FINGERPRINTS:

HISTORY, LAW AND ROMANCE

a

HENRY FAULDS

FINGERPRINTS:

HISTORY, LAW AND ROMANCE

BY

GEORGE WILTON WILTON, B.L.

One of His Majesty's Counsel in Scotland, and of the Middle Temple, Barrister-at-Law

With FOREWORD by Dr. ROBERT HEINDL

Formerly Chief, C.I.D., Saxony, and latterly Privy Councillor, Foreign Office, Germany, author of "Daktyloskopie"

LONDON   EDINBURGH   GLASGOW

WILLIAM HODGE AND COMPANY, LIMITED

1938

MADE AND PRINTED IN GREAT BRITAIN
BY
WILLIAM HODGE AND COMPANY, LIMITED
LONDON   EDINBURGH   GLASGOW

Photo Blocks by Hislop & Day, Limited
Edinburgh

TO
MY WIFE

HENRY FAULDS

(1843-1930)

Pioneer

of

Modern Fingerprint Crime Detection

acknowledged

by

Otto Schlaginhaufen, Switzerland,

Tighe Hopkins, England,
in 1905

Charles Ainsworth Mitchell, England,
in 1911

William Herschel, England,
in 1917

Bert Wentworth and Harris Hawthorne Wilder,
United States of America,
in 1918

Robert Heindl, Germany,
in 1921

Sydney Alfred Smith, Scotland,
in 1925

John Edgar Hoover,
United States of America,
in 1931

Dr. Henry Faulds in " Nature," 28th October, 1880

" WHEN bloody finger-marks or impressions on clay, glass, &c., exist, they may lead to the scientific identification of criminals. . . . Other cases might occur in medico-legal investigations, as when the hands only of some mutilated victim were found."

———

Sir William J. Herschel in " Nature," 18th January, 1917

" HIS (Faulds's) letter of 1880 announced . . . that he had come to the conclusion, by original and patient experiment, that finger-prints were sufficiently personal in pattern to supply a long-wanted method of scientific identification, which should enable us to fix his crime upon any offender who left finger marks behind him, and equally well to disprove the suspected identity of an innocent person. (For all which I gave him, and I still do so, the credit due for a conception so different from mine.) "

FOREWORD

MR. WILTON'S book takes the reader back to those interesting days when the police adopted completely new methods in their fight against the criminal, that is to say, to about the year 1880.

The reforms effected about that time in the laws and methods of criminal procedure in all civilized countries completely did away with the robust methods of the Middle Ages. Even the smallest of thumb screws was forbidden, and as a result there was a painful lack of technical assistance. Thus the rise of the natural sciences about 1880, which revolutionized every field of man's activity, was of the greatest importance in that it provided the police with new implements to replace the old methods they had lost. These were anthropometry and the fingerprint.

In Paris, Alfonse Bertillon invented anthropometry, basing his work on the investigations of the physicist and astronomer, Quételet, and became internationally famous. From all over the world police specialists made pilgrimage to Paris to study his procedure. Paris became the Mecca of the police and Bertillon their prophet. His services were lauded in books printed in every language and even that back door propagandist, the sixpenny novel, took up his name and made it popular.

Such outward success was not accorded to the pioneers of the fingerprint, although their method was shown to be more dependable and extensive than anthropometry. To provide a memorial to one of these pioneers, which has so far been denied him, is the aim of Mr. Wilton's book. In this he has done me the honour to quote several times from a work of my own. That book, which I wrote twenty years ago on the occasion of a visit to India and the Far East, was until now, perhaps, the most comprehensive history of Dactyloscopy. Mr. Wilton's book surpasses mine as far as the Herschel-Faulds question is concerned, both in its skilled documentation and in its comprehensiveness; Mr. Wilton has spent an enormous amount of labour in tracing and studying his sources.

Mr. Wilton, with zeal for the *suum cuique*, discusses, what I did not do, the delicate question of whether justice and fairness were exhibited by all parties in the disputes over the respective claims of Faulds and Herschel. My judgment of this question, which is to a certain extent a personal one, is not entirely that of Mr. Wilton.

The association of ancient China with fingerprints, a topic with which I have also dealt in " Daktyloskopie," the particular cases in modern times that have occurred in different parts of the world and chosen by Mr. Wilton to illustrate the value of fingerprints in crime detection and other subjects pertinent to fingerprints, with which his book treats, all seem to me most interesting in their wide appeal.

I am very glad to introduce " Fingerprints : History, Law and Romance " to the public. I trust that it may find many interested readers, not only in the circles of jurists and police officials, but also among scientists, so that it may spur them on to invent new means for the police to combat crime. R. HEINDL.

BERLIN.

ROBERT HEINDL

PREFACE

THE first chapter of this book explains how it came to be written.

Investigation into the facts relating to the life and work of Dr. Henry Faulds, the main theme of the book, and, in particular, to his connexion with fingerprints, has meant much research. No other writer has gone, I believe, so fully into the claim of Faulds to be the pioneer of our modern police fingerprint method, by which criminals are tracked from finger impressions left on crime scenes. That exclusive claim of Faulds, dating from 1880, is distinct from his other claim of sharing with Herschel (in his case from 1877, both independently of each other) in the merit of the conception of finger-print registers for the identification of registered wrong-doers. The essential writings of Faulds, with those of Herschel, Galton and Henry, are fully set out or noticed in the text. Vindication of Faulds stands upon these writings.

In collecting my data about fingerprint development, cases, and other cognate matters, Chiefs of Police and their Officers in this country and abroad have rendered me notable service.

I am specially indebted to Dr. Robert Heindl, Berlin, for his Foreword. Dr. Reyna Almandos, La Plata, supplied me with the Spanish publications of Vucetich and other criminologists, including his own. Mr. Bert Wentworth, New Hampshire, U.S.A., Dr. Charles Sannié, Paris, and M. Louis Baraduc, Procureur Général Honoraire, Bordeaux, my friend of Parisian student days, also gave me important information.

I consulted, as disclosed in the text, experts in Arabic,

Chinese and Persian, connected with the British Museum and the London University School of Oriental Languages. They checked the renderings of French and other translators of the works of old Eastern writers.

In the preparation and revision of the text and in other ways, amongst other friends, Mr. Rolland J. B. Munro, Mr. John S. Robertson, Mr. W. Marshall Henderson, S.S.C., and Mr. James A. Christie, Edinburgh; Mr. W. S. Gibb, Mr. Robert Macdonald, and Mr. David Willox, Glasgow; and Mr. John Ritchie, Barrister, London, have assisted and guided me.

My grateful acknowledgments and thanks are tendered to every one.

May the wish expressed at the end of the book be fulfilled and my labour in a cause so good be thus repaid. G. W. WILTON.

LANARK.

ABBREVIATIONS IN NOTES

B.M.J.	=	British Medical Journal.
C.C.C.	=	Crown Criminal Cases (England).
C.I.D.	=	Criminal Investigation Department.
Cr.App.R.	=	Crown Appeal Reports (England).
F.B.I.	=	Federal Bureau of Investigation (U.S.A.).
H.M.	=	His Majesty's.
H.M.S.O.	=	His Majesty's Stationery Office.
Ill.	=	Illinois (U.S.A.).
I.L.R.	=	Indian Law Reports.
N.E.	=	North Eastern (U.S.A.).
Nev.	=	Nevada (U.S.A.).
Pac.	=	Pacific (U.S.A.).
Pat.	=	Patna (Indian).
Phil. Trans.	=	Philosophical Transactions.
S.C.(J.)	=	Session Cases (Justiciary) (Scotland).
Sess.	=	Session.
V.L.R.	=	Victorian Law Reports (Australia).

CONTENTS

CONTENTS

ILLUSTRATIONS

FINGERPRINTS

I

INTRODUCTION

SOMEWHERE about 1878, while walking on the beach
in the Bay of Yedo in Japan, Henry Faulds[1]
(1843-1930), then residing in Tokio, found fragments of
" sun-baked " prehistoric pottery ware. They bore the
finger-impressions of the Japanese potters left on
the clay while still soft. Closer observation of these
impressions during his residence in Japan, where he was
located as the first Scottish medical missionary, led to his
serious study of our finger-tip lineations, or " furrows "
as he styled them, with all their possible bearings on
questions of race and other matters. He came to the conclusion that our finger-patterns, so varied in design,
arched, looped, whorled and mixed, as he described them,
differed, in every individual, irrespective of race and
sex. In his striking phrase these patterns were " for-
ever-unchangeable," so that it appeared to him, as he
announced in 1880 by a communication to a British
scientific journal, " nature-copies " of such finger-
impressions would be of advantage in the detection of
crime. I refer to *Nature* of 28th October, 1880, Vol.
XXII, p. 605.

Our finger-pad peculiarities had been long ago observed
by anatomists and others. But, in modern times, no one
prior to Faulds had seen their forensic importance. This
conception in the course of some ten years led in
Argentina and later in all other countries to a complete
revolution in criminal detective methods. The officials,

A   1

chiefs, and subordinates of the premier British police force, distinguished, for short, by its familiar name of " Scotland Yard," have repeatedly proclaimed that no more powerful weapon, as an aid to justice, has ever been placed in their hands. " Scotland Yard," now known as " New Scotland Yard," by this weapon refers to the discovery of criminals from their fingerprints left on their crime scenes.

It seems incredible that, up to the present time, Scotland Yard does not appear to be aware that this instrument was placed in its hands by Faulds. Indeed, in publications sponsored by Scotland Yard and by the Government, credit for the conception has been given to Sir William J. Herschel, Bart. (1833-1917). Up to the present time, Scotland Yard does not seem to have discovered that Herschel disclaimed that credit and expressly acknowledged that Faulds was alone entitled to it. The Bengal career of Herschel, grandson of the astronomer, is mentioned in Chapter III.

When my interest in fingerprints was first aroused, I did not think that investigation into the origin of their use would render it necessary for me to make inquiries, literally, all over the world. Such, however, has been the result of my trying in Glasgow in 1933 a " fingerprint " prosecution brought before me as one of the Sheriff-Substitutes of Lanarkshire. The more I inquired and investigated, the more engrossing the subject became. How great the interest in fingerprints has been and is to the people of every country, subsequent chapters of this book, I hope, will abundantly show. But first, in a little more detail, let me deal with my judicial introduction to fingerprints.

On 21st June, 1933, Mr. John Drummond Strathern,[2] Procurator-Fiscal for the Lower Ward of Lanarkshire, on the information of the Glasgow City Police, brought a complaint in the Sheriff Court, Glasgow, against a man for breaking into a public-house. The man pleaded not guilty.

The Police possessed and adduced no other proof of his alleged guilt than that led by fingerprint experts from New Scotland Yard, London, of the identity of an impression of his dirty left middle finger (of the ulnar loop type) found on an empty bottle in the premises with that same fingermark (among his ten) as photographed on his arrest. His New Scotland Yard record contained his fingerprints as that of one previously convicted in England. The photograph of the glass-bottle impression was communicated by the Glasgow Police to New Scotland Yard. Through its system of fingerprint classification, his record was easily found. When the record was given to the Glasgow Police, his arrest followed. This was, of course, not proved in Court. Nothing setting up his prior record could be laid in evidence before the Court until after conviction. If previous convictions relate to charges of a different nature, they may not be libelled at all in complaints. Sixteen points of proved identity between the two fingerprints[3] were regarded by the accused's solicitor as so convincing that the accused on his advice withdrew his plea of not guilty. I was thus relieved of the necessity of determining whether, by the Criminal Law of Scotland, I could find an accused guilty of crime upon evidence solely of his finger-impressions left by him on materials on the scene of his alleged crime.

In September, 1933, a jury in Glasgow, under the direction of Mr. Sheriff Macdiarmid, returned a verdict of guilty against an accused upon an indictment for shop-breaking and stealing, and upon no other evidence than that of fingerprints. The accused, who was sentenced to eighteen months' imprisonment, appealed to the High Court of Justiciary against his conviction, on the ground that he was illegally so convicted. In October, 1933, that tribunal dismissed his appeal, and thus settled positively that anyone might be convicted of charges of, say, murder or theft, solely upon evidence of his fingerprints.[4] In England, this was decided in 1909.[5] In Australia, the Supreme Court of Victoria in 1912 gave a like decision.[6] I deal at length with the law generally in Chapter XXX.

In June, 1933, the Scottish tribunal had affirmed the right at common law of the Scottish Police to take, as soon as arrests were made, fingerprints of persons charged with, or suspected of crime. No formal warrant was held necessary. Fingerprints might be taken before committal to prison of an accused for trial.[7] It was satisfactory that the accused in my first case had suffered no injustice by accepting the advice of his solicitor to plead guilty.[8] In Plate I are shown the comparative fingerprints produced by the Crown in his case.

My association with that first case and other fingerprint cases led me to inquire into the origin in Britain of such detective methods. I contributed two special articles to *The Glasgow Herald*, one of the leading Scottish daily newspapers, upon "Conviction by Fingerprints as a conclusive method of Bringing Offenders to Justice." In the first of these articles, published on 26th December, 1933, the share of Scotland in that origin was treated by reference to Faulds,[9] through his researches and experiments, when acting as superintendent of the first Scottish Medical Mission set up in Tokio, Japan. The second article, which appeared on 29th December, 1933, mentioned the application of the fingerprint system in Glasgow, and narrated the recent successful establishment there of a fingerprint bureau under the direction of its Chief of Police, Captain P. J. Sillitoe, C.B.E., thus dispensing in most, if not all, of the Glasgow cases from that time with any assistance by way of expert testimony from New Scotland Yard.[10] During the past five years, police officers from all over the world have visited the Glasgow bureau for the purpose of learning its methods. In many instances the Glasgow system of identification has been adopted. Criminologists from abroad have also visited Glasgow and interested themselves in the working of its Fingerprint Department. The very notable success of that Department in its investigations generally, and in particular in connexion with the Lancaster double murder by Dr. Buck Ruxton in September, 1935, has placed Glasgow in the front rank.[11]

I expressed the hope in the first of my *Glasgow Herald* articles that by further research I might be able to show that " Faulds did not receive from the British Government the recognition to which many think he was justly entitled." Further and fuller research has amply confirmed my opinion that Faulds did not receive anything like the recognition which his services deserved from Scotland Yard and its high officials, particularly, between 1885 and 1900. The officials of that period appear to have allowed themselves to be completely " Galtonised " as to the relative positions in the matter of fingerprints of Herschel and of Sir Francis Galton (1822-1911) himself. Succeeding officials have thus no doubt been unaware of Faulds and his work.

NOTES

[1] For the sake of brevity in the case of prominent persons mentioned in the book and now deceased, the birth and death years are given with Christian names, as a rule, on first mention only.

[2] Mr. Strathern died on 14th October, 1937. He was then the leading Fiscal in Scotland. Charged with the prosecution of crimes in its most important area, he had long and great experience in criminal matters. Over some of the Chaps. in this book I had his generous assistance.

[3] Agreement in comparison of fingerprints and its sequence are explained in Chap. XXVIII.

[4] *Hamilton* v. *H.M. Advocate*, 1934, S.C. (J.) 1.

[5] *Castleton*, 1909, 3 Cr.App. R. 74.

[6] *Rex* v. *Parker*, 1912, V.L.R. 152.

7 *Adair* v. *M'Garry*, 1933, S.C. (J.) 72.

8 Glasgow Sheriff Court Books record a conviction on 10th March, 1931, against an accused for some housebreaking or other offence. The Police had no evidence against him beyond his fingerprints. Before going to trial, the accused withdrew his plea of not guilty and then pleaded guilty.

9 His baptismal names were "Henry Martyn." In all his published writings, he dropped "Martyn."

10 Leading cities in England outside the Metropolis have fingerprint bureaux. The City of Edinburgh has followed Glasgow in this respect.

11 The full story of its achievement in Ruxton's Case is given in Chap. XXVIII.

II

FAULDS AND DARWIN : 1880

FROM Japan, Faulds on 15th February, 1880, wrote to Charles Darwin (1809-82) a letter on the subject of fingerprints. An engraving, made under his supervision by a Japanese engraver and illustrative of impressions made of the fingers, &c., of a right hand, accompanied this letter. Darwin replied to Faulds by letter dated 7th April, 1880, stating that he would forward his letter to his cousin, Galton. This reply, so pleasantly characteristic of Darwin, was in these terms :—

> Via Brindisi,
> April 7th, 1880.
> Down, Beckenham, Kent, Railway Station,
> Orpington, S.E.R.
>
> Dear Sir,
> The subject to which you refer in your letter of February 15th seems to me a curious one, which may turn out interesting; but I am sorry to say that I am most unfortunately situated for offering you any assistance. I live in the country, and from weak health seldom see anyone. I will, however, forward your letter to Mr. F. Galton, who is the most likely man that I can think of to take up the subject to make further enquiries.
> Wishing you success,
> I remain, dear Sir, Yours faithfully,
> CHARLES DARWIN.

Darwin died on 19th April, 1882.

Faulds's letter to Darwin is not extant. Faulds kept no copy. Darwin's reply to him (of which he had kept a copy), with the postmarked envelope, was handed in or about 1886 by Faulds to the then Secretary and Librarian of the Royal Faculty of Physicians and Surgeons in Glasgow, together with an original proof-sheet engraving from the copper-plate of the Japanese engraver. It was a duplicate of that sent to Darwin. The Faculty still possesses the engraving. Darwin's letter cannot be found.[1]

Most probably Faulds's letter to Darwin only called Darwin's attention to the ethnological aspect of finger-patterns, then very prominent in the mind of Faulds. That interest was likely to appeal to Darwin. There is a very strong presumption that Darwin would do what he said to Faulds he would do, and that Galton accordingly received Faulds's letter, with a covering letter from Darwin.

Like Galton, Faulds originally deemed the bearing of fingerprints on anthropological subjects of first importance. That was the main and, perhaps, the only ground on which in January, 1880, Faulds circularized from Japan many scientific people for information to assist him in his investigations.

Faulds states, however, that some time in 1880 (and there is no reason to doubt his word) he wrote to the Chief of the Police, Paris, recommending the use of finger-prints.[2] Plainly, such a communication could have had reference only to the juristic bearing of fingerprints on crime discovery. In all probability, Faulds made this communication to the Paris Chief of Police after he had sent his letter from Japan to the Editor of *Nature*. That letter appeared in its issue of 28th October, 1880.[3] In regard to this matter, for some time after his return to England, and specially in 1886, when, by personal inter-

7

views, Faulds tried to persuade officials at Scotland Yard of the far-reaching effects of his discovery of the importance of fingerprints, he was regarded as a visionary. Other police detective agencies, European and American, have praised the work of Faulds. Herschel, to whom both Galton and Scotland Yard gave so much praise, acknowledged after Galton's death the pre-eminence of Faulds in his contribution to crime detection.[4]

NOTES

[1] See Faulds's " Guide to Finger-Print Identification," 1905, p. 40; also his " Dactylography," 1912, pp. 20 *et* 22; and his " Manual of Practical Dactylography," 1923, p. 30. Darwin's letter to Faulds appears *in extenso* in his " Dactylography," *supra*, pp. 21, 22, *et* 23, and also in his article on " Finger-prints " in *Knowledge*, Vol. VIII, for April, 1911, p. 136. A facsimile of the Japanese copper-plate is reproduced in his " Manual."

[2] See " Guide," *supra*, p. 30.

[3] Vol. XVII, p. 605.

[4] See Chap. XXII.

III

HERSCHEL'S FINGERMARK REGISTERS: "HOOGHLY LETTER": 1858-77

FROM his examination of the skin-furrows of the hand, Faulds first suggested in modern times that: " When bloody finger-marks or impressions on clay, glass, &c., exist, they may lead to the scientific identification of criminals."[1] Such finger-impressions, of course, need not be bloody. Probably Faulds had mainly before his mind crimes of violence. Two instances which Faulds gave with his suggestion were bloodless. They were connected with thieving or pilfering. In one of these cases, the suspected offender was tracked and identified by his greasy fingermarks. In the other, an innocent suspect was absolved where sooty fingermarks had been left on a wall.

15th August, 1877, to the Inspector of Jails and Registrar-General, Bengal, the officer in question. It is referred to afterwards in this work as the "Hooghly Letter." It does not in any way embrace, touch, or suggest the topic first publicly broached by Faulds in his *Nature* Letter about the feasibility of finger-impressions being discoverable upon crime *loci* or otherwise and of their discovery leading to criminals being brought to justice. Galton will, however, be found later asserting this, if not expressly, at least by implication, and that without any justification. Herschel himself never thought of this development.

Here is the "Hooghly Letter."[3]

Hooghly, August 15, 1877.

My Dear B——,—I enclose a paper which looks unusual, but which I hope has some value. It exhibits a method of identification of persons, which, with ordinary care in execution, and with judicial care in the scrutiny, is, I can now say, for all practical purposes far more infallible than photography. It consists in taking a seal-like impression, in common seal ink, of the markings on the skin of the two forefingers of the right hand (these two being taken for convenience only).

I am able to say that these marks do not (bar accidents) change in the course of ten or fifteen years so much as to affect the utility of the test.

The process of taking the impression is hardly more difficult than that of making a fair stamp of an office seal. I have been trying it in the Jail and in the Registering Office and among pensioners here for some months past. I have purposely taken no particular pains in explaining the process, beyond once showing how it is done, and once or twice visiting the office, inspecting the signatures, and asking the omlah* to be a little more careful. The articles necessary are such as the daftari† can prepare on a mere verbal explanation.

Every person who now registers a document at Hooghly has to sign his "sign-manual." None has offered the

---

* Clerks.
† Man in charge of stationery.

smallest objection, and I believe that the practice, if generally adopted, will put an end to all attempts at personation.

The cogency of the evidence is admitted by every one who takes the trouble to compare a few signatures together, and to try making a few himself. I have taken thousands now in the course of the last twenty years and (bar smudges and accidents, which are rarely bad enough to be fatal) I am prepared to answer for the identity of every person whose " sign-manual " I can now produce if I am confronted with him.

As an instance of the value of the thing, I might suggest that, if Roger Tichborne had given his " sign-manual " on entering the Army on any register, the whole Orton case would have been knocked on the head in ten minutes by requiring Orton to make his " sign-manual " alongside it for comparison.

I send this specimen to you because I believe that identification is by no means the unnecessary thing in jails which one might presume it should be. I don't think I need dilate on that point. Here is the means of verifying the identity of every man in jail with the man sentenced by the court, at any moment, day or night. Call the number up and make him sign. If it is he, it is he; if not, he is exposed on the spot. Is No. 1302 really dead, and is that his corpse or a sham one? The corpse has two fingers that will answer the question at once. Is this man brought into jail the real Simon Pure sentenced by the magistrate? The " sign-manual " on the back of the magistrate's warrant is there to testify, etc.

For uses in other departments and transactions, especially among illiterate people, it is available with such ease that I quite think its general use would be a substantial contribution towards public morality. Now that it is pretty well known here, I do not believe the man lives who would dare to attempt personation before the Registrar here. The mukhtears‡ all know the potency of the evidence too well.

Will you kindly give the matter a little patient attention, and then let me ask whether you would let me try it in other jails?

The impressions will, I doubt not, explain themselves

---

‡ Attorneys.

12

to you without more words. I will say that perhaps in a small proportion of the cases that might come to question the study of the seals by an expert might be advisable, but that in most cases any man of judgment giving his attention to it cannot fail to pronounce right. I have never seen any two signatures about which I remained in doubt after sufficient care.

Kindly keep the specimens carefully.

Yours sincerely,

W. HERSCHEL.

Until 1894, Herschel made no public announcement about having written this "Hooghly Letter." He referred to it then in a letter he wrote to *Nature* with the apparent view of depriving Faulds of any credit in his published revelations in 1880 over fingerprints. Galton was aware by 1892 of the existence of Herschel's "Hooghly Letter." It was not apparently until after 1894 that he knew its terms. Digesting the letter slowly and with deliberation, some ten years later he came, to use a Hibernicism, to find in it something which was not there. Thereby he exalted Herschel and discredited Faulds: how unduly in the one case and how unfairly in the other, later chapters disclose. In the end, his extravagant praise of Herschel miscarried. The damage to Faulds was never wholly repaired.

NOTES

[1] See his Letter to *Nature*, of 28th October, 1880, in Chap. IV.
[2] See Chap. XXIX.
[3] Reprinted from *Nature* of 1894, Vol. 51, p. 77.

IV

FAULDS: LETTER TO "NATURE": 1880

BEYOND all dispute, Faulds was the first person to announce and describe to the world his discovery of the importance of finger and thumbmarks or fingerprint-impressions, and to suggest in particular their application in the detection of such crimes, *e.g.*, as murder and theft. Faulds did this by the publication of his letter to the Editor of *Nature* in its issue of 28th October, 1880.[1] In that letter he used the expression " finger-marks " and also referred to " thumb-marks." His letter does not seem to have been reprinted in any of the books afterwards published by Faulds on the subject matter of fingerprints. It is not to be found in English in its entirety in any treatise or textbook, British or foreign, on fingerprints or on medical jurisprudence.[2] Accordingly, here it is:

ON THE SKIN-FURROWS OF THE HAND

In looking over some specimens of " prehistoric " pottery[3] found in Japan, I was led, about a year ago, to give some attention to the character of certain finger-marks which had been made on them while the clay was still soft. Unfortunately, all of those which happened to come into my possession were too vague and ill-defined to be of much use, but a comparison of such finger-tip impressions made in recent pottery led me to observe the characters of the skin-furrows in human fingers generally. From these I passed to the study of the finger-tips of monkeys, and found at once that they presented very close analogies to those of human beings. I have here few opportunities of prosecuting the latter study to much advantage, but hope to present such results as I may attain in another letter. Meanwhile, I would venture to suggest to others more favourably situated the careful study of the lemurs, etc., in this connection, as an additional means of throwing light on their interesting genetic relations.

A large number of nature-prints have been taken by me from the fingers of people in Japan, and I am at present collecting others from different nationalities, which I hope may aid students of ethnology in classification. Some few interesting points may here be mentioned by way of introduction.

Some individuals show quite a *symmetrical* development of these furrows. In these cases all the fingers of

14

one hand have a similar arrangement of lines, while the pattern is simply reversed on the other hand. A Gibraltar monkey (Macacus innus) examined by me had this arrangement. A slight majority of the few Europeans I have been able to examine here have it also.

An ordinary botanical lens is of great service in bringing out these minor peculiarities. Where the loops occur the innermost lines may simply break off and end abruptly; they may end in self-returning loops, or, again, they may go on without breaks after turning round upon themselves. Some lines also join or branch like junctions in a railway map. All these varieties, however, may be compatible with the general impression of symmetry that the two hands give us when printed from.

In a Japanese man the lines on both thumbs form similar spiral whorls; those of the left fore-finger form a peculiar oval whorl, while those of the right corresponding finger form an open loop having a direction quite opposite to that of the right fore-finger in the previous example. A similar whorl is found on both middle fingers instead of a symmetrically reversed whorl. The right ring-finger again has an oval whorl, but the corresponding left finger shows an open loop.

The lines at the ulno-palmar margin of this particular Japanese are of the parallel sort in both hands, and are quite symmetrical, thus differing from the Englishman's considerably. These instances are not intended to stand for typical patterns of the two peoples, but simply as illustrations of the kind of facts to be observed. My method of observation was at first simply to examine fingers closely, to sketch the general trend of the curves as accurately as possible, recording nationality, sex, colour of eyes and hair, and securing a specimen of the latter. I passed from this to " nature-printing," as ferns are often copied.

A common slate or smooth board of any kind, or a sheet of tin, spread over very thinly and evenly with printer's ink, is all that is required. The parts of which impressions are desired are pressed down steadily and softly, and then are transferred to slightly damp paper. I have succeeded in making very delicate impressions on glass. They are somewhat faint, indeed, but would be useful for demonstrations, as details are very well shown, even down to the minute pores. By using different

15

colours of ink useful comparisons could be made of two patterns by superposition. These might be shown by magic lantern. I have had prepared a number of out-line hands with blank forms for entering such particulars of each case as may be wanted, and attach a specimen of hair for microscopic examination. Each finger-tip may best be done singly, and people are uncommonly willing to submit to the process. A little *hot* water and soap remove the ink. Benzine is still more effective. The dominancy of heredity through these infinite varieties is sometimes very striking. I have found unique patterns in a parent repeated with marvellous accuracy in his child. Negative results, however, might prove nothing in regard to parentage, a caution which it is important to make.

I am sanguine that the careful study of these patterns may be useful in several ways.

1. We may perhaps be able to extend to other animals the analogies found by me to exist in the monkeys.

2. These analogies may admit of further analysis, and may assist, when better understood, in ethnological classifications.

3. If so, those which are found in ancient pottery may become of immense historical importance.

4. The fingers of mummies, by special preparation, may yield results for comparison. I am very doubtful, however, of this.[4]

5. When bloody finger-marks or impressions on clay, glass, etc., exist, they may lead to the scientific identification of criminals. Already I have had experience in two such cases, and found useful evidence from these marks. In one case greasy finger-marks revealed who had been drinking some rectified spirit. The pattern was unique, and fortunately I had previously obtained a copy of it. They agreed with microscopic fidelity. In another case sooty finger-marks of a person climbing a white wall were of great use as negative evidence. Other cases might occur in medico-legal investigations, as when the hands only of some mutilated victim were found. If previously known they would be much more precise in value than the standard *mole* of the penny novelists. If unknown previously, heredity might enable an expert to determine the relatives with considerable probability in many cases, and with absolute precision in some. Such

a case as that of the Claimant even might not be beyond the range of this principle.[5] There might be a recognisable Tichborne type, and there might be an Orton type, to one or other of which experts might relate the case. Absolute identity would prove descent in some circumstances.

I have heard, since coming to these general conclusions by original and patient experiment, that the Chinese criminals from early times have been made to give the impressions of their fingers, just as we make ours yield their photographs.[6] I have not yet, however, succeeded in getting any precise or authenticated facts on that point. That the Egyptians caused their criminals to seal their confessions with their thumb-nails,[7] just as the Japanese do now, a recent discovery proves. This is however quite a different matter, and it is curious to observe that in our country servant-girls used to stamp their sealed letters in the same way. There can be no doubt as to the advantage of having, besides their photographs, a nature-copy of the for-ever-unchangeable finger-furrows of important criminals. It need not surprise us to find that the Chinese have been before us in this as in other matters. I shall be glad to find that it is really so, as it would only serve to confirm the utility of the method, and the facts which may thus have been accumulated would be a rich anthropological mine for patient observers.   HENRY FAULDS.

Tsukiji Hospital, Tokio, Japan.

(Here follows note by Editor of " Nature.")

(Some very interesting examples of nature-printed finger-tips accompanied this letter.—ED.)

So interesting a communication attracted the attention of scientists and others all over the globe. Faulds received many letters on its subject-matter from well-known biologists and others.[8]

In view of controversial developments, it was, however, unfortunate that Faulds did not put in the forefront of his *Nature* Letter his suggestions on—

I. " The scientific identification of criminals " by the use of finger-impressions found " on clay, glass, etc.," and

II. " The advantage of having, besides their photo-graphs, a nature copy of the for-ever-unchange-able finger-furrows of important criminals."

This arose, as his letter itself indicates, from the great interest Faulds had taken in racial questions, first in India and afterwards in Japan. Upon these questions the importance of scientific investigation into finger-patterns was stressed in his Letter to *Nature*. This was clearly in line with the trend of his mind on racial and sociological matters. Faulds then thought that these matters were the most important of all the issues set up by his researches over papillary ridges. The determina-tion of matters of criminal guilt or innocence was in his eyes then of minor and subsidiary value. This minor and subsidiary point was destined, however, to become, and remains up till at least the present time, the sole matter of real value.

Faulds was an earnest student of ethnology. This is attested by his membership of several learned societies concerned with that branch of knowledge and by his contributions to scientific and other magazines.[9] His medical studies and experience well equipped him for research in it.

In an article on " Finger Prints " in *Knowledge* of April, 1911,[10] Faulds describes how he became interested in fingerprints from finding finger-impressions on old sun-baked pottery fragments picked up from the beach of Yedo Bay. There he states—

" I examined directly many thousands of living fingers, then passed on to consider impresses on putty, bees-wax, sealing-wax, clay and other sub-stances, taken from my own fingers, those of students under my care, and medical men, native and foreign, and out-patients who might visit the hospital. These were at first very roughly classified

18

and analysed. I am quite sure that at this point the conception of a wide and general method of identification flashed upon me with suddenness."

Faulds also narrates in this article that in many hundreds of cases in which finger pads had been shaved or powdered down, after careful scrutiny he found that " not one solitary example of a variation was detected " when the skin had grown again.[11] In short, as has been well said by Dr. Reyna Almandos, of La Plata, distinguished as an authority on finger-print identification, the finger-tip forms the anthropological number of every person: invariable, perfect, mathematical, and absolutely unforgeable.[12]

Faulds was of opinion before he left Japan that Egyptian mummies would still retain their finger-patterns sufficiently to enable them to be studied. He referred to them in the fourth branch of the questions for inquiry set out in his 1880 *Nature* Letter. On his return to England, he verified that his opinion was correct by visits to the British Museum.[13]

NOTES

[1] Vol. XXII, p. 605.

[2] The Letters of Faulds and Herschel to *Nature* in 1880 and 1894, respectively, have been translated into Spanish. See Chap. XVI. The all-important Letter by Herschel to *Nature* in 1917, which concedes to Faulds his pre-eminence in fingerprint discoveries, has been overlooked; but it will doubtless also now be translated into Spanish. See Chap. XXII for reprint from *Nature* of Herschel's 1917 Letter.

[3] Fingerprints of ancient potters have been clearly made out on unearthing wine jars and other clay-ware from the ruins of Mizpah. These fingermarks date back a thousand years B.C. See *re* W. F. Bade's Palestine Exploration work in *The Scientific American*, 1935, Vol. 152, p. 4.

[4] Digital lines are preserved in mummification. Their dactyloscopic formulas have been made out with absolute clearness by experts, such as Dr. René Forgeot, of Lyons, Kamillo Windt, of Vienna, and Juan Vucetich, of La Plata. See article on " Identification of Suspects " by Dr. Edmond Locard, of Paris, in *Revista de Identificacion y Ciencias Penales*, 1936, Vol. 13, p. 23. La Plata. So also did Faulds upon his return to Britain by visits to the British Museum. It does not appear that ancient Egyptians used fingermarks as signatures to documents. Mr. A. Lucas, O.B.E., F.I.C., Cairo, an acknowledged authority on Egyptian *papyri*, informed me that he knew of no instance.

[5] Lord Maugham does not refer to fingerprints in his " The Tichborne Case," 1936. London. Hodder & Stoughton.

[6] Henri Cordier, Paris, in a Note by him as Editor of the revised 1914 edition of Yule's " Cathay and the Way Thither," Vol. III, p. 123, calls attention to this observation. It is punctuated by Dr. Robert Heindl, of Berlin, in his " Daktyloskopie," p. 19, 3rd edition, 1927. See further Chap. XXIX.

[7] Faulds corrected this as a blunder on his part. See his " Guide to Finger-Print Identification," *supra*, p. 32.

[8] Professor Bowditch, Harvard University, among others, in 1880. See " Guide," *supra*, p. 34. Faulds's Letter to *Nature* is noted as the first printed contribution on fingerprints in the U.S.A. *Index Medicus* for January, 1881, p. 6, under " Anthropology and Ethnology." It was obviously in the mind, if he did not, in fact, mention it, of John S. Billings, M.D., Surgeon, United States Army (the joint supervisor of this extraordinarily useful catalogue of medical articles in magazines of the world), when addressing The International Medical Congress in London in August, 1881, upon " Our Medical Literature." See *The British Medical Journal* of 13th August, 1881, p. 264. The *Index Medicus* is now merged in " The Surgeon-General's Catalogue." It contains both articles and books and is the most comprehensive catalogue of its kind.

[9] Faulds contributed an interesting article on " The Origin of Man," to *Sunlight*, a Glasgow magazine, which he edited. See Vol. I, p. 135, 1884.

[10] Vol. XXXIV, p. 136.

[11] The large coloured plate illustrating Faulds's article in *Knowledge*, *supra*, of the tattooed back of a Japanese workman once employed by him, is, by the way, of very great interest in regard to the subject of personal identification generally. The back of this Japanese from neck to feet is covered in colours with an intricate and beautiful pattern, finely wrought, over the whole skin.

[12] " Ciencia y Derecho de Identidad," p. 11. 1929. La Plata.

[13] See Note 4, *supra*.

V

HERSCHEL: LETTER TO " NATURE ": 1880

HERSCHEL was in England at the time Faulds's Letter to *Nature* appeared. It drew from Herschel a response in the form of a Letter to the Editor of *Nature* in its issue of 25th November, 1880.[1] It has not hitherto been reprinted in English anywhere else. It is as follows:—

SKIN FURROWS OF THE HAND

Allow me to contribute the information in my possession in furtherance of the interesting study undertaken by your Japan correspondent (Vol. xxii, p. 605).

I have been taking sign-manuals by means of finger-marks for now more than twenty years, and have introduced them for practical purposes in several ways in India with marked benefit.

The object has been to make all attempts at persona-tion, or at repudiation of signatures, quite hopeless wherever this method is available.

(1) First I used it for pensioners whose vitality has been a distracting problem to Government in all countries. When I found all room for suspicion effectually removed here, I tried it on a larger scale in the several (2) registration offices under me, and here I had the satisfaction of seeing every official and legal agent connected with these offices confess that the use of these signatures lifted off the ugly cloud of suspiciousness which always hangs over such offices in India. It put a summary and absolute stop to the very idea of either personation or repudiation from the moment half-a-dozen men had made their marks and compared them together. (3) I next introduced them into the jail, where they were not unneeded. On commitment to jail each prisoner had to sign with his finger. Any official visitor to the jail after that could instantly satisfy himself of the identity of the man whom the jailor produced by requiring him to make a signature on the spot and comparing it with that which the books showed.

The ease with which the signature is taken and the hopelessness of either personation or repudiation are so great that I sincerely believe that the adoption of the practice in places and professions where such kinds of fraud are rife is a substantial benefit to morality.

I may add that by comparison of the signatures of persons now living with their signatures made twenty years ago, I have proved that that much time at least makes no such material change as to affect the utility of the plan.

For instance, if it were the practice on enlisting in the army to take, say, three signatures—one to stay with the regiment, one to go to the Horse Guards, and one to the police at Scotland Yard—I believe a very appreciable diminution of desertions could be brought about by the mere fact that identification was become simply a matter of reference to the records.

And supposing that there existed such a thing as a

21

fingermark of Roger Tichborne, the whole Orton imposture would have been exposed to the full satisfaction of the jury in a single sitting by requiring Orton to make his own mark for comparison.

The difference between the general character of the rugæ of Hindoos and of Europeans is as apparent as that between male and female signatures, but my inspection of several thousands has not led me to think that it will ever be practically safe to say of any single person's signature that it is a woman's, or a Hindoo's, or not a male European's. The conclusions of your correspondent seem, however, to indicate greater possibilities of certainty. In single families I find myself the widest varieties.

W. J. HERSCHEL.

15, St. Giles, Oxford, November 13.

P.S.—It would be particularly interesting to hear whether the Chinese have really used finger-marks *in this way*. Finger-dips (mere blots) are common in the East, as " marks."

In this letter, Herschel makes no reference to his " Hooghly Letter " of 15th August, 1877, printed in Chapter III. With that " Hooghly Letter " and both of these 1880 *Nature* communications before us, the position of Herschel at that time in regard to fingermarks is clearly seen. His reply in *Nature* does not directly record, but his " Hooghly Letter " does suggest, the setting up of a criminal register of fingerprints. In this, Faulds and Herschel are entitled equally to credit.

Herschel's vision, however, limited the application of a fingerprint register to the checking or prevention of personation or " passing off " cases.

Faulds in his *Nature* Letter expressly made the suggestion for a criminal fingerprint register. By clear implication, Faulds also visualized the use of fingerprints not only in the identification of convicts as fresh offenders by comparison of their finger-impressions left on the scene of their felonies or misdemeanours, but also in the further discovery of unknown and unregistered criminals upon comparison of their fingerprints after arrest with their finger-impressions left behind them in the place of their offences.

Upon this idea of Faulds, as stated in the fifth proposition of his *Nature* Letter with regard to " bloody " fingermarks, Herschel in his *Nature* Letter made no comment. It is plain that this aspect of the use of fingerprints was then absolutely new to Herschel. In that regard Faulds stands alone.[2]

Herschel, but only some thirty-seven years after 1880, acknowledged the pre-eminence of Faulds. Through Galton in 1905 asserting, unjustifiably, that Herschel's " Hooghly Letter " covered the whole field of all subsequent developments in fingerprints, and that there was nothing new in Faulds's contribution to *Nature* in 1880, Faulds suffered grievous prejudice.

No one could possibly carp at the terms of Herschel's first contribution to *Nature* as in any way belittling the merit of the facts previously disclosed by Faulds. The same simple and dignified manner characterizing that first contribution was not maintained by Herschel and likewise by Faulds, when they subsequently differed with each other.

NOTES

[1] Vol. XXIII, p. 76.

[2] See opinion of Professor Otto Schlaginhaufen, of Zurich, written in 1905, as set forth in Chap. XXXIII.

VI

FAULDS : EARLY CAREER : INDIA : 1843-74

FAULDS, of Scottish descent on both sides, was born on 1st June, 1843, at Beith, in Ayrshire. After some schooling at Beith Academy, he went at the age of twelve years to Glasgow, entering there the office of his maternal uncle, Thomas Corbett, J.P.[1] Three years afterwards he passed into the employment of R. T. & J. Rowat, Shawl and Dress Manufacturers, Glasgow, a firm with Paisley connexions, and was with them for five years. His experience with this firm in the arrangement and classification of shawl patterns had no little bearing upon his equipment in the making of his great discovery. Neither Herschel nor Galton had his practical training.[2] Improving himself by attending, first, private classes, and then, during the years 1864 to 1867, the classes of Latin, Greek, Logic, and Mathematics in the Faculty of Arts of the University of Glasgow, Faulds in 1868 resolved upon a medical qualification. He became a student of Anderson's College, Glasgow, and passed his final examination in 1871 as a Licentiate of the Royal Faculty of Physicians and Surgeons in Glasgow. Regarded as a student above the average, he received testimonials from various professors, and from surgeons and physicians with whom he had been associated in clinical work. He went to London and got further experience at St. Thomas's Hospital, and returned to Glasgow for more infirmary work there.

During his student days, Faulds was a Sunday-school teacher in Barony Parish, Glasgow, under the famous pastor of Barony Parish Church, the Rev. Dr. Norman MacLeod. Strong religious convictions induced him towards foreign missionary work; and, offering himself as a medical missionary to the Foreign Mission Committee of the Church of Scotland, the Committee accepted him for service in India.[3] In November, 1871, he was appointed to that Church's Darjeeling Station, receiving " the right hand of fellowship." His medical work was declared at the same time to be " subsidiary."

Faulds arrived in India about March, 1872. By January, 1873, there was disagreement between him and the clerical missionary in charge of the station. Faulds

24

returned to Scotland in July, 1873, when, after " being cordially welcomed " by the members of the Foreign Mission Committee, his engagement under them was then terminated, and their decision was intimated to him by their Convener.

On 10th September, 1873, Faulds married Isabella Wilson, a lady of Shawlands, Glasgow. His and her people were then settled there. In his marriage-registration paper, Faulds described himself as a surgeon. This qualification is a fact about Faulds, rather overlooked by others afterwards in dealing with his work in fingerprints.

Still imbued with missionary zeal, Faulds turned to the United Presbyterian Church of Scotland. His parents were connected with that body. His father was an elder of Erskine United Presbyterian Church, Glasgow.

NOTES

[1] His eldest son, Archibald Cameron Corbett, sat in Parliament (1885-1911) for the Tradeston Division of Glasgow, and became Baron Rowallan.

[2] See " Dactylography," *supra*, p. 46, where Faulds says : " Part of my duty was to deal with the arrangement, classifying and numbering immense varieties of patterns, printed with every conceivable variation of combined colours." See also *ibid.*, p. 84.

[3] By courtesy of the Officials in the Central Offices of The Church of Scotland, perusal was made of the Minute Books of the Foreign Mission Committee of the Church as existing between 1871 and 1873 and of the Minute Books of the Foreign Mission Board and the *Missionary Record* of the United Presbyterian Church of Scotland as existing between 1873 and 1886, all now in the possession of the Church of Scotland. The United Presbyterian Church was united with the Free Church of Scotland in 1900 under the name " The United Free Church of Scotland." That Church was united with the Church of Scotland in 1929.

VII

FAULDS : JAPAN : 1874-85

FAULDS applied in July, 1873, to the Foreign Mission Board of the United Presbyterian Church of Scotland to be sent to Japan. The Committee approved. On 24th December, 1873, he sailed from London for Yokohama to establish under the auspices of that Church the first Scottish Japanese Medical Mission. He arrived in Yokohama on 5th March, 1874.

Faulds soon had a hospital and dispensary built and equipped in Tsuki, " the foreign Concession," contiguous to Yedo (Tokio). This hospital, of which he was medical superintendent, set up on the lines of our cottage hospitals, was the first of its kind in Japan.

Faulds started a journal or magazine, embracing matters of medical interest.[1] By 1881, his connexion with this paper displeased the Church's Home Board. They pressed him to give up its editorship. His active interest in medicine must have been of advantage to him and the Church in his missionary appeals to the Japanese. So thought one member of the Home Board, William Gray Dixon (1854-1928), formerly a professor of English Literature in the Imperial College, Tokio, and for some time recording secretary of the Asiatic Society of Japan, of which he was a life member. He protested against the attitude of the Home Board to Faulds, maintaining that Faulds was specially fitted for such work as " a man of science and general culture."[2] Faulds himself saw no good ground for the surrender of his editorship. The Home Board in 1883 still considered that his service with them was incompatible with journalistic work. The resignation of his post then seemed inevitable. Probably it was not easy for the purely ministerial mind to appreciate the scientific side of Faulds as any aid at all to mission service. His missionary colleagues in Japan certainly did not do so. By the end of 1883, moreover, the Japanese Government had erected hospitals with a medical college, all with the best equipment. This advance affected the continued usefulness of the Medical Mission of the United Presbyterian Church of Scotland.

Little fruit in the way of Christian converts had apparently resulted. The abandonment of the Mission was then seriously considered. But Faulds, coming home on leave to Scotland, prevailed with the Home Board for its continuance. The question of his resignation was dropped.[3]

In Japan, Faulds was a powerful personality. By July, 1875, he reported to his superiors in Scotland that he had received overtures from officials of the Japanese Government on behalf of a Prince of Japan to become his physician with the equivalent in salary of £1000 a year, besides a house to be built in the English style to his own design, provided that he gave up his Mission work. These overtures, as he told the Home Board, he did not entertain.[4] About 1876, he set about the establishment of a medical school in connexion with the Mission, arranging a weekly course of lectures, in which as one of the lecturers he himself participated, with physiology as his subject. He gave also a series of popular lectures on Darwinism, and so successfully that for a time these were delivered in one of the largest theatres in Tokio. Further, he introduced the Japanese to the milk-treatment of typhoid fever as well as to the antiseptic methods of Lister, with whom as a student in Glasgow he had come in contact.

Some idea of the activities of Faulds in Japan may be gauged from his reporting his Mission expenditure for 1876 to the Home Board as not far short of £5000.[5] Hospital cases and out patients, treated by his hospital, rose in a year to 9000.[6] The Japanese Government made him honorary Surgeon-Superintendent of their Tsuki Hospital in Tokio. This post, while retaining his position as Medical Missionary, he held from March, 1874, till the eve of his final departure from Japan in 1885. Faulds helped in the publication, in raised letters, of a Bible for the Japanese blind. Fees he received from Japanese patients went to the credit of the Mission.

In November, 1885, Mrs. Faulds, who had gone out in May to Japan, became very ill, and her immediate return to Britain with Faulds was resolved upon. He and his wife landed in England on 19th December, 1885. Faulds did not go back to Japan.

The Foreign Mission Committee of the United Presbyterian Church of Scotland, in accepting the resignation of Faulds, recorded their sense of the value of his medical work at Tokio during his twelve years' period of " excellent service " under them " as a medical missionary." The Church paid the passage money home of Faulds and his wife, provided for the education of their eldest son and eldest daughter at Shawlands Academy, Glasgow, and granted to Faulds one full year's allowance as from 1st February, 1886.[7]

Before leaving Japan, Faulds published in 1884, through a Scottish London publisher, " Nine Years in Nipon : Sketches of Japanese Life and Manners."[8] This book, in which Faulds makes no reference to fingerprints, was reviewed in *Nature* as a " beautiful and entertaining volume."[9] The anonymous reviewer, who the editor of *Nature* states was not Galton, credits Faulds with making the " original suggestion " about the universal spread of education throughout Japan as due to Buddhism with its " new and genial enthusiasm of humanity." *The Saturday Review* of 17th January, 1885, among other journals, had also a very full and appreciative notice, in which Faulds was referred to as " a keen naturalist."

NOTES

[1] This journal is believed to have been a monthly magazine, called *The Chrysanthemum*, published, it is understood, in Japanese in Tokio, and " devoted to the discussion of Japanese topics of literary, scientific or antiquarian interest." See " Dactylography," *supra*, p. 85. Unfortunately, this journal has not been accessible to me. It is

possible that there are contributions in it by Faulds with reference to fingerprints.

2 See Minute of Foreign Mission Board of 3rd August, 1881.

3 See Minutes of 25th September, 1883, and 29th January, 1884. Faulds resigned his post; but later, with the approval of the Committee, he withdrew that resignation.

4 See Minutes of 1st July, 1875, p. 562.

5 *Per* Minute of 1st December, 1876.

6 *Ibid.*

7 See Minute of 26th January, 1886.

8 A second edition was published in 1887. Alexander Gardner, London and Paisley.

9 Vol. XXXI, p. 288.

VIII

FAULDS: MEDICAL SCIENCE INTERESTS: 1868-1930

FROM student days, Faulds was aware that Jean Evangéliste Purkinje (1787-1869), a very distinguished Bohemian professor of physiology in the Universities of Breslau and Prague, had dealt with the nerves of touch. In connexion with his own experiments in Japan in relation to fingermarks, Faulds surmised that this famous physiologist could not have failed to observe, with more particularity than other physiologists or anatomists, the related patterns on human fingers. In this country, and over a period of three or more years, Faulds made extensive inquiries with regard to unpublished papers by Purkinje among Dutch and German scholars and American friends. In June, 1886, some two years before Galton had taken any active interest in fingerprints, Faulds saw the Librarian of the Royal College of Surgeons in London, and expressed his belief to him in the likelihood of Purkinje's having recorded his researches over finger-furrows in some still possibly extant manuscript or print. Faulds was accompanied by his friend, Dr. Charles Bagge Plowright, of King's Lynn. The Librarian agreed in this matter with the belief of Faulds.[1] By a rather wonderful coincidence, however, Galton, after he took up in earnest the subject of fingerprints, also thought in the same way about Purkinje.[2]   There can be little doubt that Galton became desirous of finding Faulds forestalled in the subject-matter of his Letter to *Nature* in 1880.   Galton ranged in search over all quarters.   His motives may be surmised.   Friendship with Herschel was certainly an incentive.   In his observations with regard to finger-furrows in his " Finger Prints," Galton refers to several cases of individuals, besides Purkinje, as interested in fingerprints, some as medical men, others as engravers, and so forth.   Not one of the varied activities of these persons, including the researches of Purkinje, had the slightest bearing on the deductions Faulds had made from his own researches in regard to the permanence of finger-prints and their use as aids in the formation of criminal registers and in the detection of crime.   No one disputed that, before and after Faulds, many others had independently noticed the peculiarities of finger-pads. Galton referred, for example, to Thomas Bewick, the Newcastle engraver and naturalist, making prints of his finger-pads on his books about 1820 (probably the first person to use this mode of " artist proof signature "), and to a San Francisco photographer in 1882.[3]   But, of course, these particular examples in no way anticipated Faulds or Herschel in their discoveries about the permanence of finger variations and of the application of this fact as aids to justice.   Galton made efforts to see and examine the suspected still existing writings of Purkinje, and he likewise enlisted the services of the same Librarian as Faulds had already done.   Their independent surmises proved well founded.   It was the good fortune of Galton to get possession through this Librarian of a Continental copy of a Latin thesis of Purkinje printed in 1823.[4]

In this paper, Purkinje did deal with the peculiarities of the tactile furrows of the hands, and his paper disclosed the first attempt by anyone of their classification. Purkinje found from his observations "nine principal varieties" of "the curvature." His observations, however, were made from the purely physiological aspect. He was altogether silent on their use as a means of personal identification, and did not deal with their variations not recurring in other individuals or with the subject of their unchangeability through life. Purkinje, so far as can be traced, had no interest in forensic medicine. Even Galton, for at least some years prior to 1890, took no interest in finger-furrows as related to crime detection, His interests were at first directed to the ethnological bearing of finger-furrows. Purkinje's classification was of no material assistance in the classifications subsequently made, for the purposes of criminology, by Faulds, Galton, Sir Edward R. Henry (1850-1931), Juan Vucetich (1858-1925), and others. Faulds clearly foreshadowed the main classification into arches, loops, and whorls, in his 1880 Letter to *Nature*.[5] That classification, as I believe, was at the base of classifications suggested or made by Galton and Henry.

NOTES

[1] See "Guide," *supra*, p. 34.

[2] Galton had studied medicine at King's College, London.

[3] Galton mentions some of these "prior claims" in reviewing Faulds's "Guide." See the "Review" printed in Chap. XIX. In Chap. XII, I refer to a woodcut of the thumbprint of James Nasmyth, the great mechanical engineer, found at the end of his "Autobiography" (Smiles) as probably suggested by Bewick's "thumbmark" woodcuts.

[4] See "Personal Identification," p. 334. Wentworth-Wilder, 1932. Chicago. Cooke.

[5] Of course, Purkinje did not observe these peculiarities for the first time. Malpighi (1628-94) perceived the "ridges to be drawn out into loops or spirals." See "Dactylography," *supra*, p. 16; and Wentworth-Wilder on "Personal Identification," *supra*, p. 333. The Chinese long ago characterized whorls as "snails." Rashid, the Persian historian, as I relate in Chap. XXIX, records, on Chinese information, that no two individuals had fingers precisely alike.

IX

FAULDS AND SCOTLAND YARD: 1886-89

BETWEEN 1886 and 1888, by personal interviews with officials at Scotland Yard and in particular at his own home with Inspector John B. Tunbridge (1850-1928), of the Criminal Investigation Department (afterwards Commissioner of Police from 1897 to 1903 in New Zealand), Faulds endeavoured to enlist Scotland Yard in the proposed application of his method of identification by fingerprints. He offered " to work a small bureau, free of expense, in order to test its value and practicability."[1] High officials regarded Faulds as a crank. They refused to entertain his views as of any real value. So, tests were rejected. " How could anyone be convicted," said one of these officials to him, " on identification of features confined within so small a space as the tip or pad of a finger? "[2]

Faulds understood, however, that Tunbridge, who was an able officer and sympathetically interested in his suggestions, was commissioned to make a report to the Commissioner of the Metropolitan Police for his and Government purposes. Faulds believed that Tunbridge in or about 1887 did make a report; that the report was unfavourable to him on the grounds that, although scientific and accurate, his system was too delicate for ordinary police manipulation; and that, before anything could be done, legislation would be necessary.

After his retirement from New Zealand to Kent, Tunbridge wrote the following letter to Faulds:

> I have a most distinct and pleasant recollection of our interview, and, since the " F.P." system has been adopted as a means of identification of criminals with such marked success, have often wondered how it was that you have not been more actively connected with the carrying out of the system. When the Home Authorities

recognised the value of the system, I was Commissioner of Police in New Zealand, and it was owing mainly to my recommendation that the system was introduced into the New Zealand prisons, although the Prison Authorities were somewhat opposed to it. . . . Some of the Australian States also adopted the system, with the result that an interchange of prints took place, which soon manifested its value. The system is now in full working order in Australia, and is carried on by the police, of course, with the assistance of the Prison Authorities.

It is believed that this letter was written to Faulds in 1907.[3]

Disclosure now of Tunbridge's report would be of the greatest importance in view of what Faulds must have represented to Tunbridge and other police officials could be done in crime detection as the result of his researches and the methods he then suggested. Tunbridge initiated, as he told Faulds in the letter quoted, the adoption of fingerprints in New Zealand.

From the outset, Faulds had recommended to the officials of Scotland Yard a registration system based on a ten-finger method in serial form. Faulds prepared forms to receive imprints. That method and those forms were substantially, I believe, adopted, and are in official use.[4] Herschel worked out no system. Galton's plan was too complicated for official adoption. Henry made great improvements in classification.

I have found no reference to Faulds in the Annual Reports to Parliament of the Commissioner of the Metropolitan Police for the period embraced in this Chapter IX. In 1878 the Metropolitan Police set up a Criminal Investigation Department. Thereafter the Annual Reports deal with the position and progress of that Department.[5]

NOTES

[1] See " Guide," *supra*, pp. 63 *et* 113 : also " Dactylography," *supra*, pp. 25 *et* 88.

[2] See " Guide," *supra*, p. 86.

3 See Faulds's article on " Finger Prints " in *Knowledge, supra.*
I have no idea why Faulds missed out some part of Tunbridge's letter : probably the omitted part was unimportant.
Tunbridge was not Superintendent of the C.I.D. at the time,
but one of the Detective-Inspectors. I applied " in the interests of
science " to the Commissioner of Police of the Metropolis for exhibition of this report. He replied by letter of 14th July, 1936, " that he
regrets that no record of the report by Mr. Tunbridge . . . can be
traced at this office " (New Scotland Yard). Great Scotland Yard was
given up in 1890. It may be taken now as altogether lost. An article
on " New Scotland Yard " in *The Times,* p. 6, of 3rd May, 1890,
refers to the " hopeless confusion " in which stores of books, papers,
&c., then were over removal from Whitehall Place and Great Scotland
Yard.

4 See " Daktyloskopie," *supra,* p. 53, and Chap. XVIII.

5 See the Annual Reports H.M.S.O.

X

FAULDS : LAST YEARS : 1885-1930

AFTER residing in London for a few years from 1886, and
acting as assistant to Dr. William Joseph Dawes, Long-
ton, Staffordshire, Faulds settled as a medical practi-
tioner at Fenton, in the Potteries. There he was
police-surgeon for eight years from 1892 or thereabout.
Thereafter he moved to Hanley. After selling his practice there, he retired in 1922, in ill-health, with deafness
increasing, to Wolstanton, Stoke-on-Trent. He died
there on 19th March, 1930, over eighty-six years of age,
his wife having predeceased him by some two years.
Besides his dwelling-house, he left very little estate.

Faulds was known among his friends as a very interesting man, versatile and fluent and entertaining in
conversation. Loyal to his parents and to his family,
his deeds of piety in the noble Roman sense are for
remembrance elsewhere.

Faulds was a member of, among other learned societies,
the Royal Asiatic Society (1884-86), the Royal Anthropological Institute (1911-26) and the Classical Association
(1919-22). It is understood that he was also a member

34

of the Royal Archæological Institute and the Sociological Society, and an honorary fellow of the International Association for Identification, U.S.A.; but, although correspondence has been held with these London and American Associations, Faulds's memberships and fellowship have not been authenticated.[1] Their membership registers do not seem for the material periods to have been complete. From the various publications of Faulds, it is clear that he had considerable knowledge of the Classics, besides being acquainted with French and German. He had mastered the language of Japan, and lectured to Japanese audiences in their own tongue.

According to *The Glasgow Herald* of 20th March, 1930, in its short obituary notice, Faulds was " the pioneer of the path in opening up the system of fingerprints in crime detection." This appears to be strictly true of Faulds, both as a theorist and an experimentalist, and true of him in Japan before and up to October, 1880, and thereafter in his work in England in his endeavours to get his identification method adopted by the Government and the Police Authorities. In all this he was a pioneer in crime detection, sharing its origination with Herschel so far as concerns the registration of criminal fingermarks. But, if regard be paid to his original suggestion about the detection of criminals from the impressions of their fingermarks—really a fundamental revolution in detective methods—Faulds was truly the only pioneer of the modern system in all its wide significance. In *The Times's* obituary notice of Faulds in its issue of 20th March, 1930, he was merely described as " an authority on the fingerprint system of detecting criminals." In the obituaries of that newspaper of Herschel in its issue of 25th October, 1917, and of Henry in its issue of 21st February, 1931, Faulds is not mentioned. The obituarist of Henry credits him, in association with Herschel, with the detection of the criminals in the " Blackheath murder " through the finding of a single finger impression on an empty cash box. This case occurred in March, 1905, and is otherwise known as the " Deptford murder." See Chapter XVIII.

Faulds was the author of several books and brochures on fingerprints, and, of these, his " Guide to Finger-Print Identification," published in September, 1905, was the most notable. His " Manual of Practical Dactylography," published in 1923, and his " Guide," are full of general information on the subject of identification and are still worthy of study by medico-legal students and especially by all aspirants for promotion in the detective branches of police administration and service.[2] It is to be hoped that some new edition of his works or a textbook based on them may yet be published in connexion with Police Educational Colleges at Hendon and elsewhere and with the proposed new Central College of Medical Jurisprudence.[3] Some of Faulds's publications were published by the proprietors of *The Police Review*.[4]

Through the Editor of *Nature*, Galton got the opportunity of reviewing Faulds's " Guide." Galton took full advantage of this opportunity to exalt Herschel at the expense of Faulds as a man with " an old grievance." His well-known initials, " F. G.," appended to the review, advertised its authorship. That review, which did, as it was bound to do, very great harm to Faulds, is dealt with more fully in Chapters XIX and XX.

NOTES

[1] See title page of " Dactylography," *supra*.

[2] Some of Faulds's articles or publications on fingerprints and identification, besides those specially mentioned in the text, are—

1904. " Dactyloscopy." *St. Thomas's Hospital Gazette*—January. This magazine had only a limited circle of readers.

1911. " Finger Prints : A Chapter in the History of their Use for Personal Identification." *Scientific American Supplement*, Vol. LXXII, p. 326.

1912. " Dactylography " or " The Study of Finger Prints " in Twentieth Century Science Series.

1913. " Poroscopy; The Scrutiny of the Sweat Pores for Indenti- fication." *Nature*, Vol. XCI, p. 635.

[3] Some of Faulds's publications are out of print. The University Library of Cambridge in February, 1931, had an inquiry from America for a photostatic copy of his " Guide " if no copies were procurable.

[4] His " Manual of Practical Dactylography," *supra*, was issued by The *Police Review* Publishing Co., Ltd.

XI

GALTON: NO INTEREST IN FINGERPRINTS: 1880-88

GALTON has been rightly described as one of the great British scientists of the period from 1860 to 1895.

Galton, despite the probabilities that he received a letter from Darwin about April, 1880, over the communi- cation of 15th February, 1880, by Faulds to Darwin, does not seem, prior to May, 1888, to have taken any special interest either in the letter one assumes he received from Darwin forwarding that communication, or in Faulds's Letter in *Nature* of 28th October, 1880.

From its commencement in 1869, Galton was a sub- scriber to *Nature*. Prior to October, 1880, he had been a frequent contributor. Indeed, in the very same volume as that in which that Letter of Faulds appears, there is a contribution by Galton. Galton may not have read the contribution of Faulds, and may not even have noticed it. Until 1888, Galton took no interest whatever in skin- furrows or in fingerprint-impressions. In dealing with impressions of fingerprints, it has to be kept in view that an impression is, so to speak, a mirror-image, and is the reverse of a direct examination of the finger tip itself.

At the outset of his interest in fingerprints, Galton concerned himself about them only as affecting his investigations into matters of race and heredity. Equally with kindred speculations by Faulds and others, Galton's researches into these matters yielded negative results. Some still hope for positive gains.[1]

For the purpose of this book, the crucial point in reference to Galton is that, up to 1888 and for some considerable time thereafter, he never saw the significance of the discovery made by Faulds, even if he were aware of it, either in enabling crime to be brought to light by the use of fingerprints or in making use of them for the creation of criminal records for identification purposes, in which latter aspect Herschel also was entitled to credit.

It is rather strange that Galton should not have been earlier attracted to the subject of fingerprints. As a student of forensic medicine, he had distinguished himself at King's College, London. He tells in his " Memories of My Life " that he delighted in that course. " It had," he observes, " a sort of Sherlock Holmes fascination for me."[2] After his attention was specially called to finger-furrows in relation to crime, Galton did not advocate resort to fingerprint evidence. His first impressions were all against its usefulness.

Galton warmly espoused the anthropometric system of Bertillon, adopted by the Parisian Police about 1880. In time he realised that he had erred in his judgment of the respective values of Bertillonage and fingerprint systems. Notwithstanding that in the meantime he had become fully apprised of the 1880 *Nature* Letter of Faulds, Galton attributed solely (but wrongly) to Herschel the discovery of the application of fingerprints in the identification of criminals.

NOTES

[1] See article by Mr. Louis Herrman on " Finger Patterns " in *The American Journal of Police Science*, 1931, Vol. II, p. 306. In " The Human Situation," p. 136 (1937. London. Edward Arnold & Co.), Emeritus Professor W. Macneile Dixon, states : " His fingerprints,

if closely examined, reveal the race or community to which a man belongs." No authority for this statement is cited. Sex, I believe, is not disclosed by fingerprint examination.

2 1908. p. 42. London. Methuen & Co.

XII

GALTON'S FLIRTATION WITH BERTILLONAGE : 1888-90

IN his " Memories of My Life,"[1] Galton states that his interest in fingerprints arose in 1888 through his being requested to lecture at the Royal Institution, London, on Bertillonage. In preparation for that address he inquired into the alleged use of thumb marks " especially by the Chinese " ; and he adds : " I also wrote a letter to *Nature,* asking for information."

Faulds's Letter to *Nature* of October, 1880, must have been widely noticed by men of science all over the world. Reference has already been made to this and to the letters Faulds himself received after the appearance in *Nature* of that letter. His contribution was officially indexed in 1880 in the *Index Medicus* of the United States Librarians as the first on fingerprints.

In an unsigned leader on " Fingermarks " in *St. James's Gazette,* of 17th December, 1880, the writer observes :

" The application of a finger mark either as an autograph in lampblack on ordinary paper, in wax, or on prepared paper, which would instantly print the most delicate *rugæ* of the damp finger impressed on it, ought immediately to take the place of the clumsy cross—which, in spite of school boards, will for a long time yet continue in various documents."[2]

It seems clear that the contribution of Faulds to *Nature* in October, 1880, had been widely noticed in the United States. Mr. John S. Billings, Surgeon, United

States Army, could be referring to no other person than Faulds, when, in addressing in London in August, 1881, the International Medical Congress upon the subject of " Our Medical Literature," he observed—

> " Just as each individual is in some respects peculiar and unique, so that even the arrangement of the minute ridges and furrows at the end of his forefinger differs from that of all other forefingers and is sufficient to identify him."

See report of this address in *British Medical Journal*, under date, 13th August, 1881, Vol. 1, 262, at p. 264.

In " The World of Wonders " for 1883, published by Cassell & Co., London and New York, an article (p. 114) upon " Thumb Portraits " appeared. The contributor made no reference in it to Faulds or Herschel and cited no authorities. No record of the contributors at that time to this magazine is extant. So his name is unknown. The writer referred, however, to Chinese customs and one of two letters (that by Joseph F. James, of Miami University, O.) written to the Editor of *Science* in 1886, quotes from a newspaper, presumably American, a passage from that article. Galton afterwards referred to these two letters, as appears from Note 6 at the end of this Chapter. " Thumb Portraits " was illustrated by the representation of two thumbmarks— right and left. Bewick's " thumbmarks " in his Natural History books are well known, published early in the nineteenth century. I have been shown the " Autobiography of James Nasmyth " (1808-90), the inventor of the steamhammer, edited by Dr. Samuel Smiles and published by John Murray, London, in 1883. On p. 450, at the end of a paper by Nasmyth begun by him in 1829 (p. 409) and apparently revised in his later years, upon the origin and mode of writing cuneiform characters, he appends an engraving of his thumbmark with the words,

" My mark—an impression before Letters." Nasmyth
does not relate how he came to insert this thumbmark.
It is possible, from the original 1829 date of his paper,
that he had become acquainted with Bewick's engravings.
Nasmyth's father was a well-known artist.

In 1883 Clemens (1835-1910), in his " Life on the
Mississippi," under the *nom de plume* of " Mark
Twain," made his first reference to " thumb marks."[3]
Facts about fingermarks were observed generally by
others in the United States from about 1882.

No doubt Galton had heard or read of all or some of
these references to fingermarks. He may also have
attended the International Medical Congress in London
in August, 1881, and listened, or read the reference in
The Times or elsewhere, to the address already referred
to on " Our Medical Literature " by Dr. Billings, one
of the Librarians responsible for the *Index Medicus*. All
this may have been in addition to his reception of
Darwin's letter of April, 1880, and his knowledge of
Faulds's Letter in *Nature* of October, 1880. The probability of this is great. If he did, he might, nevertheless,
easily forget the sources of his knowledge or belief.
Galton must have been the recipient of countless letters;
many cranks, doubtless, were among his correspondents.
It is somewhat significant that in 1888 Galton first wrote
for information to the Editor of *Nature*.

No trace of any publication of Galton's letter to
Nature's Editor can be found. It is not unlikely that
the Editor dealt with it privately and in answer referred
Galton to Herschel, and that Galton then wrote a letter
to Herschel. Galton relates that his letter, it is assumed,
to Herschel, " had the important effect of drawing a
response." This " response " does not appear to have
been preserved. Obviously, Galton had then overlooked
or was unaware of the contributions of Faulds and
Herschel in *Nature* of October and November, 1880,

respectively. It may be that the Editor did not think of mentioning Faulds in replying to Galton. Nevertheless, it is possible both these contributions were subconsciously in the mind of Galton in prompting his letter of inquiry to the Editor of *Nature*. His "Memories of My Life," however, mentions Herschel only. Galton, doubtless, thought it was right to omit all reference to Faulds in his "Memories of My Life," except in the item, No. 171 of the Appendix—a list of all his Lectures, Writings, &c., of which Galton was naturally proud. No. 171 was his "Review" in *Nature*, 1905, of Faulds's "Guide." That "Review" did Galton little credit. Galton was aware, in composing these "Memories," that he had dealt Faulds an almost deadly blow in reviewing for *Nature* Faulds's "Guide," his first book on "Finger Prints," published in September, 1905. But, of that later.

Tracing, in chronological order, the development of Galton's interest in fingerprints, one finds that on 25th May, 1888, he read at the Royal Institution a paper on "Personal Identification and Description."[4] It was a laudation of Bertillonage. Of the anthropometric system of Bertillon (1853-1914), Galton was then completely enamoured. Only casually in this address did he refer to fingerprints, stating that, in so far as the paper dealt with that method of identification, it was based largely on experiments of Herschel. "He," i.e., Herschel, Galton proceeded to say, "found it to be most successful in preventing personation and in putting an end to disputes about the authenticity of deeds," mentioning that Herschel had "described his method fully in *Nature* in 1880, Vol. XXIII, p. 76." That paper, he added, "should be referred to by the reader"; and then, most amazingly, he states: "also a paper by Mr. Faulds in the next (*sic*) volume." Anyone listening to Galton's address would naturally infer that, contrary to the fact,

Herschel's was both the first and the more important contribution to *Nature* of these two papers. It was a most
inaccurate and misleading reference for Galton to make
about Faulds's contribution.[5] Obviously, the reference to
Faulds, however, was not intended to be sympathetic.
Galton made this matter worse. In permitting the substance of his lecture to be printed in *Nature*, he had the
opportunity of correcting his error both for *Nature* and
for the Royal Institution Proceedings, in which it
appeared " as reprinted from *Nature* of June 21 and 28 "
and " after some slight revision by the author."[6] He did
not correct the error. Such carelessness seems unpardon-
able. Galton never called the attention of *Nature* to his
blunder, and, although he stated the correct sequence of
the contributions of Faulds and Herschel afterwards (in
1905) in his " Review " of Faulds's " Guide," many of
the readers who saw *Nature* of 1888 and the Royal Institution Proceedings of 1888 might never see *Nature* of 1905.
So Galton, in this way, apart from others, damaged the
interests of Faulds. In the address itself, Galton made
no reference of any kind to the use of fingerprints left
in or on places of crime, or on articles used or touched
in crimes, as a means of detecting the criminals.
Faulds's contribution to that, the most important
development of the use of fingerprints, was, therefore,
not mentioned. Bertillonage and fingermark registers
do not come into that sphere. Indeed, Galton was
sceptical at this date about the possibility of taking
proper impressions of fingermarks; for, in this address,
he observed :

> " If a cleanly and simple way could be discovered
> of taking durable impressions of the finger tips,
> there would be little doubt of their being service-
> able in more than one way."[7]

Faulds had treated of this very matter in his *Nature*
Letter of 1880.

On 5th December, 1888, Galton sent a paper to the Royal Society on " Co-relations and their Measurement, chiefly from Anthropometric Data."[8] He made no reference at all in this paper to fingerprints.

On 27th November, 1890, Galton read a memoir before the Royal Society on " The Patterns in Thumb and Finger Marks." In this memoir, after observing that " My attention was drawn to the subject nearly three years ago when preparing a lecture for the Royal Institution," Galton expressed his opinion (not accepted by other scientists) that the origin of these patterns was due to " the existence of the thumb nail."[9] Galton based their permanency through life on data supplied to him by Herschel. Faulds was ignored. In this paper, Galton further asserted that the truth of the statement about this permanence " had never been adequately investigated." Adequacy is, of course, a question of degree. No other person than Faulds, apart from Herschel, had made investigations (if Herschel's observations fall under the term " investigations ") into their unchangeability. The reference to Faulds was oblique. Faulds's investigations and experiments and tests as described in his 1880 *Nature* Letter were surely to any unprejudiced mind acid proof of the permanency of the lineations throughout life. They were far superior in value to the observations relied upon by Herschel from the examination of marks of fingers of individuals at intervals, long or short. Fingerprint authorities, as mentioned later, confirm these criticisms. Such generalizing by Galton suggests in charity that he had not scrutinized Faulds's Letter with sufficient care. If he did, in fact, mean Faulds by his oblique reference (and no one else can be imagined, and he was, in fact, well aware of Faulds's part in the matter), then his perception of " adequacy " was peculiar. Indeed, any " adequacy " not related to his own speculations apparently fell to be discounted or disregarded.

Galton in this same paper made this further observation—

> "The popular idea [of the life-long persistence of finger-ridges] that has hitherto been jumped at without adequate evidence is now shown to be strictly correct."[10]

It is not doing " adequate " justice to Galton to suggest that he had " Mark Twain " in his mind by this observation. If he meant Faulds, and it is difficult to conceive of any other person, then his observation was a travesty in every particular of the facts and conclusions of Faulds in his *Nature* Letter. " Popular idea " in his case? Surely not. " Jumped at "? How ridiculous! And " without adequate evidence "? How unjustifiable! If, however, he was not referring to Faulds, then his ignorance of the facts and of the conclusions of Faulds was the more astounding.

The Metropolitan Police do not appear at this period to have been interested in fingerprints. During 1890 the Criminal Investigation Department at Scotland Yard commenced the registration of photographs for the better identification of habitual criminals.

At the Anthropological Institute on 9th December, 1890, Galton again lectured on the same subject, and declared—

> " There is a statement that the Chinese—who seem to be credited with every new discovery—had used thumb impressions as proof of identity for a long time."

This statement, he then announced, pontifically, was " an egregious error."[11] Perhaps, he was indirectly referring, consciously or otherwise, to Faulds's original and correct belief in the matter as expressed in his 1880 *Nature*

Letter. Galton no doubt thought the surmise of Faulds was the childish view of an amateur in knowledge. It is presumed, however, that Galton had no great knowledge of the Chinese or of their literature. Indeed, there is no evidence that he had sought for information, positive or negative, from reliable sources, about the position of fingerprints in Chinese history. The opinion of Galton, one of the High Priests of his time in the Temple of Science, has turned out to be wrong on this matter; the original surmise of Faulds, a minor Canon in that Temple, has proved to be right. Clearly, up to 1890, Galton had not the least conception of the legal incidence of fingerprints in ancient Chinese history.[12]

NOTES

[1] *Supra*, p. 252.

[2] This leader, p. 12, refers both to Faulds and Herschel, and was obviously based to a large extent upon facts stated in their Letters to *Nature* in October and November, 1880, respectively : no direct reference is made to these Letters.

[3] See " Mark Twain and Fingerprints : 1883-94," Chap. XXIII, *infra*.

[4] Royal Institution Proceedings, 1888, Vol. XII, p. 346.

[5] I notice that Vucetich, of whom I write at length in Chap. XVI, observed this mistake made by Galton, " equivocando totalmente las fechas . . . cuando la verdad es lo contrario," and characterized it " como demonstración de algún prejuicio contra Faulds." See " Historia Sintética de la Identificación " by Vucetich, published after his death in *Revista de Identificación y Ciencias Penales*. Tomo VI, p. 383, 1930. La Plata. I am under the impression that Faulds never noticed this inaccurate citation by Galton of his epoch-making Letter.

[6] See *Nature*, Vol. XXXVIII, pp. 173 *et* 201. In this lecture, Galton stated what no one ever disputed : " It has occurred independently to many persons to propose finger marks as a means of identification." See Royal Institution Proceedings, Vol. XII, *supra*, p. 357. Galton there gives certain instances of this, without disclosing actual dates. All in fact occurred after 1880. They might be consciously or unconsciously inspired by the contributions of Faulds and Herschel to *Nature* in that year. After so referring to these instances, Galton proceeds : " I may also allude to articles in the American Journal, *Science*, 1886, Vol. VIII, pp. 166 and 212." There were no articles, but simply two short letters *re* " Thumb Marks," viz. : (1) in issue of August 20, 1886, No. 185, under the signature of Walter Hough, U.S. National Museum, with reference to the Proceedings of the Royal Asiatic Society of 1847 (of course, prior to Herschel's being in India) and (2) in issue of September 3, 1886, No. 187, under the signature of Joseph F. James, Miami University, O. I refer later to the subject matter of these two letters in Chaps. XIV and XXIX.

[7] See Royal Institution Proceedings, *supra*, Vol. XII, p. 360.

[8] Proceedings of Royal Society, Vol. 45, p. 135.

[9] Royal Society Proceedings : Abstract. Vol. 48, p. 455 : Royal Society (Phil. Trans. B. 1891), Vol. CLXXXII, pp. 1 *et seq.*, also abstracted in *Nature*, Vol. XL, p. 455. According to Dr. Heindl, marks made by nails have nothing to do with finger-ridges, &c. Chinese authorities, he says, declare that nail-markings are representations of the new moon. See " Daktyloskopie," *supra*, p. 8. If Dr. Heindl be right in this, and he vouches his conclusions by citation of authorities, it shows how great intellects sometimes ventilate baseless theories. It is understood that both the nose and the ears have their own permanent and varied markings. Some identification experts would call these markings also in aid of criminal detection. No nails are, of course, present to account for any peculiarities in these cases.

[10] Phil. Trans. B. 1891, Vol. CLXXXII, p. 13.

[11] See report of Lecture in *Nature*, Vol. XLIII, p. 192.

[12] See Chap. XXIX.

XIII

GALTON : DESERTION OF BERTILLONAGE : 1891

EARLY in 1891, Galton, having apparently made fuller investigation, had better thoughts of fingerprints in regard to crime discovery.

On 30th April of that year, he sent a paper to the Royal Society, which, however, was not read until 27th November, 1891. Its title was " Method of Indexing Finger-Marks."[1] Galton here refers to the three divisions of such marks into " primaries, whorls, and loops," as if he were the sole originator of that classification. He now reaches the conclusion that " the practical efficiency " of any such method as that of Bertillon would be " vastly " increased by the adoption of a fingerprint system on the lines of his suggestions in this paper.[2] In it no credit of any kind was given to Faulds. In his 1880 *Nature* Letter, Faulds had clearly described his observation of papillary peculiarities, specially mentioning " loops," " whorls," and, obviously, it is thought, indicating " primaries " under " arches," the term now in actual use. Scotland Yard officials were in possession of Faulds's suggestions as made to Tunbridge. Neither Bertillon (1853-1914) nor Galton, however, then saw or admitted the conclusive superiority of the fingerprint system. Both were unable then to foresee how very soon thereafter in Britain, America, and elsewhere than in France, Bertillonage would be absolutely superseded, as a system unnecessarily complicated in application, very costly, and with no compensating certainty. In France it is now practically superseded by fingerprint identification.

Yet, Galton in the same year, 1891, did realize at last the high importance of fingerprints. In his article on "Identification by Finger Tips" in *The Nineteenth Century* magazine for August, 1891, Galton records his opinion that the fingerprint method is "workable at once, even in its present comparatively crude form."[3] There was then, he held, no "definitely established" method of employing fingerprints. All credit is taken in this article by Galton as being the first person to bring together and publish "trustworthy" evidence of the "lifelong persistence" of fingermarks, claiming that he had already provided this evidence in the "Memoir" read by him before the Royal Society "some months ago," being, it is presumed, his paper of April, 1891.[4]

In this *Nineteenth Century* article, his acknowledgments to Herschel were not omitted. Of Faulds, no mention was made. Faulds was a physician and surgeon, and his searching experiments and actual tests in regard to fingerprints certainly surpassed any experiments made by Herschel. Some think, and reasonably, that the recorded data of Faulds are even superior to all that Galton had collected. In no way can the evidence recorded by Faulds in his 1880 *Nature* Letter be described as unreliable or untrustworthy. It was in every way reliable and trustworthy. By some experiments of his own, Galton simply confirmed the conclusions reached in

PLATE II—LETTER OF DR. CHARLES SANNIÉ

REPUBLIQUE FRANÇAISE
——〜〜✶〜〜——

Paris, le 28 Octobre ———— 1936.

Le Docteur Charles SANNIÉ
Professeur agrégé à la Faculté de Médecine –
Directeur du Service de l'Identité
Judiciaire

à Maître Sherif WILTON
Conseil du Roi
Crosscryne,
Biggar,
Lanarkshire,
SCOTLAND.

Monsieur le Shérif,

J'ai bien reçu votre lettre du 21 Octobre, en deux
exemplaires, tous les deux signés. Je vous en retourne
un, comme vous me le demandez.

Le système anthropométrique, tel qu'il a été créé
par Bertillon, s'est transformé dès ses débuts. Bertillon
lui-même n'a pas tardé à adjoindre aux mensurations osseuses
le relevé des empreintes digitales.

A l'heure actuelle, et depuis 1921 environ, le
classement des fiches, pour les individus nés à partir de
1905, se fait uniquement à l'aide des données dactylosco-
piques. Pour les individus nés avant 1905, on utilise encore
comme subdivisions les mesures de la tête : longueur et lar-
geur, et la longueur du médius gauche suivant les cas,
les divisions initiales étant fournies par les empreintes
digitales.

Nous appelons le procédé d'identification par les
empreintes digitales : la dactyloscopie.

Je vous prie d'agréer, Monsieur le Shérif,
l'expression de ma considération très distinguée.

1880 by Faulds. To no other person than Faulds could Galton be taken as referring in connexion with the question of prior evidence on the reliability of fingerprints.

Again, in the same *Ninteenth Century* article, Galton professed to make a very exhaustive statement of all the uses to which, in addition to the identification of habitual criminals, he thought the system of fingerprints could be put. Not one of these uses mentioned by Galton in connexion with passports, corpse identity, &c., was very original. Somehow, Galton altogether missed the highly valuable method of identification of criminals from fingermarks left on bottles, safes, &c. It is possible, of course, that, notwithstanding Faulds's observations and instances, Galton thought no impressions of such marks could be effectively taken for evidential purposes, and thus he omitted to refer to such a use. Not so Faulds. Refer back to his 1880 *Nature* Letter.

Finally, in this *Ninteenth Century* article, Galton ends his flirtation with Bertillonage. He mentions, somewhat satirically, the stupid rebuff, as it has proved, he received from Bertillon. Galton states that Bertillon (who afterwords somewhat recanted his hasty judgment) assured him that he (Bertillon) " does not use fingerprints in connection with his system of anthropometric identification which is now employed in the French criminal service." France, or, rather, Bertillon, was averse to any detective assistance from Britain, just as Scotland Yard, it would seem, could not accept or acknowledge any assistance from anyone without the apparent possession of a halo of some kind. Yet Bertillon in 1905 wrote to Faulds officially that since 1894 the two methods were jointly used and " that greater security was now felt in identifying."[5] I believe it is more correct to say that Bertillon formally adopted in 1903 the fingerprint system and that he did so then by introducing the system of Vucetich, of La Plata.[6]

The extraordinary fact remains, as Dr. Robert Heindl, of Berlin, has noticed, that Bertillon is still regarded in France as " the spiritual father of finger prints "![7] Quite illusory! Dr. Edmond Locard, of Lyons, has recorded that

> " Le grand public en attribue la découverte à Bertillon, qui execrait cette méthode. Mais on ne prête qu'aux riches "![8]

Bertillon himself never gave any ground for such an idea. It is the result of rash surmise or perfunctory investigation.

Galton, as President of the Anthropological Institute, gave a demonstration in London on 10th November, 1891, of the methods of Dr. René Forgeot, of the Lyons Criminal Laboratory, in taking imprints of impressions left by suspected persons on crime scenes. He explained that London detectives were not then alive to Dr. Forgeot's methods. Not even to the simple methods of Faulds described in his 1880 *Nature* Letter!

Galton, as late as 16th October, 1902, is found writing to the Editor of *Nature* a letter on " Finger Print Evidence." Scotland Yard had sent him enlarged photographs, as he states, " lately submitted in a Court of Law to prove the identity of (a) the mark left on the window pane of a house after a burglary had been committed, with (b) the impression of H. J.,[9] a criminal then released and at large, whose finger prints are preserved and classified in Scotland Yard." Galton in this letter presents his views of " the readiest way of explaining to a judge and a jury the nature of the complete identity between (a) and (b)." Again, of course, not a word of or about Faulds! No wonder some American writers thought Galton was himself the discoverer of this mode of crime detection! In his November, 1891, demonstration, Galton declared that a recent London burglary had

baffled the London detectives. They could not take
imprints of impressions made on glass! Not a word that
but for Faulds this revolution in fine detective work
would not then have been thought of by Dr. Forgeot or
Galton himself! Henry was not installed at Scotland
Yard as Assistant Commissioner until in or about 1900.
He was in India, as Galton's protégé in this matter,
doing his best there to establish Bertillonage, and in
1897 actually profiting, not by Bertillonage, but by the
application of Faulds's ideas. I tell of this in Chapter
XVII.

The most interesting episode with regard to Bertillon
and Bertillonage is surely this—

In the night between 16th and 17th October, 1902,
and in the residence of a dentist in the rue du Faubourg,
St. Honoré, Paris, his manservant, Reibel, was
murdered. The imprints of four bloody fingers were
found upon a window of the house. Impressions of these
compared and agreed with those recorded of one, Henri
Scheffer, of Léon, Brittany, listed among the classified
fingermarks of convicted criminals. No suspicion had
attached to him. So, thanks to Bertillon's largeness of
mind in latterly calling in aid of justice the fingerprint
system, Scheffer was arrested. He confessed. On 14th
March, 1903, he was sentenced by the Seine Assizes *aux
travaux forcés à perpétuité.*[10] But for Faulds, Bertillon
would not have achieved this, his first great success in a
case where, so far as records go, there was absolutely
nothing but fingermarks to indicate the culprit. The
registered fingermarks completed the identity. In the
merit of the conception of this register Faulds and
Herschel mutually share. All the elaborate anthropological measurements of Bertillon's own system were of
no assistance without Faulds's window-glass fingerprints
in the discovery of Scheffer as the murderer. Dr. Locard
indicates that there may have been some additional facts

relied upon in Scheffer's case. He describes "L'affaire de la Rue Ravat, Lyons," in June, 1910, as the first case in France of any conviction (it was for house-breaking) obtained " sur l'unique preuve dactylosco-pique."[11]

Since about 1921, the fingerprint system has been alone in operation in France. It is only as regards persons born before 1905 that the French Service of Criminal Identification employs Bertillon measurements of the head, with the length and size of the left middle finger, according to circumstances. These are used in conjunc-tion with the fingerprints of the individuals. The accom-panying photostat (Plate II) of the letter, dated 28th October, 1936, to me from Dr. Charles Sannié, the Director in charge of the Police Identification Bureau in Paris, vouches these facts.

NOTES

[1] Proceedings of Royal Society, Vol. 49, p. 540. See also *Nature*, 1891, Vol. XLIV, p. 141, under date 11th June, 1891, for " Finger Print Indices " by Galton.

[2] See Proceedings of Royal Society, Vol. 49, p. 540.

[3] Vol. 30, p. 303.

[4] Proceedings of Royal Society, Vol. 49, p. 540.

[5] See Faulds's article on " Finger Prints " in *Knowledge* for April, 1911, and his " Guide," *supra*, pp. 4 *et* 5, where the French text is given. In a communication to me by one, high up in the judicial administration of France, " Le système d'identification des malfaiteurs basé sur les empreintes digitales " is referred to as " Le Système Bertillon." How widespread is this error ! Even in Scotland, I have found it so described. The letter to me of Dr. Charles Sannié noted at the end of this Chap. dispels all doubt. See Plate II facing page 49.

[6] See Chap. XVI and Número Extraordinario, in memory of *Vucetich, of Revista de Criminalogia Psiquiatria y Medicina Legal*, January, 1926. Buenos Aires.

[7] " Daktyloskopie," p. 72.

[8] See his article on " The Identification of Suspects," *supra*, Vol. 13, p. 20.

[9] I believe this case is that noted by me under the name of Harry Jackson, and under date 13th September, 1902, in the series of convic-tions through fingerprints between 1898 and 1909 given in detail in Chap. XXIV.

[10] The particulars of Scheffer's case were supplied to me by the

PLATE III—CHINESE LAND CONTRACT

Finger mark, 1839

Chief of the Parisian Service of Judiciary Identity by letter, dated 24th July, 1936.

[11] " La Preuve par les Empreintes Digitales " in *Archives d'Anthropologie*, 1911, Vol. XXVI, p. 254. There is considerable confusion in fingerprint textbooks about a case in Kansas, U.S.A., known as that of " the two Wests," in which the superiority of fingerprint identification over that of Bertillonage was demonstrated. Some, including Faulds, narrate it as a case over a murder charge. It seems to have concerned only the identity of two individuals. Bertillonage found no difference between them in measurements, appearance, &c. Only fingerprints solved the puzzle. See " Personal Identification," *supra*, p. 28.

XIV

GALTON'S " FINGER PRINTS " : 1892

IN 1892 Galton published his first book on fingerprints.[1] In the Introduction, as elsewhere, he acknowledged his " large indebtedness " to Herschel. It is not surprising that all Galton's eulogistic references went to Herschel's head, accounting in no little measure for his fanciful idea, to which he adhered to the end of his life, that from him the Chinese had derived their knowledge of fingerprints and of their application in crime discovery. The clear and grotesque implication of his fancy was that in this roundabout way Faulds had obtained in Japan the genesis for his conclusions upon the investigations he had made there into the character of finger-ridges.

Galton's work was reviewed anonymously for *The Times* in its issue of 10th November, 1892, and, in the course of flattering comments, the reviewer observed—

" It is needless to say that the whole subject is handled with that rare patience and thoroughness in investigation and that keen, but cautious, acumen in interpretation, which are characteristic of all Mr. Galton's work."

In view of what this chapter discloses, it seems impossible to endorse this certificate.

In his Introduction, Galton observed—

> " It seems difficult to believe . . . that our criminal
> administration can long neglect the use of such a
> powerful auxiliary."[2]

It took the London Metropolitan Police wellnigh ten
years from 1892 to institute a system of fingerprint identification and more than twenty years from the time when
the project was first promulgated by Faulds. In 1894
their Criminal Investigation Department resorted to
anthropometric methods in addition to the photographic
system commenced in 1890 for the better identification
of habitual offenders; in 1900 the Department experienced
the defects of Bertillonage; and it was only in the second
half of 1901 that the fingerprint system was introduced.
See the Annual Reports of the Commissioner for these
years. H.M.S.O.

Galton was unaware in 1892, and I assume that Police
Authorities in London did not know, that Vucetich, of
La Plata, before the publication of Galton's book in
1892, had devised and put in operation his system of
classification, and so successfully that it was adopted in
many countries besides Argentina.[3] It is fair to Galton
to record that but for an article in a French Scientific
Review by a French writer, expounding a thesis of
Galton on " Finger Prints " as taken from one of his
lectures in 1891, Vucetich and his system might never
have been heard of. Galton became aware of Vucetich
and his work as a dactyloscopist; but, so far as I know,
he never did much to make British readers aware of him.

Galton further in his Introduction, as he does at more
length in Chapter V, refers to his "A. L. W." (arches,
loops, and whorls) system of classification. He could not
of course claim credit for this as an original discovery.
Faulds mentioned such a grouping in his 1880 *Nature*
Letter. Galton never devised any " armario-casillero,"
the very foundation of every proper system in " fecha

de impresiones sobre puestas." So far as Galton's classification went, he had only three types. Vucetich termed
his four groups, derived from the French article he had
read, as arcos=arches (primaries of Galton), vertillos=
whorls or spirals, and presillas or loops, which he divided
into inner and outer.[4]

It is only in the second chapter of his book that any
reference is made by Galton to Faulds. The title of this
chapter is " Previous Use of Finger Prints." After stating that Bewick, the Newcastle engraver and naturalist,
was " the first well-known person who appears to have
studied the lineations of the ridges as a means of identification," Galton proceeds to say—

> " Occasional instances of careful study may also
> be noted, such as that of Mr. Fauld (sic) (Nature,
> XXII, p. 605, October 28, 1880), who seems to have
> taken much pains."

Not much in the way of an invitation to consult Nature!
In association with " Mr. Fauld," Galton next mentions
" Mr. Tabor " and " Mr. Gilbert Thompson," two
Americans, and alludes to them in such complimentary
terms from the very detailed description he gives of their
uses of fingerprints as to suggest to his readers that
any work of Faulds was not of commensurate importance. Their uses were quite unimportant. How far all
others fell short of Herschel in interest, Galton then
fully describes.

In this same Chapter II, Galton underestimates the
significance of the evidence of ancient fingerprints in
regard to their identification value. A striking illustration of his attitude up to this time to every suggestion
of their existence prior to 1858, when, as Galton knew,
Herschel's interest in fingerprints originated as a
" hobby,"[5] is the following passage from this chapter—

> So, when a chief presses his hand, smeared with blood
> or grime, upon a clean surface, a mark is left in some

degree characteristic of him. It may be that of a broad stumpy hand, or of a long thin one; it may be large or small; it may even show lines corresponding to the principal creases of the palm. Such hand prints have been made and repeated in many semi-civilised nations, and have even been impressed in vermilion on their State documents as formerly by the sovereign of Japan. Though mere smudges, they serve in a slight degree to individualise the signer, while they are more or less clothed with the superstitious attributes of personal contact. So far as I can learn, no higher form of finger printing than this has ever existed, in regular and well-understood use, in any barbarous or semi-civilised nation. The ridges dealt with in this book could not be seen at all in such rude prints, much less could they be utilised as strictly distinctive features. It is possible that when impressions of the fingers have been made in wax, and used as seals to documents, they may sometimes have been subjected to minute scrutiny; but no account has yet reached me of trials in any of their courts of law, about disputed signatures, in which the identity of the party who was said to have signed with his finger print, had been established or disproved by comparing it with a print made by him then and there. The reader need be troubled with only a few examples, taken out of a considerable collection of extracts from books and letters, in which prints, or rather daubs of the above kind, are mentioned.

Galton was so enamoured of his thought that nobody had known or heard anything of fingerprint signatures until, as he believed, Herschel had brought them to light through his experiences in India, that any reference to a " semi-civilized " people, such as the ancient Chinese seemed to him to be, was for him in its effect very much like that of a red rag to a bull. The discussion of this passage of special pleading for his preconceived views would be a waste of ink. One wonders how Galton could expect to find records of trials from early times of the kind to which he alludes.

Galton proceeded as follows:—

A good instance of their small real value may be seen in the *Trans. China Branch of the Royal Asiatic Society,*

Part I, 1847, published at Hong-Kong, which contains
a paper on " Land Tenure in China," by T. Meadows
Taylor (*sic* for " T. Taylor Meadows "), with a deed
concerning a sale of land, in facsimile, and its translation : this ends, " The mother and the son, the sellers,
have in the presence of all the parties, received the price
of the land in full, amounting to sixty-four taels and five
mace in perfect dollars weighed in scales. *Impression of
the finger of the mother, of the maiden name of Chin.*"
The impression, as it appears in the woodcut, is roundish
in outline, and was therefore made by the tip and not
the bulb of the finger. Its surface is somewhat mottled,
but there is no trace of any ridges.

The first observation upon this passage that occurs to
anyone upon its consideration is why, in the face of a
facsimile of the whole deed with the finger-impression, Galton should base his conclusion not on
that impression, but on the impression " *as it appears
in the woodcut.*" I italicize these words. Galton
could not intend to convey the idea that the woodcut
representation of the seller's finger-impression was
really better than the facsimile impression. It would
be natural for most readers to infer that both the
facsimile and the woodcut impressions were at least
identical. If, as might be the fact, there was no finger-
marked impression on the facsimile in the particular
volume, examined by Galton, containing the article in
question, then Galton should have made this fact known.
It is inexplicable why he did not deal with the ricepaper
facsimile impression on the assumption that it contained
the fingermark or if it were somehow omitted, he did
not refer to that fact.

The accuracy of Galton's opinion upon this alleged
" good instance " cannot be tested without referring to
(1) the very interesting paper of Meadows; (2) the ricepaper facsimile of the Chinese conveyance in question,
with its fingermark inserted between pages 12 and 13 of
Meadows's article, the first in the volume of the China

Branch Transactions cited by Galton; and (3) the translation by Meadows of the Chinese characters relative to the receipt of the price as found by the district magistrate, together with the "woodcut."

Upon investigation, the observations of Galton are found to be inaccurate and misleading. No one suggests that this result was designed. But it shows how a scientist, credited with almost infallibility in his propositions and speculations, when obsessed with partisan views, can err. His attitude to Chinese literature was narrow and almost perverse. In making use specially of the particular passage quoted from this article by Thomas Taylor Meadows (1819-68), a very able writer on Chinese topics, to support his argument, Galton went far astray. I deal at length in Chapter XXIX with the part played by the Chinese in the history of fingerprints.

In regard to this particular Chinese document, my attention was first called to it from perusing the article on "The History of the Finger-Print System," by Berthold Laufer (1874-1934) in the Annual Report of the *Smithsonian* Institution for 1912.*[6] For the purpose of illustrating his paper, Laufer there reproduced as Plate I from the ricepaper facsimile in the copy he possessed of the volume containing Meadows's article, the part appended to the original deed of 1839, narrating the receipt of the price for the land sold, with the facsimile of the impression of the finger of the mother, mentioned in the quotation made by Galton. This part of the ricepaper facsimile is also reproduced here as my Plate III.[7] Further, the "receipt" part of the translation, as quoted by Galton, with the accompanying "woodcut" is here also shown by photostat as my Plate IV. It is taken from the article of Meadows, as contained in the 1847 volume in Cambridge University Library.[8]

---

* For brevity, this article is afterwards referred to as his "1912 *Smithsonian* article."

I could not understand how this facsimile of the
mother's finger-impression shown in Laufer's Plate I could
be characterized by anyone as a " daub." Anyone would
correctly describe the " woodcut " representation as
nothing else than a " daub." It was natural to infer
from Galton's reference to this " woodcut " that it was
an absolutely correct copy of the woman's fingermark.
Galton intended his readers to draw the conclusion that
such a " daub " was of no use in fingerprint identification. Of course, it was of no value whatever. No one
with any knowledge of finger-ridges, despite the paren-
thetical statement of Meadows, however, could correctly
describe this " woodcut " representation as an " impression." Meadows merely placed the " woodcut " where he
did, as indicating the place in the original ricepaper
facsimile of the position of the actual fingerprint, very
much in the same way as legal seals are represented
on share transfers or other documents printed in this
country. The daub is, indeed, in this case a very crude
representation of a fingermark, compared with engravings made by men like Bewick. Its engraver took no
trouble to etch anything like a resemblance to finger-
furrows or ridges. It is doubtful whether in 1847 and
in China a photostat could have been made.[9]

Under the impression that Galton, in dealing with
the " woodcut " was using the ricepaper facsimile fingermark as seen in the volume he consulted and assuming
it was the same as Laufer's Plate I, I had that fingermark as copied from that Plate independently examined
by Detective-Lieutenant Bertie J. Hammond, Fingerprint Expert, Glasgow City Police, and Captain Frederick
E. Zwirz, of the Criminal Identification Bureau, New
York City Police. Both returned opinions to the same
effect, bearing out what inspection by the eye itself
discloses. It is sufficient to state the conclusions of the

American expert. The impression of the woman's finger, according to him, was made by the bulb as well as by the tip of the finger, and the imprint shows clearly defined ridge-characteristics serviceable for identification purposes.

Such a mistake on Galton's part in dealing with the " woodcut " or " daub " as the basis of his prejudicial comment upon old Chinese fingerprints does not appear to have any excuse. It was singularly unfortunate, in any event, for Galton to base his criticism upon this illustration, as if it applied generally to all Chinese fingerprint signatures. Readers of Galton's " Finger Prints," without consulting for themselves Meadows's paper, would accept as absolutely correct his dogmatic opinion. Galton fell foul of Faulds as one who, in his opinion, too easily jumped to " rash " conclusions; but in his case, if rash, they proved true. Galton's " jump " in this instance was both rash and baseless.

For the purpose of illustrating his 1912 *Smithsonian* article, Laufer reproduced, as he there says, the original document of 1839; but, in fact, he reproduced for that article in his " Plate I " from the ricepaper facsimile only the relevant part of it covered by my photostat of Meadows's translation. Laufer narrates that the finger-impression of Mrs. Ch'ên (" Chin " Meadows renders the Chinese characters) is headed by the words " Impression of the finger of the mother, née Ch'ên."

Laufer made this reproduction because, as he states, it " furnishes actual evidence of the use of an individual finger-impression in China before the system was developed in Europe." Obviously, he thought the finger-impression was good for identity purposes. He further observes that " Sir Francis Galton comments on this fingerprint in the words: ' The impression, as it appears in the woodcut, is roundish in outline, and was therefore made by the tip and not the bulb of the finger. Its surface is somewhat mottled, but there is no trace of any ridges.' " Laufer, strangely it now seems, made no comment of his own upon this extract from Galton's " Finger Prints." The absurdity of Galton's comment on comparison with Laufer's " Plate I " is transparent. Clearly, in the mind of Laufer, despite the words " as it appears in the woodcut," Galton was commenting on the finger-impression on the original deed according to the ricepaper facsimile of it that he found incorporated with his copy of the 1847 " Transactions." That is what his " Plate I " demonstrates. It has no resemblance to the translation " woodcut." My reproduction of the Chinese facsimile impression is, I think, clearer in definition than Laufer's Plate I. My Plate III is taken from the original facsimile in Laufer's possession. Galton's comments applied, however, solely to that " woodcut," and could not possibly apply to the impression on Laufer's ricepaper facsimile. Probably, Laufer was mystified, and so made no comment.

Dr. Heindl, in his " Daktyloskopie," *supra*, reproduces Laufer's " Plate I " in citing his valuable article. He has apparently not noticed that Galton and Laufer dealt with two different things: Galton with a make-believe; Laufer with what, I think, he inferred from the ricepaper facsimile was Mrs. Ch'ên's actual finger-impression. Dr. Heindl does not traverse the criticism of Galton.[10] Both Laufer and Dr. Heindl assumed, as at first I did myself, that Galton's criticism was based on the fingermark as shown on Laufer's Plate I: my Plate III.

The Chinese, both ancient and modern, must be credited with the intelligence that " daubed " or " smudged " finger-impressions had and have no place in the execution of solemn contracts. They could not be referring to such finger impressions of which it is

61

said they "verify the lines on a man's fingers, in connection with the impression on a deed,"[11] or record in A.D. 782, for example, in a contract, that "The two parties have found this just and clear and have affixed the impressions of their fingers as a distinctive mark."[12]

I refer upon this subject to Chapter XXVII, where I deal at length with the very striking illustration of the conclusive identification of a murdered Hindu. His head and face were so mutilated that no one who had known him could recognize him. Identification was rendered possible only by the complete correspondence found between the thumbprint impression taken from his corpse and that of his thumbprint signature to a lease of his bazaar in Delhi which he had thus authenticated some years before his murder. Assuming Mrs. Ch'ên had been murdered and likewise mutilated, and that her thumbprint could have been obtained, there could have been absolutely no doubt that her thumbprint on her sale deed would have enabled her corpse in the same way to have been absolutely identified. I may mention that Messrs. Hammond and Zwirz, in making their individual examinations for me, based these upon the illustrative plate of Laufer as found in the 1912 Annual Report of the *Smithsonian* Institution. The plate as reproduced by me is taken not from that published illustration but from the actual ricepaper facsimile in the 1847 volume of the China Branch Transactions, belonging to Laufer and now in the possession of the Field Museum of Natural History, Chicago. The Director, Mr. C. C. Gregg, of that Museum, graciously had this photostat so made for me. The lineations of Mrs. Ch'ên's thumbprint come out in this photostat so clearly that with it before one, the layman can see how thoroughly instrumental it could be for criminal or other identification purposes.

The second chapter of Galton's " Finger Prints " ends thus:

> " If the use of finger prints ever becomes of general importance, Sir William Herschel must be regarded as the first who devised a feasible method for regular use, and afterwards officially adopted it."

So put, no one can or does dispute this statement. It does not, however, reveal the whole truth. Herschel certainly began the registration of fingerprints chiefly for the recognition of convicted persons. But he devised no system of classification, and the use to which he put his collection of fingermarks had no application to the detection of crime through fingermarks being left in or on places of crime, whether by recidivists or other criminals.

In the third chapter, Galton only incidentally refers to the employment of fingerprint-impressions in tracing criminals by alluding to the work of the Lyons Laboratory of Criminal Anthropology. He does not, as in fairness he might have done, refer to the prior experiments of Faulds in Japan, as described in his 1880 *Nature* Letter. The Lyons Laboratory owed its origin much more to that Letter of Faulds than to the *Nature* Letter of Herschel in response to Faulds's.[13] Whether or not, in the light of ancient Chinese literature, Herschel's use of fingerprints merits a claim to originality (the same criticism, of course, applying also to Faulds; with, however, in his case his first surmise of what research into that literature might reveal), it is absolutely clear that until 1880 Herschel never thought of the employment of fingerprint-impressions in tracking criminals. Of that possibility he knew for the first time only from Faulds's letter to *Nature*.

In the sixth chapter of the book, dealing with " Persistence," Galton, again, mainly relies on the examination of fingermarks of individuals made at different dates as proving their permanency. While he refers, and properly so, to Herschel's experiences over a long period as supporting the unchanging character of the papillary ridges, it is remarkable that, in a considered treatise of this kind, he should in no way have specifically noticed Faulds's valuable experiments, which were of a wholly different and more truly scientific nature.

In this sixth chapter, somewhat cynically and with obviously clear reference to Faulds (no one else can be suggested), Galton also repeats his views as expressed in his Royal Society Paper of 27th November, 1890—

> Very good evidence and careful enquiry is thus seen to justify the popular idea of the persistence of finger-markings that has hitherto been too rashly jumped at and which wrongly ascribed the persistence to the general appearance of the pattern, rather than to the *minutiæ* it contains.

Comments already made upon similar observations of Galton need not be repeated.

The opinion of Mr. C. Ainsworth Mitchell, M.A., D.Sc.(Oxon.), F.I.C., &c., Editor of *The Analyst*, ex-President of the Medico-Legal Society, and author, among other works, of " The Scientific Detective and The Expert Witness," may be usefully quoted—

> The ridge patterns in the skin are not only unchangeable but also cannot be permanently removed by any means short of complete mutilation of the finger or hand. This was clearly proved by a series of experiments made by Dr. Faulds in Japan.[14]

In " Science and the Criminal," published by Dr. Mitchell in 1911, the study of finger-lineations made by Faulds is described as " exhaustive."[15]

Dr. J. Edgar Hoover's opinion, quoted by me in Chapter XXXIII, among American tributes to Faulds, may be also referred to as being in accord with the conclusions of Dr. Mitchell.

In the tenth chapter of his book, it is noteworthy that

PLATE IV—MEADOWS'S TRANSLATION OF CHINESE LAND CONTRACT

Leang, district magistrate of Nan-hae, and bearing by Imperial authority the title of sub-prefect, finds on inspection the price in the deed to be sixty-four taels and five mace.

Negotiators, } Hoo-yu-ming.
 } Hoo-yuen-chang.

1. The mother and son, the sellers, have in the presence of all the parties, received the price of the land in full, amounting to sixty-four taels and five mace in perfect dollars weighed in scales.

(*Impression of the finger of the mother, of the maiden name of Chin.*)

This deed of absolute sale in perpetuity was executed on the 15th day of the 3d month of the 19th Taoukwang year, by Hwang-kwei-lung, in his actual handwriting.

(A true Translation.)

T.T.M.

Wood-cut impression of finger mark

Galton definitely abandoned his previously declared admiration and exclusive preference for Bertillonage, stating that—

> " it can rarely supply more than grounds for very strong suspicion; the method of fingerprints affords certainty."

Galton calculated that the risk of duplication of a single fingerprint, or dactylogram, is as one in sixty-four thousand millions.[16] Wentworth and Wilder, leading American authorities, in their " Personal Identification," point out that Galton's is the lowest of all calculations by various investigators.[17] It is sufficient for all practical purposes, and comes as near as reasonably can be to " absolute " certainty.[18] And, if such is the calculation for one finger, how much more for all ten fingers! Tighe Hopkins (1856-1919), in an article on " Crime and the Finger Print," substantially based on Galton's " Finger Prints," observed—

> " It is improbable that once in ten thousand years, the imprints of the finger tips of two pairs of hands would be found to coincide."[19]

It is not perhaps surprising that, in the latest addition to criminological bibliography, the authors should assert that Galton really derived his classification system from the Chinese. I refer to " Modern Criminal Investigation," by Dr. Harry Söderman, of Sweden, and Mr. John J. O'Connell, Deputy Chief Inspector, New York City Police Department, and Dean of the Police Academy.[20]

They say, page 57—

> " The German criminologist, Robert Heindl, has thoroughly studied the history of fingerprints in the Far East and found that they were already commonly used for identification purposes during the T'ang dynasty (618 to 906 A.D.). Later the Chinese

developed a classification of fingerprints based upon loops and whorls for the identification of criminals. This Chinese system of classification was described by a Dr. M'Carthy (*sic*) in an American journal in 1886.[21] Galton learned of this contribution. Heindl is convinced that Galton derived his classification system from the Chinese. The Galton-Henry system, the one most widely used, is therefore said to be derived from China.''

The apologists of Galton would strongly dispute this statement, putting him, as it does, into a very ironical situation. It appeared to me to be inaccurate and to convey more than Dr. Heindl could have intended by any statement made in his '' Daktyloskopie.''

I communicated this passage to Dr. Heindl, and, as I anticipated, he informed me that the joint authors of this most informative work were in error in stating that he '' is convinced that Galton derived his classification system from the Chinese.'' Dr. Heindl (translating his own words) informed me that, in his opinion, stated briefly, Herschel's attention was drawn to the value of fingerprints for purposes of identification by Chinese coolies in Calcutta, and that Galton finally used for *primary* classification the grouping into whorls and non-whorls, a classification already known to the Chinese and of which he says Galton knew from the contribution in the American *Science* Journal of 1886. Dr. Heindl referred me to his '' Daktyloskopie,'' pp. 48 and 218, note 2. By far the larger part of Galton's formula of his registration method cannot be traced back, in Dr. Heindl's view, to Chinese models. In substance, as I have already also indicated in another chapter, Messrs. Söderman and O'Connell are right in suggesting that Herschel's inspiration and Galton's application of his experiences are derived indirectly from Herschel's knowledge of Eastern coolies. Dr. Heindl points this out in his "Daktylos-kopie," which, according to these American writers, " is unique in the literature of identification."

No one perusing " Finger Prints " can fail to see and admire the intellectual brilliance of Galton and the value of all his calculations and deductions.

It was unfortunate that Faulds was never personally introduced by some influential friend to Galton. There is little doubt that Herschel's introduction to Galton, with his title, his relationship to the great astronomer, his social position, and his residence in Oxford, would unconsciously bias Galton in his excessive estimate of Herschel's share in fingerprints. The discovery of the registration use of fingerprints for identification purposes by Herschel, and his introduction through it to Galton, naturally led to their mutual friendship, as Galton practically admits, or, at least, implies, in his " Memories of My Life."

NOTES

[1] Galton's supplementary chapter, published in 1893, under the title of " Decipherment of Blurred Fingerprints," is an analysis of further *data* supplied to him by Herschel. It does not bear materially on controversial points in this book. Galton's " Finger Print Directories," published in 1895, and dedicated to Herschel " in recognition of your initiative in employing finger prints as official signatures " was based on the Report of 12th February, 1894, of the Troup Committee into the " Best Means of Identifying Habitual Criminals." Galton gives in this brochure long extracts of his evidence before the Troup Committee.

[2] p. 16.

[3] See Chap. XVI for life and work of Vucetich.

[4] See Article by Don Antonio Herrero on " El Sistema Dactilo-scópico Argentino," pp. 20, 33 *et seq.* 1926. Buenos Aires. It is understood that loops, ulnar and radial, account for 60 per cent. of the four different types, whorls, single or double cored, and composites between them for 35 per cent. and arches the remaining 5 per cent. Inner and outer *termini* control ridge counting and tracing and pattern orientation.

[5] Herschel indicates this in " The Origin of Finger Printing," p. 10. 1916. London. Oxford University Press.

[6] Washington, D.C., 1913. See p. 639.

[7] The Director of the Field Museum of Natural History, Chicago, instructed the photostat to be taken for me from the ricepaper

facsimile in the 1847 volume of the " China Branch Transactions,", which belonged to Laufer and is now in the Museum Collection.

8 Kindly borrowed for me by Dr. Norman M'Lean, late Master of Christ's College, Cambridge.

9 I have explained in a paper entitled " Facsimile Dissimilarities " in *Notes and Queries,* under date, 8th January, 1938, Vol. 174, No. 2, p. 20, facts that I have ascertained to the effect that the ricepaper facsimile is not uniform as regards the finger-impression in all the published volumes of 1847. Some have no fingerprint at all. This disconformity has no bearing on Galton's mistake. The printer's devil by inadvertence shows the Chinese thumb-print, &c., upside down in *Notes and Queries.*

10 " Daktyloskopie," *supra,* p. 25.

11 See Laufer's Note 1 on p. 639 of the *Smithsonian* Institution's Report, *supra,* where he cites No. 13, being No. 133 of Giles's Chinese-English Dictionary. Cf. Dr. Heindl's reference to this same citation in " Daktyloskopie," *supra,* p. 28.

12 Quoted by Laufer from a French writer in an article contributed by Laufer in *Science,* 25th May, 1917, Vol. 45, p. 505, New York. The Science Press. I refer in Chap. XXI more particularly to this article by Laufer, and in Chap. XXIX to this document, among others, discovered by Sir Aurel Stein in Eastern Turkestan, and now in the British Museum, London.

13 Dr. Heindl expresses the view that the legal-medical men of the University of Lyons continued the work of Faulds, but their sympathies were more with Bertillonage. See " Daktyloskopie," p. 69.

14 p. 63. 1931. Cambridge. W. Heffer & Sons, Ltd.

15 p. 66. London. Sir Isaac Pitman & Sons, Ltd. It is now out of print.

16 Chap. VII, p. 110.

17 p. 319, *supra.*

18 Absolute certainty is not required in courts of law. See Lord President Clyde's opinion in *Hamilton* v. *H.M. Advocate,* quoted in Chap. XXX on " Evidential Admissibility and Value of Fingerprints."

19 *Cassell's Family Magazine,* May, 1902, Vol. 33, pp. 323 and 327.

20 1936. New York and London. Funk & Wagnalls Co.

21 I can find no article such as is here suggested. I believe these authors must be referring to a sentence in the letter of Mr. Walter B. Hough to *Science,* in 1886, Vol. VIII, p. 66, in which he says : " Dr. D. B. M'Cartee informs us that the Chinese class the *striæ* at the ends of the fingers into ' pots,' when arranged in a coil and ' hooks,' when they form a curving loop." By 1888 Galton knew of the contents of Mr. Hough's letter.

XV

FAULDS AND HERSCHEL : PEN DUEL : 1894

IF Galton erred, as it is submitted he did, in failing to acknowledge in just measure the merits of Faulds's experiments, researches, and conclusions, no unbiased person can justify the wholly negative attitude Herschel developed towards Faulds. Ignorance of Faulds was an impossible excuse for Herschel, in view of his own contribution to *Nature* in 1880, admittedly evoked by Faulds's earlier Letter in that journal. Herschel's subsequent writings showed a distrust of Faulds's sincerity. If Herschel conveyed such a sentiment to Galton about Faulds, it may go far to explain the rather unchivalrous treatment of Faulds in their respective publications, with the not unnatural consequence of creating prejudice against Faulds in the minds of Government officials whom Faulds met subsequent to 1892.

It is just, however, both to Galton and Herschel, to say that Faulds, who appears under their treatment to have somewhat forgotten himself, offended both by the terms of his communication[1] to *Nature* in October, of 1894. He was unjustifiably sceptical of Herschel. His communication was, however, in just protest against the place assigned to Herschel by Galton before a Government Committee presided over by Mr. Charles Edward Troup, of the Home Office. Here is a reprint of it—

On the Identification of Habitual Criminals by Finger-Prints.

A PARLIAMENTARY Blue Book on " The Identification of Habitual Criminals," which has recently been issued, reports on *The Finger-Print System*, stated to have been " first suggested, and to some extent applied practically, by Sir William Herschel."

The chairman of the committee appointed by Mr. Asquith, whose report contains the above statement, refers me for his evidence on this point to Mr. Galton's work on " Finger-Prints " (Macmillan & Co., 1892).

My " careful study " of the subject is mentioned there, and an article of mine in *Nature*, October 28, 1880 (vol. xxii. p. 605), is referred to. It is correctly indexed in the " Index Medicus " for the year, published in 1881, although Mr. Galton spells and indexes my name incorrectly. That article, I believe, is absolutely the first notice of the subject contained in English literature, and the conclusion I reached therein was that the patterns of the skin-furrows, with their distinctive loops, whorls, and lines, breaking and blending like the junctions in a railway map, were capable of being readily used as a reliable and permanent basis for the " scientific identification of criminals." I conclude my paper with the statement that " There can be no doubt as to the advantage of having, besides their photographs, a nature-copy of the forever-unchangeable finger-furrows of important criminals."

Sir William Herschel wrote in *Nature*, November 25, of the same year, alleging that he had " been taking sign-manuals by means of finger-marks for now more than twenty years." It does not yet appear that anything had been published on the subject by that gentleman till my contribution called forth his letter a month afterwards. The collections made by Sir W. Herschel were recently placed in Mr. Galton's hands, and that writer states that " they refer to one or more fingers, and in a few instances to the whole hand, of fifteen different persons." (" Finger-Prints," p. 9.)

It is not stated how many of these had been imprinted prior to my first calling attention to the subject. At present it would seem that Sir W. Herschel had not accumulated the impressions at a more rapid rate than that of one person in two years! As we are informed in the letter to *Nature*, referred to above, that the identification of pensioners had been secured in this way, that the method was in use in all the registration offices of the district, and that " on commitment to gaol, each prisoner had to sign with his finger," I should have expected that a somewhat more extensive collection might have been secured. As priority of publication is generally held to count for something, and as I knew absolutely nothing of Sir W. Herschel's studies, nor ever heard of anyone in India who did, some little evidence on the point of priority would be of interest even now.

Mr. Galton says, of Sir W. Herschel, " He informs me that he submitted, in 1877, a report in semi-official form to the Inspector-General of Gaols, asking to be allowed to extend the process; but no result followed." (p. 28.) A copy of that semi-official report would go far to settle the question of priority, as its date is nearly two years previous to my having noticed the finger-furrows. No reference to them was then to be found in any anatomical work that I could find access to, and no writer on identification had ever thought of them as a means to that end. My interest, like that of Purkenje, arose from a special study of the sense of touch, and I was then lecturing to medical students on the " Physiology of the Senses." Having myopic eyes which enable me to write with ease the Lord's Prayer three times in the space of a sixpence, I soon noticed the unique patterns which the papillary ridges formed. I happened to be studying the prehistoric pottery of Japan at the same time, and became interested in observing that these patterns were similar, but, I thought, finer and more slender than those of the present day, which pointed, I conjectured, to the employment of children in early fictile art. However that may be, my knowledge of the subject had a natural and independent genesis.

The subject of identification by this means has been brought under the notice of the authorities on criminal matters of different countries by me from time to time, and some years before Mr. Galton's work was published, Scotland Yard placed one of its most enlightened officers in communication with me on the subject. Inspector Tunbridge studied the subject with me during a forenoon. Even in 1880, I prepared copper-plate outlines of the two hands, accompanied with instructions as to obtaining finger-prints, and some two chief points on the palm, where the *rugæ* are characteristic. Sir W. Herschel's letter mentions prints of one finger only as being obtained from prisoners on commitment. On page 79 of the Blue Book mentioned above, " Instructions for taking Finger-Prints " are given for the benefit of prison warders, and the ten fingers are to be printed from, as I have advocated. I may add that I have not the slightest wish to diminish the credit that may be due to Sir W. Herschel. What I wish to point out is that his claim ought to be brought out a little more clearly than has yet been done, either by himself or by Mr. Galton. What precisely did he do, and when ?

HENRY FAULDS.

It is noteworthy that in this letter Faulds does not allude to, far less stress, his best, and now admitted, claim in the identification of criminals. He deals only with fingerprint registration. Both Faulds and Herschel share the honour there.

Unfortunately for Faulds's doubt, Herschel was able to produce his " Hooghly Letter." Unquestionably, it proves Herschel's claim to have discerned, as he put it, the more or less permanent nature of fingermarks and to have originated the limited use of fingermarks for identification purposes in prisons and otherwise.

Herschel's response appeared in *Nature* of 22nd November, 1894.[2] It was in these terms : —

Finger-Prints.

I have been quite unable, since I saw Mr. Faulds's letter in your issue of October 4, to take the matter of it in hand hitherto ; and I do so now only because I think Mr. Faulds is entitled to raise the question if he pleases. To the best of my knowledge, Mr. Faulds' letter of 1880 was, what he says it was, the first notice in the public papers, in your columns, of the value of finger-prints for the purpose of identification. His statement that he came upon it independently in 1879 (?1878) commands acceptance as a matter of course. At the same time I scarcely think that such short experience as that justified his announcing that the finger-furrows were " for-ever unchanging."

How I chanced upon the thing myself in 1858, and followed it up afterwards, has been very kindly stated on my authority by Mr. Galton, at whose disposal I gladly placed all my materials on his request. Those published by him are only a part of what were available. (See his " Finger-Prints," page 27, and his " Blurred Finger-Prints.") To what is there stated I need now only add, at Mr. Faulds' request, a copy of the demi-official letter which I addressed in 1877 to the then Inspector-General of Jails in Bengal. That the reply I received appeared to me altogether discouraging was simply the result of my very depressed state of health at the time. The position into which the subject has now been lifted is therefore wholly due to Mr. Galton through his large development of the study, and his exquisite and costly methods of demonstrating in print the many new and important conclusions he has reached.

I take the opportunity, in reference to a late article on Anthropometry (in the *Nineteenth Century* of September, 1894, p. 365) to deprecate, as being to the best of my knowledge wholly unproved, the assertion that the use of finger-marks in this way was " originally invented by the Chinese." I have met no evidence which goes anywhere near substantiating this. As a matter of fact, I exhibited the system to many passengers and officers of the P. and O. steamship Mongolia in the Indian Ocean, during her outward voyage in February, 1877; and I have the finger-prints of her captain, and of all those persons, with their names. It is likely enough that the idea, which caught on rapidly among the passengers, may have found a settlement in some Chinese port by this route, and have there taken a practical form; but whether that be so or not, I must protest against the vague claim made on behalf of the Chinese, until satisfactory evidence of antiquity is produced.

Littlemore,   W. J. HERSCHEL.
November 7.

The " Hooghly Letter," subjoined, has been printed at length in Chapter III.

Faulds and Herschel (as medical jurists of eminence, British and foreign, now agree) share the honour of using or suggesting the employment of fingermarks: Faulds in crime detection generally: Herschel mainly in the identification of habitual offenders.

The exception taken by Herschel, in his 1894 reply, to the sufficiency of the grounds stated by Faulds in coming to his conclusion of the " for-ever-unchanging " character of the finger-markings, is invalid. Scientists, other than Galton, on this matter have supported Faulds. Herschel himself could not absolutely predicate that proposition, and did not predicate it in the " Hooghly Letter " or in his Letters to *Nature* in 1880 and 1894. Without being captiously critical, all that Herschel affirmed was that he had noticed no change in comparing particular marks between periods as great as fifteen or twenty years. The inference of permanence from such observations is, no doubt, strong. But Faulds had literally cut deeper into the very flesh of finger-tips, and he was absolutely justified in announcing their life-persistence. It was, indeed, creditable to Faulds that he should have stated in his 1894 protest that he had no wish to diminish any of the credit properly due to Herschel.

Herschel, however, by voicing his opinion that there was a total want of foundation for ascribing to the Chinese any knowledge of fingermarks in connexion with crime, did not add to any prestige he had acquired. He was sceptical without having any ground for airing his scepticism. " Satisfactory evidence of antiquity " has been forthcoming to establish the far-back knowledge of fingerprints by the Chinese.[3]

The article in the *Nineteenth Century* of September, 1894, to which Herschel referred, was contributed by Edmund R. Spearman (1837-1918), then resident in Paris, a strong Bertillonist and opposed to any fingerprint system. The exact title of his article was " Known to the Police."[4] Perhaps Spearman's dogmatic statement that the fingerprint method was " originally invented by the Chinese " was very like the wish being father to the thought.[5] Apparently made satirically against Galton's conversion to the out-and-out support of fingerprints, Spearman's affirmation has since been verified as correct.

It was nonsensical on the part of Herschel to imagine and assert that his pleasant gossip (no doubt his mind in 1894 being full of fingerprints!) during his return voyage to India on board the s.s. " Mongolia " in February, 1877, and before his " Hooghly Letter " was written, led to the idea of fingerprints taking practical form thereafter " in some Chinese port." His gossip had hardly time before 1879 to percolate to Japan, and, of course, to Faulds![6]

Laufer, followed in this by Dr. Heindl, suggests that Herschel probably overlooked the fact that he (Herschel) must have hit upon the taking of his finger-pad observations from the known use in India of fingermarks in contracts or customs or from seeing thumbmarks used by " coolies " from the time he went to India up to 1858. He made no serious study of their relation to ethnology or to anything else.[7] Laufer and Dr. Heindl well remark upon this preposterous idea of Herschel that it is " naïve."[8]

NOTES

[1] Vol. L, p. 548.

[2] Vol. LI, p. 77.

[3] See Chap. XXIX.

[4] Vol. 36, p. 356, at p. 365.

[5] Spearman referred to the fingerprint method as one which " has recently found a warm advocate in Mr. Francis Galton."

[6] Herschel later recurred in 1916 to this fantasy and said in reference to this voyage : " If any one of them [passengers] had heard of the use of these marks, say, in China, I could not but have been told of it." Apparently he never consulted any Chinese authority of acknowledged standing. See " The Origin of Finger-Printing," p. 17, by Herschel (1916. London. Oxford University Press), and Chaps. XXI and XXIX.

[7] Herschel later ascribes his early knowledge of fingerprints from acquaintance as a boy with the works of Thomas Bewick, the Newcastle naturalist and engraver. See " The Origin of Finger Printing," supra, p. 34.

[8] Laufer's 1912 *Smithsonian* article, *supra*, pp. 634 *et* 636, and " Daktyloskopie," *supra*, p. 49.

XVI

VUCETICH : " PERITO IDENTIFICADOR " : ARGENTINA :
1891-1925

JUAN VUCETICH (1858-1925) devoted his life to the science of identification in all its branches, and was known all over the world as the brilliant director of the fingerprint bureau of the Province of Buenos Aires and as the inventor of a system of fingerprint classification that has been employed not only in his adopted Argentina, but in other places in South America, as well as in other continents. Very early he realized the use and value of fingerprints, and that not only as a method for the identification of criminals but as a security measure in all activities of civil life. He was a great propagandist, putting the ideas of his inventive genius rapidly into execution, finding them freely adopted as good and practical. In advancing the kindred sciences of criminology and sociology, his work appears to have been more generously acknowledged outside South America by eminent authorities in Continental Europe than by the savants of Britain or of the United States.[1] In his " Manual of Practical Dactylography," published in 1923, Faulds observed that the name of Vucetich " deserves high honour in our science." See p. 40. Throughout South America his name as a great reformer is revered.[2] Of all official fingerprint experts, he is the foremost. In inventive genius, practical application, administrative ability, forward vision, and literary distinction, no one, in these combined gifts, has approached him.

Vucetich corresponded with Galton, and Galton gave him a mild, patronizing pat. Beyond that pat, Galton does not seem to have done much in the way of spreading his fame in this country. So far as I can gather, Vucetich never fully realized the place held by Faulds in the early modern history of fingerprints.[3] In some of his published writings, Vucetich mentions Faulds in the most casual way, treating any reference to him rather as an anthropologist or physiologist than as a criminologist. For example, in an article written by Vucetich in 1916 on " Mi Actuación Daktiloscópica," republished the year after his death in the special " Vucetich " Number of *Revista de Criminología Psiquiatría y Medicina Legal* of 25th January, 1926, p. 31, at p. 33 he puts Faulds among the successors of Purkinje. If Vucetich had properly appreciated Faulds, he would certainly have acknowledged that Faulds, as well as Galton, was *un maestro* in fingerprint identification.[4]

It was through the mention of Vucetich by Faulds in his books as the first person known to him to be credited with the distinction of tracing or being associated in tracing a criminal from her bloody fingermarks on the scene of her crime that I was led to make inquiries about Vucetich. I made these inquiries through Don Pedro L. Ganduglia, the Police Chief of La Plata. I am indebted for most of the information in this Chapter to his friendly response, and specially for my introduction to Dr. Luis Reyna Almandos, of the National University of La Plata, Director of the Museo Vucetich and Identification Laboratory in connexion with the Faculty of Juridical and Social Sciences in that University. As the ardent disciple of Vucetich, Dr. Reyna Almandos has published many treatises and contributed many magazine articles about him and his labours.

Vucetich, born in 1858 in the Dalmatian island of Lessina, emigrated in 1884 to Argentina. In 1888 he became a subordinate official dealing with statistics in the Central Police Department at La Plata. His Jefe de Policía, Capitan (Navy) Guillermo J. Nunes entrusted him with the organization of an identification bureau on Bertillon lines. In July, 1891, Nunes placed in his hands, with a friendly " Read that," an article by M. Henry de Varigny upon " Anthropologie : Les Empreintes digitales d'après Mons. F. Galton," in a May number of *Revue Scientifique* of that year, published in Paris.[5] This article, read with appreciation and vision, convinced Vucetich of the use of fingerprints as superior to all other methods of identification.

From July, 1891, Vucetich was a persistent advocate in South America for the universal application of fingerprints as the determining factor in the identification of individuals in all relations, civil or criminal, of life.

By September, 1891, Vucetich had devised and initiated, with the authority of his superiors, a system of fingerprint classification for identification purposes, dealing not with one but with all ten fingers; and at first, in conjunction with Bertillonage, styling this mixed plan by the somewhat repelling title of Icnofalangométrico.

Up to this point it is clear that Henry was not then in the field,[6] and that Galton had experimented only with thumbprints, grouping his lineations into three classes of arches, loops, and whorls (Faulds having already observed these in 1880),[7] with some suggestion of a system by which varieties could be assorted. Vucetich acknowledged from the first that he based his method of classification of his four types upon Galton's " nuclear " classification, if it could in truth be described as a working classification. It seems impossible, prior to 1893 and even prior to 1897, to attribute to Vucetich the reception of any ideas from Henry. Any classification devised by Henry between 1893 and 1897 dealt only with left thumbprints based on Galton's grouping, whence his subsequently much improved classification is often referred to as the Galton-Henry system.

It is demonstrated from a Review by Galton of Bertillon's " Signaletic Instructions " for *Nature* in October, 1896,[8] that Henry had not then fully thought out his system of classification. Galton in this Review quotes from a Circular of 11th January, 1896, issued by Henry, then Inspector-General of Police for Bengal, as follows:—

> " At present a duplicate Criminal Record is being kept, i.e., a record based on anthropometric measurements *plus* thumb marks and also separately a record based solely on the impressions of the ten digits. A

system of classifying the latter is being worked out and if after being subjected to severe tests it is found to yield sufficient power of differentiation, to enable search to be unerringly made, it seems probable that measurements will be abandoned as *data* for fixing identity, dependence being placed exclusively upon finger impressions."

Discarding *anthropometría* altogether, Vucetich perfected by 1904 his ten-fingerprint classification system in such a practical manner that it was not only immediately adopted by the Argentine Republic but very rapidly also by almost all other South American governments, including Brazil.

The system of Vucetich, "práctico, perfecto e infalible," based on the registration of the lines found "en las yemas de los dedos de las manos," became known first as *Dactiloscopia*, for which name he was indebted to Dr. Francisco Latzina, a distinguished publicist, and later and more widely as "Vucetichisme" or "Vucetichismo," the name bestowed upon it by Professor Alexandre Lacassagne, of Lyons, in a letter by him to Vucetich of 4th August, 1904. Such a name distinguished it from "Bertillonage."[9]

Vucetich never claimed to be the originator of fingertip types. In that he acknowledged Galton, not knowing of Faulds's work, as his "pilot." The merit of Vucetich lay in his converting into four Galton's (or Faulds's)[10] three *tipos* of arches, loops, and whorls, by splitting loops into outer and inner *presillas*, and then by an ingenious combination of eight signs of four letters and four numbers, devising, with consequential subgrouping, a million basic variations against Galton's one hundred thousand.[11]

So valuable has the system of Vucetich proved that many of the countries of Europe, mostly Latin, have applied it.[12] China in 1913 resorted to it as the result of Vucetich's visit to Pekin. Based upon it, Dr. Sévérin Icard, of Marseilles, and Honorary Professor of Legal Medicine in Madrid University, developed a code for international use.

By decree of the Provincial Governor of Buenos Aires, dated 29th January, 1908, confirmed in the following year by decree of the President of the Republic, Vucetich, as then head of Buenos Aires C.I.D., was recognized in all matters, administrative, civil, and criminal, as " Perito Identificador." This title signified the rise of the " nueva profesión."

I have read Varigny's article that so happily fired Vucetich. No mention is made in it of Faulds. In view of Galton's opinion of and attitude to Faulds then and later, this omission is not to be wondered at. It cannot, therefore, be surprising that in all South-American Spanish literature on Fingerprints, contributed by Vucetich and others, including Dr. Reyna Almandos, I should find only very meagre references up to the present time to Faulds. Dr. Reyna Almandos graciously sent me the publications of Vucetich and of himself, as well as some minor brochures by other South-American writers. These I perused with interest. From all this literature it was easy to see that, upon his own appraisement, Galton has been accepted in South America as chief of all the apostles of fingerprint identification, with a little laudation on his *firma* for Herschel. Until very recently, in Argentine *bibliografias*, the 1880 *Nature* Letter of Faulds and his subsequent books found no prominent place.

Dr. Reyna Almandos is responsible for the publication *in extenso*, in 1930, of the Letters to *Nature* in 1880 and in 1894 of Faulds and Herschel. These appear in Spanish in *La Plata Review of Identification and Penal Sciences*, from which I have made several citations in this

Chapter.[13] Such a translation shows an increasing appreciation of Faulds in South America. I have no doubt that a translation will now appear in this well-known *Review* of the last Letter of Faulds and the " Remarks " of Herschel thereon in *Nature* in 1917. These " Remarks " finally established Faulds in front of Herschel.

It is to the United States of America that up to the present time we must chiefly look for the just recognition of Faulds. There, expert authorities have not relied upon Galton's observations about Faulds. They have made their own investigations, with the result that his outstanding distinction has been adequately acknowledged.[14]

But, as Faulds was under-estimated by Galton, Vucetich does not seem to have been much appreciated in this country or in the United States.[15] All identification bureaux in the United States are based on Henry's classification system, the first bureau having been opened at St. Louis in 1899. The Federal Criminal Investigation Bureau of the Department of Justice at Washington is the foremost of all in regard to its scientific staff and equipment for all branches of crime detection. Dr. Hoover, its director, is one of the most outstanding identity experts of the world.

There can be no doubt, it seems to me, of the simplicity and excellence of the Vucetichismo system.[16] Vucetich claims that his method, and as he improved it, was in actual and successful operation a few years before 1897, and certainly long before Henry bettered the very limited and non-practical scheme of Galton. The claim of Vucetich appears to be proved as beyond question by extant official documents. Many cases, too, from 1892 onwards are recorded of the bodies of suicides and persons unknown being identified through the registration of their fingermarks under the regime of Vucetich and long

F

before a London case in 1910 and an Amritsar case in 1911.[17]

Vucetich alleges that Henry " sólo en 1897 utilizó mi sistema de las *diez* impresiónes digitales con la clasificación de su sistema."[18] Although Henry's " Classification of Finger Prints " was first published in 1901, the " Dactiloscopía Comparada " of Vucetich, published in 1904, appears to be of more outstanding merit. The very numerous plates of Vucetich's different *tipos* seem far superior to the illustrations of Henry. It seems to be indisputable that, some six years after Vucetich had put his method into practice for criminal and other identification purposes, Henry, during the earlier period of his Bengal administration, made use only of the left thumb for these purposes. He had no classification, prior to 1897, based on the ten digits. Faulds claimed that the system he outlined to the chief officials of Scotland Yard, prior considerably in time to the inauguration of systems of any kind anywhere, whether by Galton, Vucetich, or others, was what was substantially put in force in London from 1901 onwards. Faulds was an insistent advocate of a ten-finger system. How far Vucetich applied the first concepts of Galton, and how far Henry may latterly have got assistance from the method of Vucetich, it may be difficult to say. No one has patent rights in ideas. Independently of each other, similar conceptions may have occurred both to Henry and to Vucetich. In the absence of knowledge of the terms of the Report made in the eighties " upon Faulds's scheme as submitted by him to the Scotland Yard Commissioner of Police " in or about 1886, the nature of the scheme of Faulds may be fairly well gathered from unchallenged statements made by him in his different publications.

Between December, 1908, and January, 1909, *The Times* published a series of Special Articles on " The Metropolitan Police " written by a former Superintendent of that Force. The final article appeared on 4th January, 1909. A correspondence with the Editor ensued. Various correspondents, including Galton and Herschel, discussed the claims of Galton, Henry and Herschel to the origination of the first system of fingerprint classification. The anonymous writer of these Articles had truly remarked in his last Article, which dealt with " Identification," that in the matter of fingerprints the *crux* of the problem lay in classification. I deal with this discussion in another chapter for its bearing on the claim made by Herschel.[19] The names of Faulds and Vucetich were not mentioned in the " Identification " Article, or in any of the letters to the Editor. The truth seems to be that Faulds, Henry, and Vucetich alone thought out schemes of practical use. Faulds was independent of Galton. Others were indebted to Galton in respect of his researches. Faulds does not appear to have had his attention called to *The Times* discussion. Vucetich learned of it too late to intervene. He protested in some of his writings against the claims of Galton and Herschel as authors of practical systems. Only experts in the technique of fingerprint classification can resolve or assist in resolving such disputes as the rival claims (treating Galton as non-practical) of Faulds, Henry, and Vucetich involve. But so great and impartial a critic as Dr. Heindl—held in high repute by New Scotland Yard—on this matter is in favour of Faulds. Reference to Dr. Heindl's opinion is made in Chapter XVIII in dealing with the part played by Henry. Dr. Heindl treats exhaustively of the classification systems of Henry and Vucetich, with all their modifications, called after the experts of different countries, in the adoption of one or other system. So does Professor-Doctor Thot in his exhaustive " Criminalistica " Article at p. 114 *et seq.*[20] According to Dr. Locard the system of Vucetich is scientifically the surest, and, for police purposes, the most practical and most " maniable "; offering the least chances of error.[21]

To the police administration of La Plata in 1892 undoubtedly belongs the credit of the first recorded identification of a criminal, and that, as it happened, of a murderess, Francesca Rojas, from her fingerprints left on the scene of her crime. An innocent man, whom she blamed and got arrested, was thus released and absolved. Vucetich was in charge of the Identification Service in La Plata at the time. I have been unable to discover how his Chief or himself thought of instructing the search for such prints and, upon the finding of her " chance impressions," of taking, as first suggested by Faulds, for comparison purposes the finger-impressions of the suspected man and of the woman as arrested. Varigny in his article made no reference to such a matter. Up to 1891 Galton himself had not grasped its possibility. It is probable that in some way the idea had reached Vucetich's Chief or himself or their subordinates. Doubtless all published light on fingerprints would be sought. It is difficult to say how knowledge of Faulds's *Nature* Letter of 1880 would pass to South America. Vucetich in none of his published books or articles, reminiscent or otherwise, alludes to the genesis of this search. Neither his chief nor he himself made any claim of originality in the direction for the fingermark search. The name of the successful detective in the case, I am glad to note, is recorded.[22] All that Vucetich claimed, and rightly, was the ability by his method of classification to determine the fact of identity between the woman's bloody prints and her impressions on arrest. Faulds's 1880 *Nature* Letter must have been noticed by scientists in South America.

The conviction of Rojas, with the consequent establishment of the innocence of the man she denounced, has been properly characterized as a " trascendental innovación realizada en la administracion de justicia de la Provincia de Buenos Aires."[23] I deal in Chapter XXIV as fully as available *data* allow me with this first recorded case of identification concerning the murder, by Francesca Rojas, in 1892, of her two sons. It is the chapter chronologically recording, *first*, all known capital-charge cases occurring anywhere after 1880 and prior to the end of 1908; and, *second*, non-capital cases, occurring in England during the same period, in view of their collective bearing on the strange omission to search for fingerprints in the house in which Miss Mary Gilchrist was murdered in December, 1908, and for which Oscar Slater was tried.[24]

Vucetich made a world tour of identification bureaux, including Calcutta, Pekin, and London. Many honours were conferred upon him. He died in 1925 without seeing the realization of his supreme idea of a Central Government Register of Fingerprints of every person subject to Argentine law, leading in time, as he thought, to the institution of an International Register. Civil identification has made much headway in South America. People there have realized its security value, and in fingerprint identity cards they discern no stigma. In Chile and Mexico such cards are obligatory for all inhabitants. Dr. Locard is the advocate for the adoption of civil registers in Europe. Dr. Reyna Almandos hopes to see his own reasoned and published plans for a National Personality Register before long carried into law and practice in South America.[25] Both governed and governing classes have got beyond the stage of invidiously associating fingerprints always with criminality.

So far as I can ascertain, there is no police identification bureau in Britain where citizens are invited, as in Argentina and in some parts of the United States, to enrol their names in a special register along with the registration of their fingermarks, receiving in exchange from the bureau an identity fingerprint certificate. Certificates in some countries also contain the photograph of the applicant. I see no reason why our local authorities or municipalities should not encourage the institution of such special registers, making a small charge for the privilege. It would be an excellent forerunner of a compulsory system.

In the Argentine Republic at the present day, and due primarily to the forceful personality of Vucetich, fingerprints are employed, besides crime purposes, for—

From 1891

1. Candidates for police service.
2. Identification of unknown corpses.
3. Registration on application voluntarily of any person.

From 1900

4. Authentication of civil acts by request.

From 1909

5. Registration by Bank of Spain and other Banks of their staffs.

From 1910

6. Employees of Postal Service.

From 1911

7. Matriculation of students and electoral employees of Government.
8. Emigration.
9. Government employees generally.

NOTES

[1] The writings of Vucetich do not appear in the New Scotland Yard Bibliography (to which particular reference is made in Chap. XXII), prepared by Sir John Cumming : his name is there connected, p. 54, only with the " Museo Vucetich " as the publication seat of an Argentine Review, cited *passim* in this Chap. Cf. such authors as Drs. Heindl and Locard. Dr. Locard from 1903 onwards was largely instrumental in making Europe acquainted with the system of Vucetich. See Dr. Locard's " Un Nouvel Essai de Classement

Dactyloscopique," in *Archives d'Anthropologie Criminelle*, Vol. XXV, p. 430. 1910. Paris.

[2] His portrait appears in Dr. Heindl's " Daktyloskopie," *supra*, facing p. 80.

[3] In his " Instrucciónes Generales para el Sistema de Filiación " (1896. La Plata. Solá, Sesé y Co.) Faulds is not mentioned.

[4] In his " Dactiloscopía Comparada," 1904, La Plata, Vucetich nowhere mentions Faulds. In the article on " Criminalística " by Profesor Doctor Ladislao Thot, in Vol. X, p. 107, of *Revista de Identificación y Ciencias Penales*, 1934, edited by Dr. Reyna Almandos, a very fair, though slight, reference is made to Faulds. Dr. Thot is a voluminous writer on all crime subjects. In his posthumously published " Historia Sintética de la Identificación," in *Revista de Identificación y Ciencias Penales*, *supra*, Tomos VI et VII, 1930-1931, Vucetich refers to " arches, loops and whorls " as " términos que emplearon Purkinje, Faulds y otros precursores de Galton," p. 7 of Tomo VII; cites the Letter of Faulds to *Nature* in 1880, and two of his books, p. 18 of Tomo VII. An abstract of that Letter is given in Tomo VI, p. 374.

[5] The article appeared in *Numero* 18 of date 2 Mai, 1891, and is on p. 557 of Tome XLVII. It is an interesting discussion of the grouping and subgrouping of finger-lineations with diagrams, based, I believe, on Galton's lecture printed in Phil. Trans. B. 1891, of the Royal Society, Vol. CLXXXII, p. 1.

[6] Henry was then in India and became later Commissioner of the Metropolitan Police. See Chap. XVIII.

[7] " Faulds, en 1880, publicó una carta en *Nature* respecto a las impresiónes digitales señalando los tipos arco, presilla y verticilo," *per* Don Antonio Herrero in " Breve Síntesis Histórica de la Identificación, p. 39. La Plata. 1929.

[8] Vol. LIV, p. 569. It is entertaining to find Galton in this review saying of the system of finger-impressions " which in my own, perhaps, prejudiced opinion, is far more efficient for classification and incomparably more so for final identification." How he swung round from his former opinion in favour of Bertillonage!

[9] See " Dactiloscopia Argentina," p. 55, by Dr. Reyna Almandos, 1909. La Plata. " Dactyloscopy " appears only in the Supplement of 1933 of the New Oxford Dictionary with a reference to *The Boston Transcript* of 10th October, 1908. Faulds made it the title of his short paper in *St. Thomas's Hospital Gazette*, January, 1904, p. 13.

[10] See " Guide," *supra*, p. 27.

[11] See " Proyecto de Ley de Registro General de Identificación," p. 199, by Vucetich, with Prólogo, &c., by Dr. Reyna Almandos. 1929. La Plata.

[12] His system is fully described by Dr. Locard in his " L'Identification des Récidivistes," p. 242. 1909. Paris. Maloine.

[13] See this *Revista*, *supra*, Tomo VI, p. 240.

[14] See " Criminal Identification " by Dr. Hoover, in *The American Journal of Police Science*, Vol. 11, p. 13. 1931. Chicago.

[15] But see article by Mr. August Vollmer on " Investigation, Criminal," in *Encyclopædia Britannica*, 1929, Vol. 12, p. 562, in which this writer says : " Dactyloscopy, the science which deals with identification of individuals through their finger-prints, was removed from

the realm of theory and made practical by Juan Vucetich of Buenos Aires."

16 It has the advantage, according to Dr. Locard, " d'une absolue et parfaite simplicité; il est très clair; très pratique et ne laisse place à aucune possibilité d'erreur." See " Un Nouvel Essai de Classement Dactyloscopique," *supra*, p. 431.

17 See Chap. XXXIII. The Amritsar case is noted in Chap. XXX.

18 See " Mi Actuación Dactiloscópica," *supra*, p. 34, in Número Extraordinario of *Revista de Criminología Psiquiatría y Medicina Legal*. 1926. Buenos Aires.

19 See Chap. XXI.

20 In *Revista de Identificación y Ciencias Penales*, Vol. X, 1932. La Plata, 1934.

21 See his " Un Nouvel Essai de Classement Dactyloscopique," *supra*, p. 430.

22 See the case of Francesca Rojas in more detail in Chap. XXIV, where the name of the fingerprint detective is given.

23 " Origen del Vucetichismo," p. 45, by Dr. Reyna Almandos. 1909. Buenos Aires. Alsina.

24 See Chap. XXV.

25 It is noteworthy that in the fifth edition, 1936 (as in all previous editions), of his " Forensic Medicine," p. 61, Professor Sydney Smith records his personal advocacy of fingerprint registration for everyone. I quote the passage in full in Chap. XXXIII. Vucetich's system of classification in combination with that of Henry was adopted in Egypt. Professor Sydney Smith formerly occupied at Cairo the Chair of Forensic Medicine in the University of Egypt. Much of his great experience as a medico-legal expert was gained in Egypt.

XVII

KANGALI CHARAN : NOTABLE INDIAN TRIAL : 1898

IT is a very singular fact that the second recorded instance (generally referred to in crime literature as that of Kangali Charan, a Brahmin, his real name being Ranjan Singh), illustrating Faulds's original and exclusive conception that criminals might be discovered by their bloody fingermarks, occurred in Bengal in 1897 and during the service there of Henry as its Inspector-General of Police. In Chapters XVI and XXIV the facts of the first case that happened (in Argentina) five years earlier are mentioned.

On the morning of 16th August, 1897, Hriday Nath

Gosh, a Bengali, and manager of a tea-garden belonging to Katalguri Tea Estate, Limited, on the Bhutan frontier, under the Himalayas, was found dead in the bedroom of his garden-bungalow. Obviously, he had been brutally murdered during the previous night. The contents of wooden boxes in the room were disarranged. An iron safe was rifled of cash. Three currency notes in it, of Rs.100 each, were not removed. On the previous evening the manager had been seen locking up the safe. A Kukri knife was found in the room. It had apparently been used for the infliction of the manager's wounds.

Several months previously, to wit, on 21st January, 1897, Ranjan Singh, who was a native of Birbhum, in the district of that name, in the extreme west of Bengal Province, was convicted of the theft of money from Gosh, in whose service he had been cook. He had taken the money from the iron safe. He was sentenced to six months' imprisonment by the Court of Sessions Judge of Jalpaiguri. Singh, who had gone in the tea-garden district by the name of Kangali Charan, was released on 5th July, 1897, from Jalpaiguri Jail, as an act of grace over the Diamond Jubilee of Victoria, Queen Empress. Thereafter he was seen at fairs or markets in the vicinity of the tea-garden, situated in the extreme north of Bengal Province. Many hundreds of miles separated the tea-garden district from his Birbhum home, and, except by way of Calcutta, they were inaccessible to each other. No one, however, actually saw him, so it is said, in or near the bungalow. He had told his prison mates that he would have his revenge upon the manager. Before his release from jail, his right thumbprint was taken. He and other persons were severally suspected of the murder and theft, and some of these as acting in concert for the purpose. The investigating officer,[1] whose name I have been regretfully unable to trace, found in one of the wooden boxes in the bedroom a Bengali almanac and some other papers. These were sent to the Central Office, Calcutta. The safe, the currency notes, and the knife do not appear to have been considered or examined for fingerprints, latent or otherwise. Probably, Indian detectives were not then instructed to search for fingermarks that might be invisible, or almost invisible, to the naked eye. On the Bengali almanac paper cover were found two brown smudges, as if of dried blood. Henry scrutinized these with a magnifying-glass, and saw that one was the impression of a right thumb. The records of the Central Office showed that this impression corresponded to Charan's right thumbmark as taken before he was released from jail.[2]

Upon this discovery, a warrant was issued for the arrest of Charan on the charges of murdering Gosh and stealing his money. On 9th September, 1897, he was arrested at his Birbhum home. His right thumb-impression was again taken at Calcutta on his way to Jalpaiguri for trial committal.

In May, 1898, Charan was indicted at the instance of the Queen, in the Court of Sessions at Jalpaiguri, with the commission of the murder and theft, under sections 302 and 380 of the Indian Penal Code. He pleaded not guilty to both charges, and was defended by native attorneys. The Court of Sessions Judge was Mr. Ahsanuddin Ahmad, of Ringpur, a barrister and member of the Inner Temple. He sat with two native assessors. On 25th May, 1897, Charan was acquitted of the murder charge and found guilty of the theft charge. He was sentenced to " rigorous " imprisonment for two years.

With some considerable difficulty, Mr. P. Norton Jones, the Deputy Commissioner of Police, Calcutta, aided by Mr. Noel L. Hindley, I.C.S., Barrister-at-Law, formerly Registrar of the High Court, Calcutta, and now Judge of the Assam Valley Districts, Gauhati, Assam, recovered for me full copies of (1) the judgment of the

Judge, (2) the findings of the Assessors and (3) the concurring opinion of the Justices of the High Court in the
unsuccessful appeal of Charan against his conviction and
sentence.[3] From these papers I gather that the accused
gave evidence on his own behalf at his trial; that at the
request of the Sessions Court he allowed another
impression of his right thumb to be taken; and that his
explanations as to his acquisition of money after his
release from imprisonment and some other matters were
not considered satisfactory by that Court.

The reasoned opinion of the Court of Sessions Judge
upon the topic of fingerprints is most interesting. It
reveals a strange psychology in the Mohamedan judge.
No charge of murder, whether as actor or act and part,
or as accessory, before or after, could possibly in his mind
be substantiated against Charan upon the sole proof of
his brown finger-impressions on the almanac. In all his
views, in support of this conclusion, the Assessors con-
curred. They seemed to think with him that the accused
would, or could, not use a knife unknown in the accused's
part of India and with which they said only a Bhutia or
a Nepali could make the clean cuts found on the body of
Gosh. It stood to reason, therefore, that the murderer
must have been either a Bhutia or a Nepali. Thus they
resolved that it would be " unfair and unjust to presume
him (Charan) to have murdered the deceased, without any
direct evidence, or, even, indirect evidence, to connect
him with the commission of the murder." Their responsibility on this major charge, however, was made easy for
them by the action of the native Government Pleader.
He did not move for a conviction. Presumably, the
Judge, as if approving his attitude, subtly pressed the
apparent difficulties of himself and the Assessors in the
way of a conviction for murder.

Upon the theft charge, although there were to all
appearance the same defects in the Crown case as seemed

to be present in regard to the murder charge, the Court and the Assessors unanimously found the fingerprint evidence sufficient to justify the conviction of Charan. For Charan (and, I assume, after the Government Pleader had intimated that the capital charge was not insisted in), his advisers astutely contended that the murderer must have been the thief, and, by the belated concession of the Crown, that Charan, not being the murderer, could not be the thief!

It is difficult to understand the course adopted by the Judge. On intimation that a charge of any kind has been withdrawn in the Criminal Courts of this country, it is unusual for our Judges to make any comments as to whether there are merits or not in withdrawn charges. In cases, perhaps, where no valid evidence is tendered or the charge has been transparently trumped up, the Court may observe upon the wise discretion with which an indictment has been withdrawn.

I find that the Judge, with the full approval of the Assessors, naïvely suggested that Gosh must have been murdered by

(1) another person, named, in revenge for the alleged liaison of the deceased with that person's paramour; or

(2) discontented coolies who had just left the service of the deceased; or

(3) all these people in combination.

Not one of all these suggested murderers was charged with the crime and put upon trial.

The Judge and the Assessors held that the thumb-impressions of Charan on the blood-stained almanac " proved beyond question " that he was present on the fatal night in the manager's bungalow, and that " the presumption that he committed the theft was irresistible." Then, the Judge, with their concurrence, opines, still more naïvely, that it is " possible that Charan was cognizant of the conspiracy against the manager and knowing that the manager had been killed to satisfy the grudge of the conspirators, he entered the room immediately after the murder was committed and removed the keys . . . from his body and thus stained his fingers, not knowing that their impressions might be used against him at a trial "! All that need be said upon argument of this nature is that it is far from convincing that the thief in such circumstances could not be the murderer whether as one of the alleged conspirators or otherwise. I daresay some occidental juries, not necessarily Irish, have been responsible before now for some equally, to all seeming, illogical conclusions or verdicts.

Expert fingerprint evidence, it seems, had been incompetently led before the Magistrate committing Charan for trial. Indian Law did not then allow of the evidence of fingerprint experts.[4] No such evidence was tendered at his trial. The Judge and his Assessors surmounted the want of skilled guidance by themselves (outwith the presence of the prisoner and his advocates) examining all the four thumbprint-impressions. They came to the unanimous view that all referred to the accused. Manifestly, they were right. It may seem, however, somewhat strange that the Judge and the Assessors, presumably unskilled in the interpretation or scrutiny of fingerprints, should have adopted this course instead of altogether disregarding the fingerprints of Charan. Of course, in the last resort I am aware that juries and judges respectively are entitled to believe or disbelieve expert testimony; but in this case the court was not really habile to deal with such special facts. The judgment does not reveal how many points of agreement were found, on comparison, in his fingerprints with those on the almanac.[5] It is difficult to see in such circumstances any necessity for the amendment of the Indian Civil Code. The Judge, accepting as sufficient the simple presentation of proof of the various fingerprints, inferred from his own examination, guilt therefrom *simpliciter*. No country, so far as I know, has yet reached that stage. Lord Sands, one of our Scottish Judges, predicted that, with the advance in our scientific assurance of the conclusiveness of finger-prints, the future might have in store an approach to this " short-circuit " procedure. In Charan's case the Judge recorded that, although he had no personal difficulty as a layman in finding complete similarity in the finger-impressions of Charan with those on the almanac, it took him " several hours " to explain matters to the Assessors and obtain their acquiescence in his opinion! The Judge invited Charan to submit his right thumb for a fourth impression, telling him, with Indian charm, that if it differed from the other three he should go free![6] Why did the Judge make this invitation? He must have known that there was no possibility of this issue. I can only surmise that it was desired to disprove the groundless suggestion made by Charan through his *mukhtears* that the prosecution was a plot engineered by the police against him. In the end, the court held that the evidence was " good and sufficient " to prove that the accused entered the bedroom of the deceased on the night libelled and handled the almanac. Entering " with motives of revenge,'' and finding the manager dead, the Court held that he abstracted the key, opened the box, and stole the money!

Charan appealed against his conviction and sentence as unjust. No one appeared at the diet of hearing before the High Court of Justice in Calcutta to argue the appeal on his behalf. It seems to me that there were some doubtful steps taken in the course of his trial. The appeal Judges were Kinealy and Henderson, JJ. They dismissed his appeal. No other course in the circumstances was open to them. Their concurring judgment, tersely and significantly expressed, was as follows:—

> The accused was a servant of the manager of a tea-garden who was a native of Bengal. He was found to have stolen some money, and the manager prosecuted him for theft and he was convicted. He had been a servant of the manager for some time previous to his conviction. There is evidence to show that while in Jail he threatened in some way or other to have his revenge. He was subsequently seen six or seven miles from the garden immediately before the theft, for which he has now been convicted, took place. A comparison of thumb marks by the Assessors in the court below and by this court raises a very strong probability in favour of the accused being the person whose thumb mark was found on the almanac in the house in which the theft took place. When arrested he gave a wrong name and had much more money than he could reasonably account for. Both the Judge and Assessors in the court below, although they did hesitate to convict him for the murder which was committed in the house on the night of the theft, had no hesitation whatever in convicting him of theft.

> We have no doubt whatever that the accused is guilty, and we dismiss the appeal.

No question of law was raised in the trial or in the appeal. The case was not, therefore, reported in Indian Law Reports.

Henry rightly deals with this case as a triumphant demonstration of the value of the fingerprint system. There is no evidence to indicate that he had issued any order, general or particular, to Indian Police to search in such crimes as that of the murder of Gosh for fingerprints, patent or latent, on crime scenes. The unknown investigating officer must, therefore, be credited with detective skill in recovering the bloodstained almanac. One assumes that Henry and the Indian C.I.D. did not then know of the first recorded case, in 1892, of Francesca Rojas in La Plata.[7] In that case the murderess had not been previously convicted of any crime. There was no prior registration of her finger-marks. The case of Rojas differs in this respect from that of Charan. His arrest was made easy by the registration records of his right thumbmark made before his release from jail for his previous offence. Herschel, who has the credit of the institution of such a registra-tion, had no idea of connecting its existence with the discovery of any offender, whether previously convicted or not. It is, indeed, noteworthy that both these early cases of Rojas and Charan were concerned with blood-stained fingermarks, expressly figured by Faulds in his *Nature* Letter of 28th October, 1880.

Readers of Henry's "Classification and Uses of Finger Prints," with its abstention from all reference to Faulds, would naturally infer, and erroneously, that Charan could never have been brought to justice but for Herschel. Faulds was alone entitled to the credit of rendering demonstrable Charan's presence on the scene of the murder by the trace of his bloody finger-marks on the calendar.[8]

NOTES

[1] The Deputy Commissioner of Police, Calcutta, Mr. P. Norton Jones, did everything in his power to trace this officer. His name does not appear in any records now in existence. The Superintendent of Police for the District of Jalpaiguri could not help. My " Letter to the Editor " in *The Statesman of India* of Sunday, 15th August, 1937, elicited no reliable information.

[2] The blood mark and that of Charan's right thumbmark are shown by Henry in the various editions of his " Classification and Uses of Finger Prints " : seventh edition, p. 57 *et seq.* Henry indicates six-teen points of agreement as made out upon comparison. I surmise that Henry had changed from taking left thumbprints to right thumb-prints.

[3] The full text of all these documents will be found in my article under the title : " Finger Prints : The Case of Kangali Charan : 1898," in *The Juridical Review* for 1937, Vol. XLIX, p. 417. Edin-burgh. Wm. Green & Son, Ltd.

[4] Indian Statute Law was amended in 1899. See Chap. XXX.

[5] From Note 2, *supra*, it appears sixteen points were obtained.

[6] See *Sahu* v. *King Emperor*, 1927, I.L.R. 6 Pat. 623, cited in Chap. XXVI. The seventh edition of Wills on " Circumstantial Evidence," 1937, is remarkable for the inclusion in that work for the

first time of reported Indian cases. No reference is made to unreported cases.

[7] See Chaps. XVI and XXIV.

[8] See *The Times* of 15th September, 1899, and *The British Medical Journal* of 23rd September, 1899, Vol. II, p. 803, for references to this case in (1) Henry's address on " Finger Prints " at Dover, in 1899, and see B.M.J., 1906, Vol. 1, p. 1029, in (2) an address by Dr. Vaughan Bateson of Bradford at Harrogate in 1905 to the Yorkshire Branch of the British Medical Association on " Personal Identification by means of Finger Print Impressions." Dr. Bateson refers to Charan's case as occurring when he was in Bengal. He trusted to an imperfect memory. Erroneously, he states that the victim of the murder was a Scotchman and that Charan was " finally convicted." He stated that he had never heard that the sentence was carried out. It is satisfactory that the correct facts should now be recorded.

XVIII

HENRY AND FINGERPRINTS : 1897-1931

THE adoption of the fingerprint system, first in Bengal and then throughout India in the late nineties, and afterwards by the British Government in England and Wales in or about July, 1901, was due to the immediate instigation of Henry (1850-1931). He had been Inspector-General of Police in the Bengal Civil Service, and had seen service of a similar kind in Cape of Good Hope Colony. Latterly, he was Assistant-Commissioner of the London Metropolitan Police. He became Commissioner in 1903. In the institution of the system in this country, he was undoubtedly supported by the forceful influence of Galton after his belated conversion to its merits. In one of his visits home from India, Henry was invited by Galton to his laboratory. There, Galton instructed Henry in the science of fingerprints.[1] Henry, as his pupil, gave all the credit of invention to Herschel. Nothing to Faulds! Henry never seems to have investigated for himself the respective claims of Faulds and Herschel.

Herschel never conceived or devised any system for

the interpretation and classification of finger-tip lineations. He had not the necessary knowledge or skill. As Vucetich, of La Plata, writing in 1916, puts it, Herschel secured only the dab of a finger-impression—" simple mancha de un dedo "—with no definite identification points, so that his method, if entitled to such a description, was of little use. Herschel, as Vucetich again observed, experimented " empírica y rutinariamente."[2] He knew nothing about the grouping of finger-marks.

Like Galton, and in all probability through Galton, Henry had been an admirer of Bertillonage. Henry got the sanction of the Indian Government to its application in India, as, in his mind at the time, Bertillonage was more important than any fingerprint system. So far as appears, Henry, while in India and prior at least to 1897, devised no system of classification of thumbprints.[3] It was not until Galton had made a ten-fingerprint collection of some 2500 persons that about 1897 Henry planned a method of grouping such prints and " upon a number basis."[4] There was nothing very original about Galton's grouping. Faulds had already submitted his scheme upon the obvious division of arches, loops, and whorls.[5] Vucetich, indebted for his inspiration to Galton, devised and operated his system of a ten-fingerprint classification from September, 1891.[6] As with others, including Galton, Henry perceived later the vast and absolute superiority of the fingerprint system. Rightly, Henry credited Herschel with the institution of a fingerprint system of registration. He ought, as other distinguished authorities now do, to have at least associated Faulds in that matter with Herschel. Under Henry, that system was greatly improved and extended. It was and is of great service to British and Indian officials. In that respect, the work of Herschel was of value. Galton, Herschel, and Henry never appear to have acknowledged, it is submitted, with anything like fairness the work of Faulds as an independent originator of fingerprint registration and in proving in his own authoritative way the permanence throughout life of finger-lineations. They ignored, further, his exclusive suggestion of (and his proving by actual cases) the mode in which criminals could be traced and identified through their fingermarks. Putting it very indulgently for Galton and Herschel, they under-estimated Faulds. Henry, if he knew of Faulds, ignored his existence.[7] Herschel's eleventh-hour confession of the greatest service of Faulds to the detection of crime must not, however, be overlooked.[8]

The second recorded instance in illustration of the original and exclusive discovery of Faulds occurred in Bengal in 1897, during the administration there of Henry as its Inspector-General of Police.[9] This most instructive case of Kangali Charan has been fully narrated in the previous Chapter.

Although Henry should have been aware of Herschel's admission in 1917 that Faulds alone was entitled to the credit for rendering such a crime so discoverable, all four editions of his standard textbook on " Classification and Uses of Finger-Prints " after 1917, up to the last in 1937, remain silent. Henry, who died in 1931, cannot, it must be assumed, have been aware of that admission. Henry read papers on " Finger-Prints " at the meeting in 1899 at Dover of the British Association for the Advancement of Science, and produced the calendar with Charan's bloody thumbmark.[10]

In 1900, Henry first published " Classification and Uses of Finger-Prints." It has gone, in 1937, to the eighth edition. In none of the eight is there any reference to Faulds. But after the repetition of the story of Kangali Charan in every one of these editions, without the least suggestion that anyone, save Galton, Herschel, or himself, had any say in such a matter, really no surprise at such an attitude need be expressed. Other police experts, notably in America, have not failed in this way. They have paid just tributes to Faulds.

Henry credits Galton with the merit of reducing Purkinje's nine varieties of fingerprints to three. To these Henry adds a fourth—" Composites." After all, it is understood that every finger-pad falls into one or other pattern of a loop or a whorl with its subdivisions. It is not disputed that Faulds saw this and revealed it. Readers may go back to Faulds's Letter of 1880 in *Nature* and draw their own conclusions as to the ingenuity of Henry's classification.

In the later editions of his work, Henry records various cases of criminals being discovered from the impressions of their fingermarks left on a printed Bengali calendar (the Kangali Charan case), champagne bottles, wineglasses, window-glass, &c. In particular (as he did for the first time in his fourth edition, published in 1913) he refers to the trial at the Old Bailey, London, in May, 1905, of the Stratton brothers for a double murder.[11] Mr. Justice Channell presided at that trial. It was, apart from burglary cases, the first trial in England of high importance in which the use of finger-impressions made by New Scotland Yard officials had been evidentially employed. Mr. Charles S. Collins, Superintendent of the Fingerprint Branch of the Criminal Record Office at New Scotland Yard, gave evidence for the Crown as a finger-expert. In his evidence upon the system, he did not include or refer to Faulds as in any way identified with it. If Faulds had not suggested searching for fingermarks on crime *loci*, that search might never have occurred to the London Metropolitan Criminal Investigation Department. It would have reflected the highest honour on the Metropolitan Police to have mentioned Faulds as the real and only person to whom credit was due for that striking innovation in detective crime methods. I must assume that ignorance prevailed. Nowhere in the evidence for the Government at that trial is there any allusion to Faulds with regard to all these cases from the Bengali one in 1897 onwards. But for Faulds, in not one of all these cases could conviction have been possible.[12]

Examination of the official record of the Brothers Stratton trial does not disclose the presence in any capacity of Faulds. Faulds was, however, present at this trial. He advised and sat with the solicitor for the defence. That fact may have militated against any gracious mention of his name by Superintendent Collins. After the trial, Faulds made some scathing criticisms in the public press upon the evidence led as to the particular thumbmark of one of the accused. That would make New Scotland Yard less friendly to him. Legal opinion at the time rather supported the views of Faulds. Sixteen points of identity were not obtained in the case, only eleven.[13] But there was sufficient evidence, apart from fingerprints, to warrant the conviction by the jury of the two brothers. Both were hanged.

In his Annual Report to Parliament for 1904, Henry states—

> " The finger prints of criminals left on bottles, glasses, articles of plate, cash boxes, &c., have, during the past year, been the means of enabling the investigating officers (in many cases of burglary, housebreaking and in one of murder) to place before the Courts, both in London and the Provinces, most valuable corroborative evidence." (See Annual Report, p. 10, H.M.S.O.)

It was not then apparently foreseen that fingerprint evidence might be accepted by the Courts as the sole available and conclusive evidence of guilt. I believe that the reference to the case of murder in this 1904

101

Report crept in by error. The murder referred to was that committed by the Stratton brothers and is known as the Deptford case. It occurred in March, 1905. The 1904 Report was not, I believe, completed until after March, 1905.

In 1906, fingerprint evidence was fairly prominent in the police courts around London. In one instance, that of West Ham, over which Mr. R. A. Gillespie, Stipendiary Magistrate, presided, evidence was led on the committal for trial of William Reed, an alleged burglar.[14] It was said he had broken into premises in Canning Town, and near to the shop, fingermarks of his right thumb on broken glass were discovered. The police found nineteen points of identity, distinct and clear, with his " arrested " impressions. The Magistrate expressed his " unfeigned admiration " not only of the ingenuity of the discoverer of the method, but of its extremely accurate character.[15] He mentioned that Henry had sent him his book on " Classification and Uses of Finger Prints." The Magistrate would naturally infer that Herschel was the ingenious discoverer of the method, and that Henry had no doubt improved his system! Faulds was, again, left out of the picture!

I have already referred, and refer later, to the 1912 *Smithsonian* article of Laufer.[16] In this article, Laufer sets out with an allusion to an American newspaper, calling attention to the arrest—through his fingerprints —in 1906, of a clever thief, who had robbed the wife of a novelist in London of £800 and escaped to New York. There, in the commission of another robbery, he was caught redhanded. The New York Police mailed his fingerprints to London. New Scotland Yard had his fingerprints as a convicted criminal. His identification, thus, was easy. He was convicted and sentenced in the United States to seven and a half years' imprisonment.[17]

It was, says Laufer, the first successful application of the fingerprint system in the United States.

By some mistake, for which Henry was not and could not be responsible, in a Chicago fingerprint magazine, advertising in or about 1925 one of the later editions of his work, "Classification and Uses of Finger-Prints," Henry was referred to as "the originator of the fingerprint system." It is another instance of how wrong ideas get about.[18] In America, Henry, as Bertillon in France, may be still regarded by many people as the "spiritual" father or pioneer of the fingerprint system. It is to be hoped that the "documented" memoir of Faulds in this book will dispel for the future all such illusions.

Classification of registered fingerprints by itself has no bearing on the tracing of crime from finger-impressions left on the spot, unless in cases of previous or habitual offenders, whose fingermarks are registered by the police.

Dr. Heindl states that Faulds prepared in 1880 a method for the taking of fingerprints, and proposed the collection of all the ten fingers. While Henry's classification may be more elaborate than that suggested by Faulds, Dr. Heindl declares that Faulds's method is that substantially in use to-day.[19]

Reverting to the seventh and last edition of his book (Henry died in 1931), it is stated:

> "At the present time (1933) the system has on account of its effectiveness, simplicity of working, certainty and inexpensiveness, been adopted by practically all civilised States. This is shown by the following table of figures which has been compiled at New Scotland Yard through the courtesy of the heads of the various Finger Print Bureaux of the world."[20]

The general reader of this passage is left to the natural assumption that "the system" described in Henry's book and referred to in this passage is the system known now by his name. Henry proceeds to give a list of over

103

fifty countries outside England adopting it. He includes the Argentine Republic with five times over London in the number of fingerprint slips filed up to 31st December, 1932, and almost the same ratio in identifications. In a footnote it is stated—

" The system of classification used (i.e., in Buenos Aires) is different from that described in the book."

Few would imagine from this note that the Argentine System had been in existence some years before Henry's " system " was in operation. Norway, Spain, and Brazil have no qualifying note. There is no doubt that the system employed in these countries is that of Vucetich, sometimes called " the Argentine System."[21] At the same time, the system of classification adopted by the Federal Bureau of Investigation at Washington, D.C., for the United States is based on that of Henry. It was, I believe, directly introduced from London in 1924. The Bureau has now some eight millions of cards in its collection.

The editor of the seventh and eighth editions of Henry's " standard " work is not stated. In the eighth edition of 1937, the figures for Buenos Aires remain as for 1932. This edition professes to bring statistical information up to 31st December, 1936. On page 11, dealing with " the present time," i.e. up to 31st December, 1936, the bureaux in the British Isles, outside London, are given as only Belfast and Dublin. No notice is taken of any bureaux in Scotland. The Glasgow bureau, dating from 1931, outstrips in importance both the Irish bureaux mentioned. In the short period from 1931, the number of fingerprint slips filed in Glasgow to 31st December, 1936, is 19,157. The number of identifications made with fingerprints during the year to 31st December, 1936, is 2075, or more than double that given for Dublin during the same period. *Vide*

Report of the Chief Constable of the City of Glasgow for 1936.

In 1930, Mr. Harry Battley, Chief-Inspector in charge of The Finger Print Bureau, New Scotland Yard, London, published a volume entitled: " Single Finger Prints: A New and Practical Method of Classifying and Filing Single Finger Prints and Fragmentary Impressions."[22] The principal features of Mr. Battley's method, according to Dr. C. Ainsworth Mitchell, are in securing the definition of circular areas for scrutiny by means of a magnifying-glass with a specially-prepared window at its base, and in separately filing prints of all ten fingers.[23] I believe Faulds forecasted the use of a concentric ring. Battley's " Single Finger Print System " has merit. The New York Police, I am informed, use it for their single fingerprint file. It is radically different from the system of Larson, which has never been used in New York.[24] Faulds dealt with the classification of single fingerprints in his " Manual of Practical Dactylography." There he explained his method. Vucetich was able by his own method to identify single finger " chance impressions," as he had noted the patterns of all ten fingers.[25]

The importance of single fingerprints is in the dramatic and special sphere of detection, mainly of burglars and thieves, from such prints found on crime scenes. Such detection was rendered possible only by the ingenious speculations and experiments of Faulds. I can find no recognition of Faulds in the Preface to, or in the text of, Mr. Battley's volume. It is fair to say that there he does not deal with the origin of such detective methods, and, accordingly, Herschel also is not mentioned. Mr. Battley does, however, describe " the most spectacular branch of finger-print work " as " that dealing with scenes of crime, &c.,"[26] and speaks of " the pioneers " in this science in a series of recent articles on

105

" All About Finger Prints " in *The Police Journal* for 1936 and 1937.[27] " All About Finger Prints " appeared to be so engagingly comprehensive that I scanned all the six articles, hoping to find that, at long last, New Scotland Yard had awakened from its neglect of Faulds. I was again disappointed.

Mr. Battley discourses about the prehistoric and later traces of fingerprints, and tells of the parts played by Galton, Henry, Herschel, and others, in his view, presumably, " the pioneers." Mr. Battley must be ignorant of Faulds. Not one of his six articles in " All About Finger Prints " mentions his name. Indeed, in all the fingerprint literature emanating from officials of New Scotland Yard, as well as in contributions by them to *The Police Journal*, published in London as a Quarterly Review for " The Police Forces of the Empire," the leading magazine of its class, I have come across no mention of Faulds. The only reference to him or to his publications, which I have discovered, is in Sir John Cumming's " Bibliography Dealing with Crime," issued under the patronage of the Commissioner of the Metropolitan Police. The last work of Faulds—his " Manual of Practical Dactylography," published in 1923—is there noticed! See Chapter XXII and Table V. Perhaps the knowledge of Herschel's honourable admission may lead now to a wider outlook at Metropolitan Police Headquarters.

With the wide experience of the operation of fingerprint methods, classification is always being improved and simplified, both as regards serial and single fingerprints. Police bureaux have in many cases their special adaptations different from that of New Scotland Yard. In particular, this is true of Glasgow City Police Bureau. The various uses besides that in crime detection to which fingerprints are or can be applied are noticed in the concluding chapter.

NOTES

[1] See Galton's " Memories of My Life," *supra*, p. 256.

[2] See Número Extraordinario : *Revista de Criminología, &c., supra,* p. 53. Cf. Faulds's " Dactylography," *supra*, p. 89.

[3] See Henry's Circular of 11th January, 1896, quoted in Chap. XVI.

[4] See " Classification and Uses of Finger Prints," *supra*, seventh edition, p. 5, 1934. London. H.M. Stationery Office.

[5] See his " Dactylography," *supra*, p. 89.

[6] See Chap. XVI.

[7] Henry never, I think, refers anywhere in his writings, to Faulds's evidence before the Brodrick Committee in 1902. See Chap. XXXI.

[8] See Chap. XXII.

[9] See " Classification and Uses of Finger Prints," *supra*, p 57 *et seq.* : and Chap. XVII.

[10] See *The Times* of 15th September, 1899, and *The British Medical Journal* of 23rd September, 1899, p. 803. Galton was present.

[11] 1905. 142 C.C.C. Sess.Papers, 978. Strictly speaking, this trial proceeded on an indictment charging the accused with the murder in March, 1905, of Thomas Farrow only. His wife was murdered at the same time. Fingermarks were found on the inside tray of a cash-box of the victims.

[12] In a Memorandum of July, 1904, issued from New Scotland Yard as a Government Paper, with reference to the working of Henry's system, there is no reference either to Faulds or Vucetich.

[13] The cash-box print and the impression of Alfred Stratton's right thumb showing the eleven points in agreement, is reproduced in the seventh edition of Wills on " Circumstantial Evidence," pp. 212-13. 1937.

[14] See *The Times*, of 1st August, 1906, and Chap. XXIV.

[15] See *The Times* of 1st August, 1906.

[16] See Chaps. XIV, XXIV, and XXIX.

[17] The New York City Police, as stated in Chap. XXIV, gave me particulars with regard to this criminal.

[18] See Pamphlet, printed in 1926, of Faulds, entitled " Was Sir E. R. Henry the Originator of the Finger-Print System " ? It is pathetic to read this vindication of himself, written in his old age, and to observe that he omits any notice of Herschel's admission in *Nature*, of 18th January, 1917, of his right to the sole credit in discovering the detective value of fingerprints found on crime scenes.

[19] " Daktyloskopie," *supra*, p. 53. The subject of classification is further referred to in Chap. XXXIV.

[20] pp. 11 *et seq.* Probably this table was left to some official and accepted by Henry as accurate.

[21] See Chap. XVI.

[22] London, H.M. Stationery Office.

[23] See *The Police Journal*, 1930, p. 637. Dr. Mitchell in " Documents and their Scientific Examination," *supra*, 1935, pp. 197 *et* 201, observes that Faulds suggested the use of the Kew Micrometer and the application of osmic acid in the examination of finger-impressions.

24 " Single Finger Print System." J. A. Larson. 1924. New York. D. Appleton & Co. ; see Faulds's " Manual " and, *supra*, Chap. IX, p. 39.

25 See " Modern Criminal Investigation," *supra*, p. 119. The authors credit Hakon Jorgenson, a Dane, with the first practicable single fingerprint system of registration.

26 Mr. Larson of New York says : " Never before in the history of criminal investigation has so much attention been directed toward the preservation of fingerprints found at the scene of crime." " Single Fingerprint System," p. 5, *supra*.

27 Vols. IX *et* X. 1936. London.

28 I have perused with interest the work on " Fingerprints " by F. Brewester, Document Specialist, and published in 1936 in Calcutta. His " Numerical Index " is claimed by him to be of special value for fingerprint classification and to be much simpler than the system of Henry which he describes as complicated. This writer adopts a nomenclature for finger patterns different from those of both Henry and Vucetich. Arches, loops, and whorls become with him waves, staples, and double junctions : this does not seem to make for international uniformity in coding. This writer, however, ably explains and illustrates all the peculiarities met with in fingerprints, such as rods, dots, forks, &c. Many decisions of the Indian courts are instructively set forth in Chap. VII, entitled " Fingerprint Jurisprudence " and throughout his book. " Poroscopy," the subject of Chap. VIII, is a notable feature. But Faulds dealt critically with this matter and with Dr. Locard's views in the article he contributed to *Nature* in August, 1913. See Vol. XCI, p. 635. Faulds deals with poroscopy also in his 1912 " Dactylography," *supra*. In his article, he rightly points out that poroscopy is not a separate science but that it is just a subsidiary, though all important branch, of fingerprint identification. In his article on " Finger Prints " in *Scientific American Supplement* of 18th November, 1911, Vol. LXXII, p. 326, Faulds has an illustration of an enlarged fingerprint, showing sweat pores. The Bengal and Delhi murder cases of 1897 and 1924 respectively are not referred to by Brewester. Brief, though fair, notice is made by this writer to Faulds. See pp. 7 *et* 12. On p. 12 he states " that the present-day perfection of the fingerprint method is almost entirely due to four great Englishmen : Faulds, Herschel, Galton, and Henry." It is, perhaps, a mere coincidence that Faulds, the Scot, is named first. The author does not mention Herschel's admission of the credit due to Faulds for his great conception of the use of chance finger-impressions for tracking criminals. It is this fact that gives Faulds the first place.

XIX

FAULDS'S " GUIDE " AND GALTON'S " REVIEW " : 1905

DURING the trial[1] of the Brothers Stratton, Faulds had in preparation and, in September, 1905, published his " Guide to Finger Print Identification." *Nature* con-

tained a " review " of it by Galton, under his initials
" F. G.," in a Supplement, p. iv, of date, 19th October,
1905.[2] It was not, in my opinion, a fair review. In
order that the soundness of that opinion may be tested
with the grounds upon which it is based as stated in the
next Chapter, it is right that the whole of it should be
reprinted. Here it follows : —

Finger-Print Identification.[2]

Guide to Finger-Print Identification. By Henry Faulds,
L.F.P.S., late Surgeon Superintendent of Tsukiji
Hospital, Tokyo, Japan. Pp. VIII. 80. (Hanley :
Wood, Mitchell & Co., Ltd., 1905.) Price 5s. net.

Dr. Faulds was for some years a medical officer in
Japan, and a zealous and original investigator of fingerprints. He wrote an interesting letter about them in
Nature, October 28, 1880, dwelling upon the legal purposes to which they might be applied, and he appears to
be the first person who published anything, *in print*, on
this subject. However, his suggestions of introducing the
use of finger-prints fell flat. The reason that they did
not attract attention was presumably that he supported
them by no convincing proofs of three elementary propositions on which the suitability of finger-prints for
legal purposes depends. It was necessary to adduce
strong evidence of the, long since vaguely alleged, permanence of those ridges on the bulbs of the fingers that
print their distinctive lineations. It was necessary to
adduce better evidence than opinions based on mere
inspection of the vast variety in the minute details of
those markings, and finally, for purposes of criminal
investigation, it was necessary to prove that a large
collection could be classified with sufficient precision to
enable the officials in charge of it to find out speedily
whether a duplicate of any set of prints that might be
submitted to them did or did not exist in the collection.
Dr. Faulds had no part in establishing any one of these
most important preliminaries.

But though his letter of 1880 was, as above mentioned,
apparently the first *printed* communication on the subject, it appeared years after the first public and *official
use* of finger-prints had been made by Sir William

Herschel in India, to whom the credit of originality that Dr. Faulds desires to monopolise is far more justly due. Those who care to learn the facts at first hand should turn to NATURE, vol. xxii., p. 605, for Dr. Faulds's first letter, to vol. i., p. 518, for a second letter from him in reference to the Parliamentary Blue-book on the "Identification of Criminals," then just issued, and lastly to Sir Wm. Herschel's reply in vol. li., pp. 77-8, where the question of priority of dates is placed beyond doubt, by the reprint of the office copy of Sir William's "demi-official" letter of August 15, 1877, to the then Inspector of Prisons in Bengal. This letter covers all that is important in Dr. Faulds's subsequent communication in 1880, and goes considerably further. The method introduced by Sir Wm. Herschel, tentatively at first as a safeguard against personation, had gradually been developed and tested, both in the jail and in the registering office, during a period of from ten to fifteen years before 1877, as stated in the above quoted [sic] letter[3] to the Inspector of Prisons.

The failure of Sir Wm. Herschel's successor, and of others at that time in authority in Bengal, to continue the development of the system so happily begun, is greatly to be deplored, but it can be explained on the same grounds as those mentioned above in connection with Dr. Faulds. The writer of these remarks can testify to the occasional incredulity in the early 'nineties concerning the permanence of the ridges, for it happened to himself while staying at the house of a once distinguished physiologist who was the writer when young of an article on the skin in a first-class encyclopædia, to hear strong objections made to that opinion. His theoretical grounds were that the glands, the ducts of which pierce the ridges, would multiply with the growth of the hand, and it was not until the hands of the physiologist's own children had been examined by him through a lens, that he could be convinced that the lineations on a child's hand might be the same as when he grew up, but on a smaller scale.

The literature concerning finger-prints is becoming large. An excellent index to it will be found in a memoir by Otto Schlaginhaufen, just published (*Morphol. Jahrbuch*, Bd. xxxiii., H. 4, and Bd. xxxiv., H. I., Leipzig). But even this is incomplete, for it takes no notice of Mr. Tabor's efforts in San Francisco to obtain the official registration of the finger-prints of the Chinese immigrants, whom it was found difficult to identify otherwise. This seems to have occurred at some time in the 'eighties, possibly before then, but dates are now wanting.

Dr. Faulds in his present volume recapitulates his old grievance with no less bitterness than formerly. He overstates the value of his own work, belittles that of others, and carps at evidence recently given in criminal cases. His book is not only biased and imperfect, but unfortunately it contains nothing new that is of value, so far as the writer of these remarks can judge, and much of what Dr. Faulds seems to consider new has long since been forestalled. It is a pity that he did not avail himself of the opportunity of writing a book up to date, for he can write well, and the photographic illustrations which his publisher has supplied are excellent. The experiences of other countries ought soon to be collated with those of England, in order to develop further the art of classifying large collections of finger-prints. In Argentina, for example, their use has wholly superseded Bertillonage, and one would like to know with what success.[4] A bureau that can deal effectively with very many thousands of cases would require a staff of particularly intelligent officials, and the tradition of dealing in the same way with certain transitional forms that are of frequent occurrence. The more highly the art of classifying, or as it might be phrased of " lexiconising," finger-prints is developed, the more wide will their use become. They ought to be especially valuable in checking desertions from the Army and Navy. But there may be moral objections to the use of finger-prints in these cases for, according to the present system of recruiting, many take refuge in the Army who are " wanted " by the police, and would strongly object to being finger-printed.

A few words should be added concerning the ancient usage of finger-prints in China, Japan, and India for legal purposes. Good evidence as to this has at length been supplied by Minakata Kumagusu in two letters to NATURE, vol. li., pp. 199 and 274. It is clear that it *was* used to some extent, but there is nothing as yet to show that the impressions were made and scrutinised with anything like the precautions now considered to be essential to the good working of the system. Blurred finger-prints cannot be correctly deciphered except by a trained expert, using lenses and photographic magnification. Negative evidence is often of conspicuous value, such as should leave no reasonable doubt in the mind of the most stupid juryman; but expert analysis and severe cross-examination are required when the prints to be compared are generically alike and when one of them is imperfect or blurred. F. G.

Unfortunately, there was not in 1905 and there is still not in existence any tribunal of authors, publishers, and reviewers, international or national, to which questions of literary etiquette or fairness could be submitted. It would have been of great advantage to Faulds to have been able to refer to such a tribunal the fairness or the reverse of this " review "? of his " Guide " by Galton. Armed with its subpœnas, Galton and Herschel might have been called as witnesses before the court. Upon the evidence now available, assuming its existence at the time of inquiry, their cross-examination would not have been very pleasant. Apart from the obligation upon Herschel to admit that he had positively conceded the superlative claim of Faulds in the revolutionary method of crime detection, Faulds would have been able to tender the testimony of eminent criminologists and others as supporting that claim, and doing so in ignorance of Herschel's definite admission made in 1917. One cannot doubt that such a tribunal would have made a unanimous finding in favour of Faulds.

NOTES

[1] Reported under dates 6th and 8th May, 1905, in C.C.C. Sess. Papers. Vol. CXCII, p. 958.

[2] Words underlined in the " Review " as reprinted in text are as underlined in the original.

[3] Galton only cites the " Hooghly Letter " in this " Review." He does not quote it at length. Readers have it set out in full in Chap. III.

[4] Galton probably did not know, and therefore does not here tell his readers of the real position of fingerprints in Argentina. Under

the direction of Vucetich, La Plata Fingerprint Bureau, with the system of classification invented by him, achieved distinction some years before the Metropolitan Police in London set up their Finger-print Bureau. The first Argentine Finger-Print Bureau was opened in San Nicolas in Buenos Aires on 31st March, 1892. See Chap. XVI.

XX

CRITIQUE OF GALTON'S " REVIEW " OF FAULDS'S " GUIDE "

WHERE facts justify severe criticism and condemnation, it may be the duty of an impartial reviewer to be devastating. Generally, its exercise gives no pain to the reviewer. But it always creates and is bound to create, perhaps deservedly, extreme suffering in the author reviewed. It is assumed that, although he may be wrong, the reviewer is discharging his duty in good faith. Galton's good faith and absence of malice are not disputed. Reviewing is delicate and difficult where the reviewer is himself a rival exponent (however superior) with the author of the work reviewed. Still more so is such the case, where the reviewer has been engaged in controversy with the author or has criticized him elsewhere in regard to their respective parts in the exposition or development of their special branch of science. That was Galton's position. His " review " of Faulds's " Guide " must have wounded Faulds deeply and harmed him in many ways. Galton's vision had got blurred by his Herschelian obsession.

Was Galton's " Review " fair? The answer to this query seems unquestionably No. It cannot be considered, it is submitted, as impartial or as just. The suggestions of Faulds, Galton states, fell flat. That is true. But they were correct and well founded. They fell flat on account of the obtuseness of Scotland Yard's high officials to see their significance when Faulds first submitted his propositions to them. The inference (obviously intended by Galton, in conjunction with his subsequent affirmation in the "review," that Faulds's work contained "nothing new ") is that there never was anything in Faulds's suggestions. In other words, Faulds's claims to originality, according to Galton, were without foundation.

Let first some minor points made by Galton in this Review be dealt with.

(1) He makes good, and that easily, the claim of priority on the part of Herschel as an originator of the idea of registering fingermarks. Herschel had done so by his Letter to *Nature* of November, 1880. But Galton went too far in asserting that " the credit of originality " is " far more justly due " to Herschel. The credit is shared with Faulds. Other impartial investigators of and commentators on fingerprints have since so asserted. The honour, as they maintain, of both Faulds and Herschel is equal.

(2) His apologetic reference to Oriental literature regarding fingerprints, in view of his former sarcastically negative opinions of the Chinese, is distinctly refreshing.[1]

(3) In his keenness to find Faulds's discoveries forestalled, he mentions the efforts of a San Francisco photographer to obtain in the United States official registration by the use of fingermarks of Chinese immigrants; and, he adds—

> " this seems to have occurred at some time in the 'eighties, possibly before then, but dates are now wanting."

It is believed that the year was 1882.[2] From all that appears, Tabor, the photographer in question, may have received his inspiration for his proposed regulation from Faulds's Letter of October, 1880, or from it and that of the Letter in November, 1880, of Herschel. But whether Tabor's connexion with fingerprints happened before Faulds made his experiments in or about 1878 or 1879, and sent his Letter to *Nature* in 1880, is immaterial. It has, at least, no bearing on the absolutely exclusive claim of Faulds to be the first to discover the valuable detective uses of fingermarks in or on crime scenes. Faulds called attention to the interesting references to thumb impressions in English literature made by Charles Dickens, 1850, and Walter Pater, 1871. See his " Dactylography " *supra*, pp. 18 *et* 19.

Taking up the serious propositions of the " review "—

(I) " It was necessary," says Galton, " to adduce strong evidence of the, long since vaguely alleged, permanence of those ridges on the bulbs of the fingers that print their distinctive lineations."

Who " vaguely " alleged this permanence? Not Faulds. Herschel, indeed, was " vague " in his assertions and was not absolutely convinced of their life-permanence. Could Faulds have presented stronger evidence than he did? See his *Nature* Letter; *Knowledge* article, &c.[3]

(II) " It was," again Galton proceeds, " necessary to adduce better evidence than opinions based on mere inspection of the vast variety in the minute details of those markings."

Did not Faulds base his conclusions on more than " mere inspection "? Recall his experiments.[3]

(III) " Finally for purposes of criminal investigation," states Galton, " it was necessary to prove that a large collection could be classified with sufficient precision to enable the officials in charge of it to find out speedily whether a duplicate of any set of prints that might be submitted to them did or did not exist in the collection."

Was not Faulds able to satisfy Scotland Yard that this could be done? Refer to Tunbridge's letter.[4]

Yet, Galton categorically affirms that Faulds " had no part in establishing any one of these [three] most important preliminaries." By the use only of " green spectacles," could such a dogmatic and erroneous conclusion be reached.

It is singularly striking that, at the advanced date of his " review," Galton had obviously not in his mind, or, if he had, he closed his eyes to the fact, that his own or any other classification of collected or registered fingermarks could be of no assistance in the discovery of any crime where there were no collected or registered fingermarks of the criminal in existence with which to compare transfers of his fingermarks found on the scene of his depredations. In the case of a previously-unconvicted criminal, it is only by arresting some suspect and comparing his fingermarks on arrest with the fingermarks at the *locus* that justice in so many cases has been accomplished. So, this conception of Faulds in his *Nature* Letter and expounded in his " Guide " obtained no notice in Galton's " review "; and, of course, no appreciation!

(IV) In making the very sweeping assertions in support of Herschel that the 1877 "Hooghly Letter" of Herschel

(1) " covers all that is important in Dr. Faulds's subsequent communication in 1880 "; and

(2) " goes considerably further."

Galton (however honest in his own convictions) was here definitely and positively unjust to Faulds. It is regrettable to find one of the eminence of Galton making two such gross misstatements. His extreme championship of Herschel's claims seems to have clouded his mind.

Emphatically, the " Hooghly Letter "

(1) does not cover all that is important in the com-

116

munication of Faulds to *Nature* of 28th October, 1880, and

(2) does not go " considerably further."

No one dispassionately reading the " Hooghly Letter," along with Faulds's Letter of October, 1880, could endorse as accurate these statements. Herschel himself neither in November, 1880, nor in November, 1894, made, expressly or by implication, any such assertions. Later, we shall come to Herschel's own explicit admission, refuting these extraordinary claims made for him by Galton.

Pontifically, Galton dismisses the " Guide " with the malediction—

" unfortunately it contains nothing new that is of value so far as the writer of these remarks can judge, and much of what Dr. Faulds seems to consider new has long since been forestalled."[5]

Herschel was silent at this time. He acquiesced, apparently, in all these dogmatic, slighting assertions of Galton upon Faulds. No doubt he then approved of the " review "—it lauded him so much. But, to the honour of Herschel, there was published in *Nature* of 18th January, 1917, " *Remarks* " made by him, as invited by the Editor, upon Faulds's Letter in the same issue over the publication by Herschel in 1916 of his " The Origin of Finger-Printing." In these " *Remarks*," Herschel acknowledged, in reference to this very matter, " the credit due " to Faulds " for a conception so different from mine."[6]

It was the amazing proof of detective work in trials before me that aroused my interest in fingerprints and in the origin of their use in evidence. Fingermarks in many cases seemed impossible of detection by the eye: often hidden or impressed on dark substances. Faulds's researches had resulted in their complete and masterly revelation in Courts of Justice. Mr. Bert Wentworth, formerly Police Commissioner of Dover, New Hampshire, U.S.A., and the late Harris Hawthorne Wilder, Ph.D., Professor of Zoology in Smith College, U.S.A., in the original edition of their joint work on " Personal Identification," published in 1918, devote a whole chapter to this discovery of Faulds. These authors say—

> " It is not a little singular that the one who was the first in modern times to suggest in print the use of finger-prints for identification purposes, saw, at the same time, a wider application of a system so based than did his contemporaries."[7]

Galton was the chief of these " contemporaries."

In personal references to Faulds the " review " stings. He uses his work, Galton states, for the ventilation of " his old grievance with no less bitterness than formerly." The grievance was certainly old but well founded. With this unsympathetic touch, Galton proclaims to all readers of the " review " that the " Guide " contains " nothing new that is of value." This was probably thought as the most kindly way of recommending readers of *Nature* to refrain from getting the " Guide "; or, if they had done so, to put it as valueless into the wastepaper basket. Coupled with the opening but, obviously, cold reference to Faulds as a " zealous and original investigator " (discovering " nothing new ") and the subsequent patronizing back-patting about the apparent ability of Faulds to " write well," everything was without doubt in the mind of Galton most just and in most excellent taste. " Faint praise " is damning.

The " review " had the merit of an extraordinarily subtle modesty on the part of the reviewer in withholding from readers of *Nature* the outstanding claims he had made in *Nature* and elsewhere for himself. All readers did not know or recognize " F. G."

It would have been well and discreet, it is submitted, on the part of Galton to have declined the request of the Editor of *Nature* and passed on the task of reviewing Faulds's book to an entirely neutral writer. Few readers of the " review " would discern that Galton was chafing at Faulds's criticism of himself in the " Guide " and in other publications.

In a discussion in *The Times* in January and February, 1909, over the original authorship of fingerprint classification for identification purposes, Galton took part. Some wrote in favour of Henry: some in favour of Galton: one was for Purkinje: and others backed Herschel. In his letter of 13th January, 1909, Galton observed—

> " No one who has read my two books can accuse me of ignoring the work of Sir W. Herschel or that of Purkinje."

In that Galton was right. But his books did scant justice to Faulds. This " review," no doubt in Galton's mind, justified that attitude. In *The Times* correspondence Vucetich also was never mentioned.

Of Faulds and his " Guide " other reviewers did not think so badly.[8] Some men with or without reason dislike their opponents or fellow-workers; but, still, they can admire and even praise their work. The reviewing of Faulds's book by Galton gave him a unique opportunity for magnanimity.

NOTES

[1] The two letters, written from London, under dates 18th and 31st December, 1894, and referred to by Galton, of Mr. Kumagusu Minakata (whose name, by the way, Galton reverses), a frequent contributor to *Nature* on Chinese and Japanese topics, are of great interest. Mr. Minakata states that the Japanese borrowed the fingerprint method from the Chinese; that Chinese records proved the

existence of fingerprints in a Southern Indian ancient kingdom; and, citing both Japanese and Chinese authorities, dating back to the ninth century A.D., he says that in his opinion his research " seems to justify the claim made on behalf of the Chinese " by Mr. Spearman, the author of the article on " Known to the Police," in *The Nineteenth Century, supra.* See Chap. XXIX for the result of researches by Giles, Laufer and others, taking Chinese connexion with fingerprints still further back.

2 See Chap. XIV.

3 Cf. Opinions of Dr. Ainsworth Mitchell, London, and of Dr. Hoover, Washington, D.C., cited *ibid*.

4 See Chap. IX.

5 Pleasant benedictions by men of eminence on the labours and services of Faulds will be found in Chap. XXXIII.

6 See Chap. XXII.

7 p. 351. See also p. 337. Wilder died in 1928. The Chap. remains the same in the new and revised edition, published by Mr. Wentworth in 1932.

8 " British, American and Foreign Tributes to Faulds " is the subject of Chap. XXXIII.

XXI

HERSCHEL'S " ' KONAI'S HAND ' BROCHURE " " NATURE'S " REVIEW : 1916-17

HERSCHEL published " The Origin of Finger-Printing " in 1916. For brevity, I have called it " ' Konai's Hand ' Brochure " in the title of this Chapter. It is a booklet of 41 pages. Konai was the name of a Bengali village contractor, with whom in 1858 Herschel, then a young assistant under the Old East India Company, made a contract for road-metalling. With the view of terrorizing Konai out of any attempt to repudiate his obligations, Herschel made him press his palm and fingers, dabbed with oil-ink, on the back of the contract. Herschel was so delighted afterwards with this inspiration, its consequences, and the use Galton made of Konai's hand that in this booklet he is not content with reproducing one facsimile of it. There are three, one on the face page cover, one within pages 8 and 9, and another on the inside of the back cover!

Konai's hand! I intended to reproduce it here in view of the criticism by Faulds upon it as set out in the next Chapter. The publisher of the booklet had no objection, so far as his interest was concerned, to my doing so. The copyright owner, to whom he referred me, did not give permission. Readers of Chapter XXII may judge for themselves the justice of Faulds's criticism upon "Konai's hand" by examining any of the three facsimiles in Herschel's brochure.

Undoubtedly, according to Herschel himself in this booklet, if not put in express words, at least by clearest implication, Herschel is the sole inventor of the modern fingerprint identification system in all its ramifications; "the method," as he says in the Preface, that "has been developed into a system far more effective than anything I contemplated." All sprang, as he indicates, from his giving to Galton for his Royal Society lecture in November, 1890, his "Konai" thumbmarked contract of 1858. With ill-disguised conceit he has this passage in the text:

"The decisiveness of a finger-print is now one of the most powerful aids to Justice. Our possession of it derives from the impression of Konai's hand in 1858 "!!![1]

In his Appendix to this booklet, Herschel states:

"The science of identification by means of the pads cannot, in my opinion, date further back than 1858, when I happened to use oil-ink, which was not used for *tep-sais*."[2]

If this is not a claim on Herschel's part to the sole discovery of the value of fingerprints, as including the discovery of criminals through marks left by them, it is difficult to understand his reference to "one of the most powerful aids to Justice"!

Herschel sought to exclude the Chinese from any possibility of association with the origin of fingerprints except directly through himself or indirectly through others in conversation with him. He refers again to his voyage in 1877, as mentioned by him in his Letter to *Nature* in 1894:

" We roused attention enough on board in the Indian Ocean to obtain the finger-prints of the Captain and many of his officers, stewards, and kalashis; also of many of the passengers, . . . Most of the other saloon passengers were business men on their way back to the Far East, and left us at Ceylon. If any one of them had heard of the use of these marks, say in China, I could not but have been told of it. But there was not a breath of the sort. . . . It is only reasonable, I think, to believe that such a novel and evidently useful idea would have spread by their means wherever they went."[3]

All that need be said is that Herschel's reasoning was very inconsequential.

Herschel appears to have had some qualms about his claim to the " discovery " of fingerprints. In the Appendix he adds:

" When I speak of the ' discovery ' of fingerprints nigh sixty years ago, I should wish to be understood correctly. I cannot say that I thought of it as such until Mr. Galton examined old records in search of earlier notices of the subject. What he found had been beyond my ken, and I never inquired for myself. The fascination of experiments and the impelling object of them were all I cared about. Had it been otherwise I should have had an open field for egoism to any extent, for no one questioned the novelty of the thing. The time that has elapsed since Galton's inquiries, without any material addi-

tion to his ascertained facts, justifies me, I venture
to think, in speaking of my work as the ' discovery '
of the value of finger-prints."[4]

Then, in view of all that is now known about Faulds,
he adds a truly remarkable sentence. It is this:

"I proceed to show what has been brought to light
from other sources."[4]

These " sources " are marshalled by Herschel in the
order of 1809, Bewick; 1823, Purkinje; 1858, Bengal, as
to a custom of illiterates over " token signatures ";
and China, in regard to which he refers to his " Oxford
friend," Mr. Bullock, in this way:

"Talking with him about the methods of signing
deeds in China, he told me that the finger-tip (not
finger-print) method was in ordinary use, but he was
careful to point out also that to his knowledge ever
since he went to Peking, about 1868, Chinese bankers
had been in the habit of impressing their thumbs on
the notes they issued; and he had no doubt the
custom was much older than that. This was
startling, but he kindly procured for me the bank-
note which I here show in facsimile; with it came
this explanation of such thumb-marks, given by his
friend in China:

They are imprinted partly on the counterfoil and
partly on the note itself, so that when presented its
genuineness can be tested at once.

"That is, they play the part of which is technically called the ' scroll ' in our cheques.

"My readers may accept it that the ink used was
the same Indian ink with which the Chinese
characters on the note were written. That is the
unhesitating judgement of such an expert as Mr.
Galton, who examined it. The difference between a
water ink and printer's ink for identification is

123

enormous. Blood on the fingers has occasionally left impressions that fortunately sufficed to reveal the murderer[5]; but, as a rule, wet fingers leave only smudges as useless as this one. It is quite certain, therefore, that no one in the habit of impressing his thumb-mark as this banker did, would use water ink, if he depended on recognizing it as his own. In short, the smudge on the bank-note was placed there in order to identify the two parts of a piece of paper after severance, not to prove who placed it so. My readers may see what exquisite delicacy of detail can be obtained by printer's ink, when so desired, if they will examine a fine skin impression with a magnifying-glass; even the pores along the ridges can be seen as white dots. For practical purposes, however, such extreme delicacy as this is not needed.

" This difference of ink suggests a further remark. The Chinese have used printer's ink for ages. If they aimed at identification they would surely have discovered its great value for clear impressions, and its use could never have died out. On the other hand, a method of identification depending on water ink could never have survived for such strict work as our finger-prints. On the palm of the hand it can give a fairly good impression for such simple identification as is wanted (say) for passports, because the large creases will obviously be those of the bearer of the passport, or as obviously not. These lines of the palm, so well known in palmistry, are as clear to a man as the shape of his hand, while those on the pads of his own fingers are scarcely noticed even now by one man in a million. The science of identification by means of the pads cannot, in my opinion, date farther back than 1858, when I happened to use oil-ink, which was not used for *tep-sais*."

And, lastly, Herschel mentions Japan, by a reference:

"The ablest defence of the claims of antiquity that I have seen is by a Japanese writer, Kumagusu Minakata, whose letter to *Nature*, Dec. 27, 1894, appears to be as exhaustive as it is able; but I hope that this paper will satisfy him that the finger-print system of our day has no connexion with the methods he describes."[6]

Finally, Herschel sums up his case thus:

"None of the writers who have undertaken the defence appears to perceive this need of a second impression if the issue of identity turns on any kind of finger-mark. Repudiations cannot have been rare; tribunals must occasionally have been invoked; yet no instance is quoted of decision by demand for a second impression. It seems then that these marks were not made, as ours are, expressly to challenge comparison; that, in fact, they offer no points for comparison. In conclusion, it is hard to believe that a system so practically useful as this could have been known in the great lands of the East for generations past, without arresting the notice of Western statesmen, merchants, travellers, and students. Yet the knowledge never reached us."[7]

It is difficult to find any justification for the omission of all reference to Faulds as one of the " sources " Herschel professed, exhaustively, to enumerate. Herschel specifically referred in his notice of China, as quoted, to the fact that " Blood on the fingers has occasionally left impressions that fortunately sufficed to reveal the murderer." Faulds was the only and original " source," in modern times, at least, of the way in which such a miscreant could be tracked. In the next Chapter Herschel's excuse for this serious omission will be found. Readers may appraise it for themselves.

With regard to the position of the Chinese in the matter of fingerprints, that is fully dealt with in Chapter XXIX; and, again, readers for themselves will see how very far astray both Herschel and Galton were in this matter. Galton referred to Kumagusu Minakata's letter in reviewing for *Nature* in 1905 Faulds's "Guide to Finger-Print Identification." Galton cannot have been very thorough in his examination of old records. He does not seem to have received much further light between 1892, when he published his "Finger-Prints," and 1905, when he reviewed the work of Faulds.

The express objects of Herschel in writing " 'Konai's Hand ' Brochure " were, as he sets out in the Preface:

> " first, to place on record the genesis of the Finger-print method of personal identification, from its discovery in Bengal in 1858, till its public demonstration there in 1877-8; secondly, to examine the scanty suggestions of evidence that this use of our fingers had been foreshadowed in Europe more than a hundred years ago, and had indeed been general in ancient times, especially in China."

It is submitted that Herschel achieved neither of these objects. The genesis of the fingerprint method of identification goes back far beyond 1858.

Herschel never contemplated, and the police of no country ever conceived, prior to 1880, the possibility of discovering crime from the record of a criminal left by his hands on the property he had touched in the commission of his offence. Faulds alone thought of that and of the means of obtaining that record. Why was there this seemingly studied resolution on the part of Galton up to his death in 1911, and of Herschel up to 1917, to keep Faulds out of consideration in fingermark identification? No doubt they thought that the contributions of Faulds were of no, or of little, significance.

Herschel, in the controversy raised in January-February, 1909, in the correspondence columns of *The Times*, over the discoverer of fingerprint classification, closed his share in it with this as the last paragraph of his letter to the Editor, dated 12th February, 1909 :

> " My own repetitions of true ' finger prints ' during the greater part of my 25 years' service in India are not open to dispute. If not from them, whence did the idea of persistency arise ? "

The answer is simple. In modern times, certainly from both Faulds and Herschel : from Faulds in a scientifically convincing way and of which he was the first to make the world aware : from Herschel only in a haphazard manner, prior to his " repetitions " being studied by Galton.

Herschel's book was reviewed anonymously for *Nature* in its issue of 7th December, 1916.[8] The anonymous reviewer praises Herschel and conjoins him with Galton and Henry (whom I may describe, as no doubt they esteemed themselves, as the Fingerprint Triumvirate) as alone collectively responsible for the origin and development of fingermark identification. Faulds is, of course, not mentioned in the review. The review is very short. Here it is :

> " The Origin of Finger-Printing." By Sir William J. Herschel, Bart. Pp. 41. (London : Oxford University Press, 1916.) Price with paper covers, 1s. net.
>
> When Sir Francis Galton issued " Finger-Print Directories " in 1895 he inscribed the volume to Sir William J. Herschel, Bart., in the following words :—" I do myself the pleasure of dedicating this book to you, in recognition of your initiative in employing finger-prints as official signatures, nearly forty years ago, and in grateful remembrance of the invaluable help you freely gave me when I began to study them." And now, in the year 1916, fifty-eight years after he lighted " upon a discovery which promised escape from one great difficulty of

administration in India," Sir William Herschel tells the story of how our modern system of identification by means of finger-prints was born in the magistrates' court at Jungipoor, on the upper reaches of the Hooghly. In his dedication to Sir Edward Henry, Commissioner of the Metropolitan Police, Sir William writes as follows:—
" I am offering you this old story of the beginnings of fingerprinting, by way of expressing my warm and continuous admiration of those masterly developments of its original applications, whereby, first in Bengal and the Transvaal, and then in England, you have fashioned a weapon of penetrating certainty for the sterner needs of justice."

There can be no doubt that England has given the world the most perfect system of identification—identification of an individual by means of his or her fingerprints. The method was initiated by Herschel; it was developed and created into a system by Galton; it has been perfected and applied by Henry. Nor should it be forgotten that it was on the initiative of Mr. Asquith, when Home Secretary in the Liberal Administration of 1892-95, that the method found an early recognition at Scotland Yard. All who are interested in the use and significance of finger-prints will feel grateful to Sir William Herschel for placing on record the first steps of an important development.

The anonymous reviewer, as readers must observe, does not do much more than simply piece together the laudatory dedications of Galton to Herschel in his work on " Finger Print Directories," and of Herschel to Henry in his " Konai's Hand " brochure. In his work on " Classification and Uses of Finger Prints," Henry has no dedication; but in his text Henry lauds both Galton and Herschel. So the reviewer, as we see, accepting their own estimates of themselves, states dogmatically—

The method was initiated by Herschel : it was developed and created into a system by Galton ; it has been perfected and applied by Henry.

In a measure true; but part-truths are misleading! Was it Henry that " fashioned a weapon of penetrating

certainty for the sterner needs of Justice?" Did
Galton's and Henry's works, singly or in combination,
justify Herschel in this booklet of his in speaking of
" my work " as the " discovery " of the value of fingerprints? Part-truths again! One cannot wholly blame
the reviewer for his omission of all reference to Faulds
in his " review." The classic works of the " Fingerprint Triumvirate," specified in this " review," never
mention Faulds. It was easy for the reviewer to add his
own plaudits. All credit the reviewer gives to England!
Were not the members of the " Fingerprint Triumvirate " Englishmen born!?

Sir Arthur Keith, world-renowned as an anthropologist,
was, I am informed, the author of the Review. I do
not for a moment doubt that he wrote in good faith.
Faulds being a Scotsman is a fact that redounds to
Scotland in fingerprint history. Had Sir Arthur Keith
known all the facts, he would undoubtedly have written
his " review " differently.

It was rather unfortunate, however, that so much
eulogy should have been expended in this " review "
over the Fingerprint Triumvirate, and, particularly, over
Herschel. Obviously, Sir Arthur Keith does not seem
to have gone much beyond or outside, if at all, the covers
of Herschel's booklet for his material in reviewing it.
It was in no sense a critique. He criticized nothing and
he dissented from nothing that Herschel wrote. He made
no reference to Vucetich.

Damaging observations upon or criticisms of Herschel's
brochure came first from Herschel himself, and shortly
afterwards from Laufer.[9]

In the following month of January, 1917, after the
appearance of the Review, Herschel in *Nature* divested
himself of the right to claim any share in originating
the detective values of fingermarks on crime-scenes—" a

weapon," indeed, to use Herschel's words in his " The Origin of Finger Printing," " of penetrating certainty for the sterner needs of Justice " ![10] That right Herschel for the first time there and then resigned absolutely and exclusively to Faulds.[11]

Laufer had already in his 1912 *Smithsonian* article described Herschel's artless conceit as " naïve," in proffering in his Letter to *Nature* in 1894, the theory that people in China had become aware of his " discovery " of fingerprints through the officers and passengers of s.s. " Mongolia " in 1877 passing the news to them. In a short article, entitled " Concerning the History of Finger-Prints " (afterwards referred to as his " 1917 *Science* " article), which Laufer contributed to *Science* of 25th May, 1917, he observes:

> " The principal purpose by which Sir W. Herschel was guided in writing his account is to demonstrate that he was the real ' discoverer ' of finger prints in Bengal in 1858, entirely from his own resources, and to discredit all other claims to priority in this matter, especially those on the part of the Chinese."[12]

I refer to this article by Laufer in Chapter XXIX upon " The Chinese and Fingerprints." Laufer in this 1917 *Science* article cites Professor Henri Cordier (1849-1925) of Paris, upon this question and as stating—

> " Sir W. Herschel was entirely wrong: Mr. Faulds protested against the claim of Sir W. Herschel," &c.

The authorities cited by Laufer with others mentioned in that Chapter XXIX are generally regarded as destroying the arrogant claim made by Herschel, while exposing at the same time inferentially his complete ignorance of Chinese and other Oriental literature. Laufer observes that Herschel should have found in his 1912 *Smithsonian* article " all the available evidence in favour of the Chinese, Japanese and Tibetans, all of whom applied ages ago with full consciousness the system of finger-prints for the purpose of identifying individuals "; and, further, Laufer states " the cool and impartial historian, in the light of observed facts, can reach no other con-clusion than that Herschel must have conceived his idea from observations of similar affairs made on the spot."

Laufer in the same 1917 *Science* article deals with the innocent amazement of Herschel, as expressed in " Konai's Hand " brochure, that

> " a system so practically useful as this could have been known in the great lands of the East for genera-tions past without arresting the notice of Western statesmen, merchants, travellers and students."

by

(a) stating that Mohamedan authors who visited China did not fail to describe this system;

(b) noting the discovery in Turkestan of three con-tracts (A.D. 782 and 786), where the parties declared that they had affixed the impressions of their fingers as a distinctive mark;

(c) citing the testimony of Soleiman (A.D. 851) with regard to bills of exchange given to creditors being authenticated by the debtor with his middle and index fingers placed together; and

(d) citing Rashid-eddin, " the famous Persian historian," who treated (*circa* A.D. 1303) of " finger-signatures " in the authentication in China of State Council resolutions and generally of contracts.

Laufer concluded his 1917 *Science* article:

Most certainly, the idea underlying Chinese finger prints was principally that of identification, as expressly stated by Rashid-eddin and all Chinese informants. If a doubt or litigation arose, all that was necessary was to repeat the finger impression of the contractor who had formerly signed the deed.

I may add that Sir Aurel Stein's work on "Ancient Khotan," which was published in 1907, and other authorities referred to by Laufer, were all available to Herschel. Galton died in 1911. Herschel died on 24th October, 1917. I do not know whether his attention was called to Laufer's 1917 *Science* article : probably not.

With Herschel's admission, and this citation of authority, the appraisement of " Konai's Hand " brochure and *Nature's* review, or rather notice of it, may be left to the judgment of readers.

NOTES

1 See p. 9.

2 See p. 40. A *tep-sai*, Herschel explains, is a black ink blot token made by wet fingertip.

3 See pp. 17 *et* 18.

4 See pp. 32 *et seq.*

5 Kangali Charan's case was no doubt in Herschel's mind.

6 See p. 40. Herschel was aware of Galton's reference to this Japanese gentleman's letter in Galton's " review " for *Nature* of Faulds's " Guide to Finger-Print Identification."

7 See p. 41.

8 Vol. 98, p. 268.

9 See Chap. XV and also Chap. XXIX as to Laufer's position as an authority on Chinese matters. " Powerful auxiliary " is the phrase used by Galton.

10 See Chap. XXII.

11 Science Press. New York.

XXII

FAULDS AND HERSCHEL : FINAL PEN DUEL : HERSCHEL'S ADMISSION : 1917

No wonder the just resentment of Faulds was roused by the publication of Herschel's " The Origin of Finger-Printing." Probably Faulds never saw the " review " of it in *Nature* before he sent to that journal a Letter, which the Editor published in the issue of 18th January, 1917, under the heading of " The Permanence of Finger Print Patterns."[1] This the Editor accompanied with " Remarks " thereon made by Herschel, to whom the Editor had first submitted Faulds's letter for that purpose.

It is of interest at this stage to observe that in the third edition of the " Bibliography dealing with Crime and cognate Subjects,"[2] compiled by Sir John Cumming, founder and first Editor of *The Police Journal*, and placed by him at the disposal of the Secretary of State for Home Affairs, the only publication of Faulds mentioned in the section dealing with Dactyloscopy is his " Manual of Practical Dactylography," published in 1923. This section, under the heading (d) " Finger Print System [Dactyloscopy]." sets out with

" *Finger Prints.* Sir W. Herschel (*Nature*, XXIII, p. 23, Nov. 25, 1880).

Finger Prints. Francis Galton (Macmillan, 1892)."

The *Nature* Letter by Faulds of 28th October, 1880, his " Guide to Finger Print Identification," published in 1905, and his " Dactylography " published in 1912 are all omitted. Having in view the high estimation in which crime detection by the use of fingerprints is held by New Scotland Yard, it seems unfortunate that this important branch of crime literature should set out with Herschel's letter of November, 1880, to *Nature* and should ignore the prior Letter of Faulds to *Nature* in October, 1880. Dr. Heindl's " Dactyloskopie," which was first published in 1921, and of which the third edition appeared in 1927, is also omitted. The works of Vucetich are not mentioned. Table V reproduces the whole of the fingerprint bibliography as appearing on p. 51 of Sir John Cumming's work with the inclusion of what is there omitted but included in Dr. Heindl's "Bibliography." With its subjoined notes, Table V explains itself.

From the Preface to Sir John Cumming's "Bibliography," it appears that, although it does not profess to be "exhaustive," the list, "after a rigorous revision," has been made "reasonably comprehensive and international, covering in the main a period of fifty years." It is suggested that no such list can be regarded as complete without the inclusion of Heindl's work and of at least the most important of the omitted contributions to fingerprint literature of Faulds and Vucetich. The respective contributions in 1917 to *Nature* of Faulds and Herschel, set out at length in this Chapter, ought also to be included in any "reasonably comprehensive and international" fingerprint bibliography. No doubt the omissions to which attention has been called will be rectified in any future revision of the "Bibliography" in question. Of course, no reference is made to Tabor *pace* Galton. See Chapter XXXIII. It must be kept in view that while the particular list under notice in Sir John Cumming's work professes to deal only with fingerprint literature, published under its special title of "Dactyloscopy" or the like, many books and articles have been published under titles, such as "Personal Identification," "Forensic Medicine" and so forth. These deal incidentally with fingerprints. Under appropriate headings, Sir John Cumming includes such publications. Here is the letter of Faulds—

THE PERMANENCE OF FINGERPRINTS.

I RECEIVED a few days ago Sir Wm. J. Herschel's brochure, "The Origin of Finger-Printing." His object—in addition to examining other claims to this method—is stated to be the desire to place on record the discovery of this method of identification "in Bengal in

1858," and the author seems to be piously grateful for the '' gift granted '' to him of that great and most useful discovery. The evidence for this early date is contained in the imprint of a single hand of one Konai, made at that time. This was issued on a single sheet some years ago, but when, as an eager student of the subject, I applied to the publishers for a copy, I was told it was issued only for private circulation, and could not be supplied to me. I now hasten at the first opportunity to give my own opinion of this impression, long guarded so carefully from the inspection of the expert critic.

The fateful lines so dear to palmistry are quite nicely shown up, and many of the skin furrows, or *rugæ*, on the palm are printed with considerable clearness. That is, the part of the hand not at all used in the official system of identification is well done, but what of those parts on which the system entirely relies? The significant pads at the last joint of each finger, which are full of intricate patterns in every human, or monkey, finger, are not shown at all. They are mere uniform blotches of ink. There is absolutely no trace of a pattern of the simplest kind in any one of the five fingers shown. I wish to be understood as not exaggerating for any controversial effect, and appeal to any trained detective if this is not as I represent. No identification could be effected on such a basis, and the system was therefore clearly *not* discovered in 1858 by the baronet. I cannot perceive that even now the author has any adequate conception of what the system is, now in general and satisfactory operation throughout the civilised world. A most curious confusion has arisen from an original police blunder that no two single finger patterns are ever alike, for which, I think, Sir William himself is mainly responsible. I am quite sure that there is no scientific basis for such an assertion. My syllabic system of classification, applied to a large collection, would enable such an assertion to be severely tested, but I know of no other method in existence which could do so. To compare finger by finger in a large collection is utterly impossible. But by giving a short syllabic name to the pattern of each finger those names can be assorted apart from the hand collection, and those which are similar can be compared individually. I have no doubt in my own mind that such a search would reveal closely similar fingers in

different individuals, so closely similar indeed that the slightest blur in printing would lead to the fallacious conclusion of identity. It was on getting a clear perception of this very dangerous fallacy, still manfully held and expounded by one or two police experts, that from 1879-80, when I first made public the method, I insisted on the use of the whole set of ten fingers, serially and consecutively printed, for criminal identification. It affords an example of mutations, but for trivial purposes fewer fingers might do very well. The English method, now practically used everywhere, cannot be greatly improved upon in this respect for identifying old convicts on reconviction.

The question of what degree of evidence a single bloody smudge may give of the identity of some supposed miscreant with a convict having a previous official record is a matter for dispute. Still more is that of a case where, say, the right forefinger of Richard Roe may be practically identical with the left ring-finger of John Doe. Such similarity would be no evidence whatever for personal identification. In labouring to be brief I trust I have not been quite obscure. Sir William, in his review of the history of this discovery, has not made any reference to my little contributions on the subject. He, however, did acknowledge my priority of publication in your columns of November 22, 1894, and for that " gift granted " I must feel grateful.   HENRY FAULDS.

Stoke-on-Trent.

Here follow " *The Remarks* " of Herschel:—

I HAVE to thank you for your courtesy in forwarding me a copy of Mr. Faulds's letter to you, and, in compliance with your request, I submit the following remarks.

The only point I feel bound to notice is his complaint that I have not mentioned his name in my story of " The Origin of Finger-Printing." Mr. Faulds's own account of his claim has been so fully placed before the public in his letters to you from Japan, of October, 1880, and later, that I think I was right in keeping to that period of history, twenty years further back than his, which lay within my own knowledge.

But his present letter breaks through all bounds of

social courtesy, and it is only his position as a professed man of science that justifies me in correcting him. Mr. Faulds has the temerity to scout my statement that I was moved to study finger-printing by the fascination of Konai's hand-mark (taken as it was for the same purpose as finger-prints now are). The finger-tips were badly smudged, but the small furrows on the palm were exquisite, and moved me to take better impressions than his from my own fingers, as I tell the reader on the same page, only Mr. Faulds ignores it. This is not the spirit of science.

I will now, with your permission, show reason why I could not honestly have introduced Mr. Faulds's name. His letter of 1880 announced that in the previous year his attention was directed to the peculiarities of finger impressions on pottery, and that he had come to the conclusion, by original and patient experiment, that finger-prints were sufficiently personal in pattern to supply a long-wanted method of scientific identification, which should enable us to fix his crime upon any offender who left finger-marks behind him, and equally well to disprove the suspected identity of an innocent person. (For all which I gave him, and I still do so, the credit due for a conception so different from mine.) But he went on to say :—" There can be no doubt of the advantage of having a copy of the for-ever-unchangeable finger-furrows of important criminals."

This expression made me protest at once, in my reply, that I could not understand how, in less than two years, he could have come to the knowledge that the furrows were unchangeable. It had taken me nearly twenty years of sustained experiment to demonstrate this persistence of the patterns for at least fifteen years of a man's life, and it is plainly impossible for any man with a scientific turn of mind to put this doctrine forward after only twenty months or so of experiment. My reply, therefore, of 1880 expressly challenged his authority for the statement, and he has never justified it. My challenge did oblige him to meet it as best he could, but the nearest approach I have seen to an answer is the following extract from an article of his in *Knowledge*, April, 1911 :—

" The mode I took to test whether the ridges ever shifted their situation or changed their form was by shaving away their elevations . . . having first taken careful imprints of the patterns. After the skin grew up again, fresh imprints were taken and compared with the old ones . . . but in many hundreds of cases, tested thus three or four times, not one solitary example of a variation in pattern was detected." His return to England broke the further investigation. He goes on to say—" The firm conviction, however, was established in my mind, which nothing has occurred to change, that skin furrows for the purposes of identification are invariable throughout life."

This quotation is his latest statement of his authority, but it needs to be read with an extract from a previous letter of his, dated June 5, 1909,[3] in which he says—

" One of my earliest experiments was to shave off the ridges of the finger-tips with razors; the pattern on the skin was reproduced with quite unvarying fidelity, unless part of the true (deep) skin was removed."

I take it that this is the only foundation he has for his claim to have known the law of persistency in 1880. I leave it to men of science to judge whether his experiments sufficed to prove persistency of a finger pattern for life. W. J. HERSCHEL.

Warfield.

These " *Remarks* " of Herschel are of the highest importance in this controversy as to the rival claims of Faulds and himself. For the first time, stung by the just reproach of Faulds about his omission to refer to him in any way in his book, and for which, it is thought he gave no valid excuse, Herschel does in these " Remarks " admit, what Galton never admitted, that Faulds did conceive that finger-patterns would " supply a long-wanted method of scientific identification, which should enable us to fix his crime upon any offender who left finger-marks behind him and equally well to disprove the suspected identity of an innocent person." He goes on to say : " For all which I gave him, and I still do so, the credit due for a conception so different from mine."

Though so very belated, this admission could not be

more handsomely made. It has a pregnant bearing on *Nature's* " review " which Galton made of Faulds's " Guide " in 1905, and with which I have dealt separately.⁴ It also destroys any value in *Nature's* review of Herschel's book in the immediately-preceding month of December.

I know of no published writing of Herschel in which, after November, 1880, and before January, 1917, Herschel ever gave any credit to Faulds and in any event so explicitly in regard to this particular and exclusive claim of Faulds to originality.

Faulds, now seventy-four years of age, was not content with extracting, if, in fact, he realized he had done so, this belated concession from Herschel. He published a small brochure in February, 1917, under the enigmatic title of " The Hidden Hand: a Contribution to the History of Finger-Prints." This document bears internal evidence of Faulds's knowledge of the publication in *Nature* of his own Letter of protest to *Nature* and of the " *Remarks* " thereon by Herschel. Faulds missed, however, the only point of importance in the " *Remarks* " so far as his interests were concerned, namely, Herschel's concession in his favour. Faulds, then so advanced in years, was probably not so alert. If he had grasped that fact, he would have acted with discretion by not publishing " The Hidden Hand." Its title is, of course, cynical in reference to " Konai's " hand. Faulds never, however, alludes to Herschel's admission in any of his subsequent publications. Until now, it is believed, no one has drawn attention to Herschel's confession that so decidedly establishes the place to which Faulds is pre-eminently entitled, and to which he is now assigned, independently of that confession, by leading medical jurists and others.

The purpose of " The Hidden Hand " was the exposure of Herschel's arrogant claim to the exclusive invention of

Fingerprints and all their developments. It was, perhaps, in any event, an ill-advised brochure. However, one cannot but feel sympathetic to Faulds. Matters presented themselves to his mind as if there had been a deliberate design on the part of several eminent persons to ignore him altogether, or, at least, to refrain from acknowledging his meritorious position in regard to fingermarks. Undue exaltation of Herschel by Galton, Henry, and others, and, worst of all, by Herschel himself, could not but irritate Faulds.

So, in this brochure, Faulds deals, and very convincingly, with Herschel's old complaint as to the impossibility of anyone's affirming the permanence of the finger-patterns in so short a time as two years, when Herschel had taken so many years to realize this. Indeed, it is doubtful if Herschel did realize it before Faulds's letter to *Nature* in 1880.

Very reasonably, in his brochure Faulds said—

> Happily, we agree as to the fact itself of the permanency of the patterns, under all known conditions of life, and that fact remains undisputable.

And, of his medical life in Japan, he narrates—

> I had under training in biology some very acute and enthusiastic Japanese pupils, many of whom afterwards attained good positions as doctors. Under my guidance these students set out to test such points carefully. We began by shaving off the ridges which contained the patterns near the finger-tips till no pattern could be traced. Yet, whenever the skin grew up, the old pattern came again into view with unimpeachable fidelity. Then we used pumice stone, sand-paper, emery-dust, various acids, caustics, and even Spanish fly. . . . An epidemic of scarlet fever, then new to Japan and very virulent, gave me a remarkable opportunity for observing the patterns— after the severe peeling of the old skin—in a great number of cases. None of them was ever observed to have changed in the least. For more than two years this had gone on before I wrote [in *Nature* of 1880] and observa-

tions have been kept up till the present time. During the period before October, 1880, many thousands of digital impressions were taken and compared mutually, while the same fingers were many times reprinted and re-examined with the greatest minuteness.

What more could Herschel, or even Galton, demand? And, as Faulds truly says in his brochure, Herschel never made any attempt at classification or devised any exact method of storing or recording indicated impressions. The number of fingers in Herschel's different cases was variable and without system. The particular finger in any series was not always the same. Yet Faulds devoted his copper-plate outline forms to precise and fixed particulars of all ten fingers in serial order. " Konai's hand " contained no fingerprints in a technical sense at all. Faulds believed, and observed, perhaps, too caustic-ally, that the problem of permanency and its vital importance never dawned upon Herschel until Galton came to his aid some eight years after Faulds had announced his own deductions in his 1880 *Nature* Letter.

" Men of science," to recur to the very last sentence Herschel ever penned in controversy with Faulds, have answered his submission to them in that sentence by affirming that the experiments of Faulds proved the persistency of finger-patterns " for life."

Let this Chapter end on the friendly note that Herschel did honourably acknowledge that what Faulds conceived about the importance of looking for imprints of bloody fingers on glass, &c., was wholly beyond his ken.

NOTES

[1] Vol. XCVII, p. 388.

[2] Printed by the Receiver for the Metropolitan Police District, New Scotland Yard, S.W.1, 1935. Heindl, in his " Bibliography," appended to his " Daktyloskopie," includes Faulds's letter to *Nature* in 1917; he makes no reference to Herschel's " Remarks " dealt with in this Chap.

[3] I have been unable to trace this letter.

[4] See Chap. XX.

XXIII

" MARK TWAIN " AND FINGERPRINTS : 1883-94

In May, 1883, Samuel Langhorne Clemens (1835-1910), under his pen-name of " Mark Twain," published in book form simultaneously in London and New York the romance, " Life on the Mississippi." In it appeared the story of Karl Ritter, the Fortune Teller, thus—

> My apparatus was simple : a little red paint and a bit of white paper. I painted the ball of the client's thumb, took a print of it on the paper, studied it that night, and revealed his fortune to him next day. What was my idea in this nonsense? It was this : When I was a youth, I knew an old Frenchman who had been a prison-keeper for thirty years, and he told me that there was one thing about a person which never changed, from the cradle to the grave—the lines in the ball of the thumb; and he said that these lines were never exactly alike in the thumbs of any two human beings. In these days, we photograph the new criminal, and hang his picture in the Rogues' Gallery for future reference; but that Frenchman, in his day, used to take a print of the ball of a new prisoner's thumb and put that away for future reference. He always said that pictures were no good—future disguises could make them useless : " The thumb's the only sure thing," said he; " you can't disguise that." And he used to prove his theory, too, on my friends and acquaintances; it always succeeded.[1]

Plainly, Clemens had become acquainted, directly or indirectly, with the letters of Faulds and Herschel in *Nature* of 1880. I have referred in Chapter XII to published comments on fingermarks in a London newspaper in December, 1880, to the address of Dr. John S. Billings in London in August, 1881, at the International Medical Congress, and to an article on " Thumb Portraits " in The World of Wonders for 1883. No one would suggest that Clemens, without any previous knowledge of fingerprints, evolved this story out of his own head. The " old French Prison Keeper " is based more, perhaps, on Herschel than Faulds.

By 1893, the interest of Clemens in fingerprints had increased, following various papers and other publications of Galton and, I have no doubt, papers and notices by others in foreign papers on that topic. Clemens was in Europe about that time. He may have heard of Vucetich and of the case of Francesca Rojas.

Between December, 1893, and June, 1894, there appeared, in *The Century Illustrated Magazine*, his next romance of " Pudd'nhead Wilson," published as a book in London and New York in November following. Wentworth and Wilder, the leading American personal identification authorities on the police side, concede that Clemens " had doubtless read what Faulds, Herschel and Galton had written."[2] But, granted that Clemens had read everything that Galton had written up to the end of 1893, it is submitted, as elsewhere demonstrated in this work, that Galton had never up to that time adverted to " the brainwave " of Faulds, in his *Nature* Letter of 1880, to the effect that " bloody finger marks or impressions on clay, glass, etc., . . . may lead to the scientific identification of criminals."

These American authors devote a special chapter[3] of their work on " Personal Identification " to this suggestion of Faulds, observing that—

> The remarkable results of this discovery, resulting in the conviction of the criminal in numberless cases, where otherwise there would have been no definite clue, are now so much matters of common knowledge that there exists a popular error to the effect that this is the sole, or at least the chief, use of the Finger Print System, while the purpose for which it was originally advocated is more or less forgotten.[4]

It is evident that Faulds's conception had captivated Clemens. His fertile imagination created the hero of his later romance, with its sole object to reveal the marvellous mysteries and consequences of a conception that was Faulds's, and his only.

" Pudd'nhead Wilson " is a young American of Scottish parentage. Faulds was a Scot. This may be only a coincidence. " Pudd'nhead Wilson " had " The fad without a name . . . which dealt with people's finger marks." He gradually collected records of all the finger-marks of the people of Dawson's Landing township, and, in particular, of the child of Percy Driscoll and of that of Roxana, both born on the same day. The " facts " of the story are taken as known to readers.

From the concluding chapters of " Pudd'nhead Wilson " are taken the following extracts[5] : —

I beg the indulgence of the court, (says Pudd'nhead Wilson,) while I make a few remarks in explanation of some evidence which I am about to introduce, and which I shall presently ask to be allowed to verify under oath on the witness stand. Every human being carries with him from his cradle to his grave certain physical marks which do not change their character, and by which he can always be identified—and that without shade of doubt or question. These marks are his signature, his physiological autograph, so to speak, and this autograph cannot be counterfeited, nor can he disguise it or hide it away, nor can it become illegible by the wear and the mutations of time. This signature is not his face—age can change that beyond recognition; it is not his hair, for that can fall out; it is not his height, for duplicates of that exist; it is not his form, for duplicates of that exist also, whereas this signature is each man's very own—there is no duplicate of it among the swarming populations of the globe ! . . .

This autograph consists of the delicate lines or corrugations with which Nature marks the insides of the hands and the soles of the feet. If you will look at the balls of your fingers—you that have very sharp eyesight—you will observe that these dainty curving lines lie close together, like those that indicate the borders of oceans in maps, and that they form various clearly defined patterns, such as arches, circles, long curves, whorls, &c., and that these patterns differ on the different fingers.

PLATE VI—" PUDD'NHEAD WILSON "

" Am I right ? "

. . . The patterns on the right hand are not the same as those on the left. . . . Taken finger for finger, your patterns differ from your neighbour's. . . . The patterns of a twin's right hand are not the same as those on his left. One twin's patterns are never the same as his fellow-twin's patterns—the jury will find that the patterns upon the finger-balls of the accused follow this rule. . . . You have often heard of twins who were so exactly alike that when dressed alike their own parents could not tell them apart. Yet there was never a twin born into this world that did not carry from birth to death a sure identifier in this mysterious and marvellous natal autograph. That once known to you, his fellow-twin could never personate him and deceive you. . . .

Upon this haft stands the assassin's natal autograph, written in the blood of that helpless and unoffending old man who loved you and whom you all loved. There is but one man in the whole earth whose hand can duplicate that crimson sign . . . and please God we will produce that man in this room before the clock strikes noon ! . . .

For more than twenty years I have amused my compulsory leisure with collecting these curious physical signatures in this town. At my house I have hundreds upon hundreds of them. Each and every one is labelled with name and date; not labelled the next day, or even the next hour, but in the very minute that the impression was taken. When I go upon the witness stand I will repeat under oath the things which I am now saying. I have the fingerprints of the court, the sheriff, and every member of the jury. There is hardly a person in this room, white or black, whose natal signature I cannot produce, and not one of them can so disguise himself that I cannot pick him out from a multitude of his fellow-creatures and unerringly identify him by his hands. And if he and I should live to be a hundred I could still do it ! . . .

Then, upon call, Wilson went to the window, made his examination, and said : . . .

" Now for the other pane; here and here are Count Luigi's, here and here are his brother's." He faced about. "Am I right? " . . . (See Plate VI.)

Here, thrown up ten sizes, are the natal autographs of the two persons who are here before you accused of murdering Judge Driscoll. I made these pantograph copies last night, and will so swear when I go upon the witness stand. I ask the jury to compare them with the finger marks of the accused upon the window-panes, and tell the court if they are same.

And the denouement !—

Tom . . . made some impotent movements with his white lips, then slid limp and lifeless to the floor.

Wilson broke the awed silence with the words :

" There is no need. He has confessed."

The court rose; the new prisoner, handcuffed, was removed.

.   .   .   .

The false heir made a full confession, and was sentenced to imprisonment for life.

Dr. Wigmore, in his " Principles of Judicial Proof " (second edition, Boston, 1931), rightly characterizes this jury speech, put by Clemens into the mouth of his hero, as " a lucid statement of the logic of finger print identification." He states that it was " written long before much use of it had been made by police departments."[6] " Pudd'nhead Wilson's " address to the jury is, indeed, a remarkable tribute to the discernment of Clemens, and to his wonderful descriptive powers and vivid realism in presenting the scientific results of Faulds's discovery in such simple language and with such remarkable accuracy.

" Mark Twain," in his amusing preface to " Pudd'n-head Wilson," informs his readers (to be taken with a pinch of salt) that all his legal procedure has been verified by " a trained barrister." I am not, though a trained advocate, abreast of American law. But, in this country, no advocate or barrister prosecutes or defends any person accused of crime and at the same time goes into the witness-box or -stand and gives evidence, as the case may be, for or against the accused. It is the privilege of the novelist, however, to make, if he so choose, his characters dance about in this way. " Pudd'nhead Wilson " illustrates this peculiarity. Of course, I am referring to Crown procedure in cases of high crime.

Clemens, in making his hero collect fingermarks for twenty years, would seem to have had Herschel more particularly in his mind. But he could not have arrived at the grand and moving climax of his story without making use of Faulds's brilliant, revolutionary detective revelation, and of his experiments in establishing its practicability. In this climax " Pudd'nhead Wilson " is Faulds. Faulds was the inspiration of Clemens.

It seems somewhat too far-fetched for the suggestion to be made that the " Old French Prison Keeper " in " Mark Twain's " " Life on the Mississippi " was a real character, by which Wentworth and Wilder say " we would be carried back to 1820 and possibly as early as 1810 " for the discovery of fingerprint registration. They admit this is " largely speculation . . . with a possibility of being partly or wholly true."[7] This interesting " speculation " for its bearing on Bertillonage has been dealt with in Chapter XIII. These authors do not apparently treat " Pudd'nhead Wilson " as based, in the same way, on fact. But equally, upon the same reasoning, they might have " carried back " the invention of fingerprints at least to 1830 as that of some American of Scottish extraction, and thus divided the honour between " Pudd'nhead Wilson " and the " Old French Prison Keeper " or his unknown prototype.

The value of Clemens's services in making his fictional characters deal with fingerprints is in the impetus it gave in America to the introduction of fingerprint registration for all police purposes. The two romances in question were not without their influence in our country. Clemens saw what the professional detective mind had failed to discover. Wentworth and Wilder justly state that Clemens

> " spread among the people correct ideas concerning the new system, and thus became a true prophet to the Gentiles in the subject."[8]

This is a fine tribute, indeed, to be paid by these authors to Clemens. Is it not also a great tribute, indirectly, to Faulds?

Of all authorities on fingerprints, writing in English, Wentworth and Wilder are the most conspicuous for the prominence assigned to Faulds. In Chapter XXXIII are fuller citations from their work on " Personal Identification."[9]

NOTES

[1] I have been unable to trace the origin of the " thumbmark," whether his own or another's, illustrating this passage.

[2] *Supra*, p. 349.

[3] *Supra*, p. 351.

[4] *Supra*, p. 352.

[5] *Supra*, p. 231 *et seq.*

[6] See note by Dr. Wigmore on p. 120, of his " Principles of Judicial Proof." Second Edition, 1931. Boston : Little, Brown & Company. There is no reference to Faulds or Herschel among the fingerprint authorities cited by Dr. Wigmore. The earliest police application of Faulds's discovery was made by Vucetich, in Argentina, in 1892. See Chaps. XVI and XXIV.

[7] *Supra*, p. 349. Bertillon lived till 1914, and never for himself or France troubled about the possibility of this fictional character having some foundation in fact. Much of Oriental literature was translated by French savants of the eighteenth and last centuries; but, so far as references to fingermarks in such literature are made, no interest in these references in this country appears to have been taken until the beginning of this century. See Chap. XXIX.

[8] *Supra*, p. 348. I had the privilege of receiving letters from Mr. Bert Wentworth, full of information about fingerprints. His colleague, Harris Hawthorne Wilder, a professor of zoology, died in 1928.

[9] It is rather extraordinary that so dramatically interesting, instructive, and moving a tale as " Pudd'nhead Wilson " has never been dramatised or filmed.

XXIV

FAULDS'S MAJOR DISCOVERY : RECORDED CASES : 1880 TO 1908

UNTIL 1891, apart from the two illustrations given by Faulds in his Letter to *Nature* of 1880, in which, in the one case, he traced a secret drinker of rectified spirits by his greasy fingermarks on a bottle, and, in the other, he proved the innocence of a man, suspected of some offence, by showing that sooty fingermarks did not correspond to the man's, I know of no recorded criminal case between 1880 and 1891, following on the publication of that Letter.

Recall to mind that Herschel erroneously credited Henry with "fashioning a weapon of penetrating certainty for the sterner needs of Justice." So far as the discovery of crime from fingermarks left on scenes of crime is concerned, Faulds alone conceived of this weapon. It is perfectly distinct from the registration of fingermarks of habitual offenders with a view to their identification on recurring lapses. According to Dr. Edmond Locard, the French criminologist: " Elle est la méthode identificatrice par excellence : sûre, applicable dans tous les cas et à tous les âges, d'un prix de revient nul, d'une execution rapide, exigeant une expérience vite acquise et presque aucune instruction."[1]

Superintendent Harry Battley, in charge of the Finger Print Branch and Criminal Record Office, C.I.D., London, has recently and truly characterized this weapon " as one of the most deadly weapons the Police have ever possessed," all unconscious, apparently, that it was discovered by Faulds and not by Galton, Henry or Herschel.[2]

In the period from 1891 to the end of 1908, many fingerprint cases are found in the records of judicial tribunals and police administrations of various countries. Dividing them into two classes, according as they deal with charges of *capital* or *non-capital* crimes and offences, these, as the result of my researches (a) for capital charge cases in any part of the world and (b) for minor cases within England only, appear to be as follows:—

I. CAPITAL CHARGES

1892

(1) *Argentina: Francesca Rojas: Murder*

This woman of Necochea, in Buenos Aires Province, in the early months of the year murdered her two sons. She wounded herself in the neck and accused a respected neighbour of cutting their throats and injuring herself. That man was arrested.[3] The Chief of La Plata Police telegraphed to Inspector Eduardo M. Alvarez to do everything possible in the way of recovering " los rastros de las impresiones digitales dejadas por el criminal y traiga las muestras."[4] The detective, in June, found various bloody fingermarks on a door jamb where the deed was done. Two pieces of wood so marked were cut out and sent to La Plata Central Identification Bureau. The officer obtained the finger-impressions of the woman and of the arrested man, and sent these also to the Bureau. The marks on the door corresponded to those of the woman's impressions. The man was released. The woman was prosecuted before magistrates. Her guilt was proved solely by fingerprint-identification methods. She confessed.[5] She was sentenced to imprisonment. Women at that time were not subject by Argentine law to capital punishment.

At this distance of time, it is impossible to state more exactly the particulars of this case. Dr. Reyna Almandos, the Director of La Plata Identification Bureau and Laboratory, states that the judicial process is not now available. I refer to this case in Chapter XVI dealing with the life and work of Vucetich.

1897

(2) *India: Kangali Charan: Murder and theft*

This is the next known case of a capital charge. Charan was convicted of theft only. The trial took place in 1898. I have dealt fully with this remarkable case in Chapter XVII.

1902

(3) *France: Henri Scheffer: Murder*

This case in its details has also been fully dealt with in Chapter XIII. Conviction followed in 1903.

1905

(4) *England: Stratton Brothers: Double murder*

Their trial and conviction are narrated in Chapter XVIII.

II. NON-CAPITAL CHARGES

The world records of such charges, between 1880 and 1909, are very numerous. My researches in regard to these are, therefore, confined to England. English cases obtained much publicity. Police honours for success up to 1909, in bringing criminals to justice in England, are fairly divided between the Metropolitan Police and the Yorkshire Police. The Bradford City Police in Yorkshire, in July, 1903, distinguished themselves by establishing the first provincial fingerprint bureau. The officials connected with this bureau were: Detective-Inspector Thomas Talbot (later Superintendent) as Chief; Sergeant Arthur Frederick Nicholson, later the Chief-Clerk at Bradford, then Chief-Constable of Exeter, and now Chairman of the Traffic Commissioners for the Western Traffic Area; and Oliver Underwood Cromwell,

Detective and Photographer, later Chief-Inspector at Bradford, and finally a Superintendent in the Borough Police at Doncaster. " Finger Print Photography," published by Cromwell in 1907, figures in Sir John Cumming's " Scotland Yard Bibliography."[6] Mr. Joseph Farndale, C.B.E., the Chief-Constable of Bradford at the time (and now Chairman of the Traffic Commissioners for Yorkshire Traffic Area), must be credited with persuading Bradford Police Authority to institute the Bureau.

Other towns in Yorkshire and elsewhere in England soon followed Bradford's example. The City of Glasgow obtained its present Constabulary Chief, Captain Sillitoe, from Sheffield. Upon his advice, as elsewhere explained, Glasgow Corporation installed a finger-print bureau, and Captain Sillitoe placed Detective-Lieutenant, now Superintendent Detective, Hammond, formerly also of Sheffield, in charge of it. That Branch has been a great success.

New Scotland Yard led off in 1902 with the first conviction for any offence.

The following represents approximately an exhaustive record during the period in question : —

1902

Metropolitan Area

On 13th September, Harry Jackson was charged at the Central Criminal Court, London, with burgling a house at Denmark Hill, and stealing billiard balls on 27th June, 1902. Other burglary charges at the same time were preferred against him. He pleaded not guilty. A plain imprint of his left thumb was found on a newly painted window sill. He was found guilty of all charges. This appears to be the first case in which the police in England relied on fingerprint evidence. The accused in this case had been previously convicted. He was sentenced by the Common Sergeant, F. A. Bosanquet,

Esq., K.C., to seven years' penal servitude. The case is reported in *The Times* of 15th September, 1902. A reference was made by the police to the position of finger-prints in India.[7]

1903

Metropolitan Area

*On 1st December, at Marlborough Street Police Court, Henry Elliott pleaded guilty to the charge of breaking into jewellers' premises in Conduit Street, London, on 16th October, and stealing over £5000 of valuables. Four of his left-hand fingermarks were found on a piece of glass broken from a skylight window. All, but the middle finger, were blurred : it was sufficient. He had previous convictions and was sentenced to twelve months' imprisonment, with hard labour.

Note.—I find a reference to a Windsor case in October, 1903, by Faulds in his " Guide," *supra*, p. 45; I have not been able to follow it up.

1904

(1) Metropolitan Area

*(i) On 18th October, William Simpson was sentenced by the Recorder at the Central Criminal Court, London, to twelve months' imprisonment, with hard labour, for breaking into premises in the City of London, some time before that date. On a fanlight his right index finger-print was found. I use " Metropolitan " area in its wider sense of including the " City."

*(ii) On 20th October, George Gage was sentenced by the Recorder at the Central Criminal Court, London, to four years' penal servitude for burglariously breaking, on 17th August, 1904, into a house at Hammersmith and stealing silver. Two of his fingerprints were found on a tumbler from which he had entertained himself with wine. The Recorder on this occasion emphasized the

---

* denotes that case has been verified for me by New Scotland Yard.

great value of fingerprint identification in the detection of crime.

*(iii) On 20th December, Walter Rose was convicted at North London Sessions of entering, on 29th November, 1904, tailoring-shop premises at Poplar, and stealing therefrom a quantity of clothing. He was sentenced to twelve months' imprisonment, with hard labour. Prints of fingers from both of his hands were found on broken glass of the basement window of the premises.

(2) *Bradford Area*

†(i) On 8th January, George Rollett was charged at the City of Bradford Quarter Sessions with breaking into warehouse premises in Bradford and stealing whisky, cigars, &c., between 10th and 11th December, 1903. He pleaded not guilty. This was the first instance, out of the London area, where the police founded their case on fingerprint evidence. The case came before the Recorder. The police deponed that a finger-impression found on a window of the burgled premises corresponded to the prisoner's. The Recorder (Mr. Thomas Milvain, K.C., M.P.) charged the jury that the impression to his mind was not sufficiently clear. The jury found the accused not guilty.

†(ii) On 30th March, James O'Hara, pleading not guilty, was convicted at the City of Bradford Quarter Sessions of shopbreaking in Bradford, between 3rd and 4th February, 1904. His fingerprint impressions were found on a broken panel of the door. He was sentenced to twelve months' imprisonment, with hard labour.

†(iii) On 26th September, Jacques Edmunds was charged at the City of Bradford Petty Sessional Court

---

* denotes that case has been verified for me by New Scotland Yard.

† denotes that case has been verified for me by Bradford City Police.

with breaking into club premises on 17th September, 1904. The charge was reduced to larceny. He was convicted and sentenced to six weeks' imprisonment. His fingermarks were found on a club beer-bottle, and some of the stolen property was recovered in his home.

†(iv) On 7th October, John Lewis Oldfield and James Bacon were convicted at the City of Bradford Quarter Sessions of housebreaking in Bradford, between 9th and 29th August. A fingerprint-impression of one of the men was found on a bathroom door. One of the prisoners was found by a constable with some of the stolen silver in his possession. Both prisoners pleaded not guilty. They received respectively six and nine months' imprisonment, with hard labour.

1905

(1) *Metropolitan Area*

None.

(2) *Bradford Area*

†On 8th February, 1905, Louis Anderson was sentenced at the City of Bradford Petty Sessional Court to imprisonment for six weeks, with hard labour, for stealing champagne and other bottles and goods to the value of £30 from premises of a Bowling Club, in Bradford, on 29th January, 1905. A very distinct fingermark was found on a club tumbler.

Detective-Inspector Talbot, who was complimented by the Bench for his fine detective work in this case, is the officer who succeeded in getting a conviction on fingerprint evidence alone in the reported case of *Castleton* (see Chapter XXX) where the Lord Chief Justice stated that he relied on his testimony there.[8] New Scotland Yard, I understand, did not come into these Bradford

---

† denotes that case has been verified for me by Bradford City Police.

cases. Detective-Inspector Talbot received his instruction in fingerprint classification at the Metropolitan Police Headquarters.

1906

(1) *Metropolitan Area*

Two men, William Reed, at West Ham Police Court, on 31st July, and William Brown, at Thames Police Court, on 15th October, were committed for trial on fingerprint evidence. See *The Times* of 1st August and 16th October, 1906. I have not been able to follow these cases further.[9]

> *Note.*—Laufer in his 1912 *Smithsonian* article, *supra*, narrates the arrest and conviction, at New York in 1906, of " a notorious criminal " through his fingerprints as taken on arrest being mailed to New Scotland Yard. The New York City Police inform me that this criminal was Henry Johnson, with four aliases in England, and seven previous convictions between 1894 and 1904. He had escaped to New York after robbing the wife of a novelist of £800 in a London hotel. He was arrested in New York on 5th April, 1906, as " a hotel sneak," on charges of " Grand Larceny " at Waldorf-Astoria Hotel, and sentenced on 27th April, 1906, to seven and a half years' imprisonment in Sing-Sing State Prison. It is believed this was the first successful instance of the international mailing of fingerprints. It does not properly belong to this Chapter except in so far as Faulds and Herschel could both claim credit for it. I mention it because it was widely noticed, and stimulated further interest in fingerprints.

(2) *Bradford Area*

†Between 7th and 9th July, a locked-up shop, No. 1 Ship Alley, was entered and a quantity of tobacco, cigars, cigarettes, &c., stolen. John Whelan was later apprehended, and an imprint of a finger found on a piece of glass on the shop window-sill was found to be

---

† denotes that case has been verified for me by Bradford City Police.

identical with the impression of the prisoner's left middle finger. At the City of Bradford Quarter Sessions, he pleaded guilty, and was sentenced to four months' imprisonment, with hard labour.

The City of Bradford Police assisted the West Riding of Yorkshire Constabulary in connexion with a burglary at St. Ives Hall, Harden, Bingley, in respect of which Aaron Cooper was subsequently arrested in Bradford on fingerprint evidence. His case is noted under the Wakefield Area.

(3) *Wakefield Area*

On 15th October, Aaron Cooper was found guilty at Wakefield West Riding Quarter Sessions of the forementioned burglary and sentenced to seven years' penal servitude. Fingerprint evidence was supplied by the West Riding of Yorkshire Constabulary, which started its fingerprint collection in 1905.

1907

(1) *Metropolitan Area*

None.

(2) *Birmingham Area*

*On 20th November, Frederick Shaw (not " Smith," as some books have it) was convicted at Birmingham Assizes of burglary at Birmingham in October, 1907, and sentenced to penal servitude for five years. His fingerprints had been left on a piece of candle used by him in burgling.

(3) *Bradford Area*

†(i) On 7th January, John Walsh was convicted at the City of Bradford Quarter Sessions of (1) housebreaking

---

* denotes that case has been verified for me by New Scotland Yard.
† denotes that case has been verified for me by Bradford City Police.

on 2nd December, 1906, and (2) stealing between 4th and 5th December, 1906, in Bradford. His fingerprint impressions were found on a fanlight. He received concurrent sentences of eighteen months' imprisonment, with hard labour. He pleaded guilty.

†(ii) On 18th October, Harry Phillips was convicted at the City of Bradford Quarter Sessions of stealing from club premises in Bradford between 10th and 11th September. His fingerprint-impressions were found on a club bottle. He received three years' penal servitude. He pleaded guilty.

1908

(1) *Metropolitan Area*

None.

(2) *Birmingham Area*

*On 19th March, George Chadwick was convicted at Birmingham Assizes of housebreaking in Edgbaston, Birmingham, on 14th January, 1908, and of stealing silver and other articles. He was sentenced to six months' imprisonment, with hard labour. No stolen property was found in his possession. His fingerprints were found on a champagne bottle. Twelve characteristics in agreement were proved of the accused's right middle finger in respect of two impressions. His defence was an alibi. The jury, notwithstanding an adverse charge from Mr. Justice Bigham in regard to fingerprint identification, returned a verdict of guilty.[10]

(3) *Bradford Area*

†Two men were arrested in October and November as suspected of several burglaries. But, their fingerprints not corresponding to fingerprints left on a writing-desk

---

* denotes that case has been verified for me by New Scotland Yard.
† denotes that case has been verified for me by Bradford City Police.

and on some broken glass, they were released. Later other two men—William Hale or Haworth and James Kennedy—were suspected and arrested, and their finger-prints were found to be identical with the desk and glass impressions. Hales's right middle fingerprint was left on the glass, and Kennedy's right fore fingerprint was left on the desk. Both men were found guilty and sen-tenced by the Quarter Sessions to five years' penal servi-tude and eighteen months' imprisonment, respectively.

I am indebted to the Commissioner of Police of the Metropolis, and, in particular, to Sir Norman Kendal, K.B.E., Assistant-Commissioner in charge of the Criminal Investigation Department, New Scotland Yard, for details of all the cases marked with a star, and to Chief-Constable Rawson, of Bradford, for details of the cases indicated by a dagger. The remaining cases I have obtained from other sources.

All these instances of capital and non-capital cases prove that by 1908 the value of fingerprint evidence was well settled. Authors of Law Books on Evidence referred, prior to 1908, to fingerprints, and, in parti-cular, medico-legalists devoted attention to the finger-print system, the premier method, as stated by Locard, of identification. It is, therefore, surprising to note that the singularly good opportunity presented to the City of Glasgow Police of tracking the murderer of Miss Mary Gilchrist, a person of means, in Glasgow in December, 1908, by searching for and obtaining fingermarks was utterly neglected. The subject matter of fingerprint evidence was specially treated in the then standard Scottish medico-legal treatise, published in 1902, of Dr. John Glaister (1856-1932), Professor of Medical Juris-prudence in the University of Glasgow. He lectured in Glasgow in December, 1906, upon this very matter.[11] The irony of the situation in Glasgow in 1908, as I indicate in Chapter XXV, was accentuated by the fact, as I have been informed, that the first detective on the scene of that crime was an enthusiastic advocate for the adoption of fingerprint methods. Medical jurisprudents called in to the case likewise failed to look for fingermarks. I assume the *amour propre* of the Glasgow Police Force was such that they could not appeal to New Scotland Yard, Bradford, or any other fingerprint bureau in existence in England at that time to come to their assistance in this obvious part of their investigation.

My purpose in calling attention to all the cases noted in this Chapter is to mark the contrast between the fingerprint lethargy of the Glasgow C.I.D. in 1908, in regard to the Gilchrist murder, as compared with the brilliance of its fingerprint identification services in 1935 in materially effecting the conviction of Dr. Buck Ruxton, of Lancaster, at Manchester Assizes, in May, 1936, for the murder of his wife (and inferentially a maidservant) in September, 1935. No fingerprint expert from New Scotland Yard gave evidence in that Lancaster case. These murder trials are made the subjects of Chapters XXV and XXVIII respectively.

I need hardly repeat, except for the benefit of recruits to the police service all over the world, that none of the fingerprint cases, other than the New York case of 1906, recorded in this Chapter, could have been established without resort to the application of the wonderful major conception of Faulds. No detective ever thought of looking for fingerprints on crime scenes until Faulds published his suggestion on the subject in *Nature* in October, 1880.

NOTES

[1] " L'Identification des Récidivistes," *supra*, p. 376. The system of Vucetich is described in this work of Dr. Locard, p. 242. A portrait of Vucetich is given in Dr. Heindl's " Daktyloskopie," p. 80.

[2] See his articles on " All About Finger Prints " in *The Police Journal*, Vol. IX, p. 30. 1936.

[3] " Dactiloscopía Comparada," *supra*, pp. 54 *et* 106. Vucetich, La Plata. 1904. Peuser. By mistake, corrected in *Errata*, the year is stated on p. 54 as 1902. The case is also noted and documented in " Dactiloscopía Argentina," *supra*, p. 171, and in " Origen e Influencia Jurídico-Social del Sistema Dactiloscópia Argentino," p. 45, by Dr. Reyna Almandos, 1912, La Plata.

[4] See " Conferencia Sobre El Sistema Dactiloscópico," *supra*, p. 21. Vucetich (with Introduction by Dr. Reyna Almandos). 1929. La Plata.

[5] " Dactiloscopía Comparada," *supra*, p. 106.

[6] " Finger Print Photography " was published by Stock, London, and Derwent, Bradford.

[7] I discovered this case through consulting " Scotland Yard," p. 285, by Mr. George Dilnot. 1929. (Centenary Edition. London. Geoffrey Bles.) It is obviously the case alluded to by Galton as that of " H. J." See Chap. XIII.

[8] The *Castleton* case was in 1909. It was not until 1910 that a conviction was secured in France by fingerprint evidence alone. This was *L'Affaire de la Rue Ravat*, in Lyons. Two men were thus convicted of housebreaking. In the case of one of these men, 100 " characteristiques homologues " were proved and 48 in the case of the other. See " La Preuve par Les Empreintes Digitales," *supra*, p. 254.

[9] See Chap. XVIII.

[10] It is reported that the Judge (afterwards Lord Mersey) pressed the jury twice to find that they were not satisfied with the fingerprint evidence. See Wills on " Circumstantial Evidence," 1937, seventh edition, p. 218. London. Butterworth & Co. In this edition increased space is devoted by the Editors to fingerprints. Faulds is, however, not mentioned. *The Glasgow Herald* of 10th September, 1920, reports the Lord Justice-Clerk (Scott Dickson) as stating his non-appreciation of the significance of fingerprint evidence in a trial before him with a jury against an accused, Robert Alexander Warren Halliday, on charges of murder, assault and robbery of a taxi-driver, William Ross. The jury found the accused guilty of assault and robbery and acquitted him of the murder charge. In a Glasgow case tried by Lord Moncrieff in 1933 that judge mentioned the " gelatine finger " as a fraudulent method of reproducing a fingerprint. See " Fingerprints," pp. 87 *et* 174. F. Brewester. 1936. Calcutta. The Eastern Law House.

[11] See the report of his lecture in *The Glasgow Herald* of 18th December, 1906.

XXV

OSCAR SLATER CASE : 1908

NO SEARCH FOR FINGERPRINTS : TRAGIC CONSEQUENCES

A MURDER, which made legal history in Scotland, occurred in a quiet, residential street in the western part of Glasgow on 21st December, 1908. The murderer

was never discovered. Fingerprints were strangely overlooked. One man was charged with the murder, tried,
found guilty, and sentenced to death. He was reprieved
and sent to penal servitude for life and, being released
after many years, he obtained by appeal the quashing of
his conviction as illegal. It is a long story; but, so far
as relevant to our theme, I give some of the facts sur-
rounding this crime.

The victim was Mary Gilchrist, a maiden lady, eighty-
three years of age. She was murdered in her dining-
room about seven o'clock in the evening. Her house was
the only one on the first flat of a street in Glasgow.[1] Her
maid, the only other occupant of her house, had gone
out at " just seven o'clock " for a newspaper to a shop
some three minutes away, leaving the old lady, " sitting
on a chair at the dining-room table with her back to the
fire. . . . She had her spectacles on and was reading."
The maid closed the outside door of the house " on the
two locks," and took both keys with her. She also
closed the door at the foot of the common stair. On her
return, that stair door was open. She unlocked the house
door, and saw " a man coming." She stepped back. He
was coming from the direction of a spare bedroom, then
lit by gas, but unlit when she left. The man passed her
in the hall, " with his head down," and went downstairs
to the street. She went into the kitchen, and then to the
dining-room. There she found her mistress " lying on
the rug in front of the fire. . . . The rug was over her
head." She then ran out and down the stair. Neigh-
bours were alarmed. At twenty minutes past seven a
police-constable entered the house and found the deceased
" lying on her back near the fireplace, just breathing
her last, with a quantity of blood about her face and below
her head." He saw " her head was battered." Her
skull was fractured, and her breast-bone and ribs were
all broken. He did not touch the body. In a spare bed-

room later that evening papers were found to have been taken out of a wooden box and scattered about the floor. The maid missed a small, diamond, crescent-shaped brooch usually kept by the deceased in a small open dish on a dressing-table.

The detective-officer first on the scene the same evening said: " I searched the house carefully to see if there were any implements left which had caused the injuries, but I found nothing."[2] He found a diamond ring in the bedroom with a gold bracelet, watch, and chain. The deceased kept in her wardrobe jewellery costing £1500, and probably worth double. All was found intact.[2] There was a box of matches, with one match spent, in the bedroom. Oscar Slater, in Glasgow at the time, was suspected of the crime. No traces of blood were found on any of his clothes, whether being worn or in some seven trunks he had when he was arrested on 2nd January, 1909, at New York on the arrival of the s.s. " Lusitania." In this vessel he had sailed on 26th December, 1908, from Liverpool. He had not " fled from justice." The maid went with the officer already mentioned to New York for identification purposes, although she had told him on the evening of the murder that she " did not know who the man was and that she did not think she would be able to identify him." His companion officer had also that same evening independently " pressed her with questions " as to the assailant's identity and to him she had said " she was quite unable to identify him."[3] Extradition proceedings resulted in Slater's returning voluntarily to Glasgow without demanding an extradition order. Slater declared and maintained his innocence of the murder and said that he had no knowledge of or acquaintance with the victim.

By a majority of nine out of a jury of fifteen, Slater, on 6th May, 1909, was found guilty of the murder of

Miss Gilchrist. One juryman was for acquittal, and five were for a verdict of not proven. Slater was sentenced to be hanged on 27th May, 1909. This sentence was commuted to one of penal servitude for life. From that punishment he was released on 14th November, 1927. On 20th July, 1928, the Court of Criminal Appeal in Scotland, specially empowered by Parliament to deal with an appeal by Slater, set aside his conviction on the ground of misdirection by the trial judge.[4] Slater accepted from the Crown a consolatory sum of £6000.

I was a practising junior member of the Scottish Bar at the time of Slater's trial. I remember well that the jury's verdict was regarded by the majority of counsel with grave doubts as to its justice. It seemed as if a non-judicial course had been taken by the prosecution. No wide berth had been given " to any possible risk of allowing a jury to be tempted into the course of giving a dog a bad name and hanging him." [5]

It is not, however, *hujus loci* to comment upon the procedure on the part of the Glasgow City Police prior to and at the trial of Slater. That procedure has been trenchantly condemned by Mr. William Roughead, Writer to the Signet, Edinburgh, in his Introduction to the Trial and Appeal of Slater in the " Notable British Trials " series.[6]

My purpose in dealing with Slater's case is in relation alone to its bearing upon fingerprint evidence.

From beginning to end of the trial, and throughout the proceedings in the appeal, no one engaged in the case at the Bar or on the Bench ever raised, even out of curiosity, any question over the absence of any search for fingerprints, whether relevant or not to the prosecution, the defence, and the conviction of Oscar Slater, or to success in his appeal.

Impressions of hands and fingers of the murderer of Miss Gilchrist must, it is thought, have been made on the disturbed wooden box, its papers, furniture, and other articles about the rooms and hall, as well as on the window-panes and door-handles of the house, besides the banisters and walls of the common stair. It is improbable that on some of these numerous places her assailant left no fingermarks, blood-stained or otherwise. Such marks may or may not be visible to the naked eye; some may be latent on glass and even on material such as cloth, and these can be discerned and " developed " only by finger-print experts.

So far as I can find, not one of the members of the Criminal Investigation Department of the City of Glasgow Police, from the superintendent downwards, seems to have thought of directing attention to, or looking for, impressions of fingerprints.

Two medico-legal experts (one a leading authority on forensic medicine) visited Miss Gilchrist's house on the morning after her murder and examined her body, then still lying in the dining-room. In evidence at the trial, they testified to the smashing of the deceased (her left eyeball " entirely missing "), and, further, they deponed: " We examined the room for any likely weapon." It did not occur to either of them, however, to look for " the weapon of penetrating certainty for the sterner needs of Justice."[7] Medical jurists, in the opinion of one of outstanding reputation, must have some knowledge of the science of identification by fingerprints in order that they may not handle or allow others " to handle material which may retain fingerprints before the expert in this branch arrives at the scene of a crime."[8]

And, again, the same authority states: " Before the body is moved the hands and feet should always be examined for the presence of blood stains, as blood-stained finger-marks . . . may be found . . ." and further: " The importance of these chance impressions cannot be over rated, and the medical examiner should never handle any weapon, glassware, door handle, or other smooth surface where a fingerprint may have been left."[8]

In the Introduction to Mr. Roughead's Report, there is this passage—

> A last point: the case occurred before the days of finger-print tests, for the application of which the circumstances of the crime afforded ample opportunity. I happen to have a " close-up " photograph of the fireplace in the Queen's Terrace house, taken at the time but not produced at the trial, showing the blood-splashed grate, together with the celebrated chair, on the back of which is plainly to be seen the imprint of a hand—possibly bloody. Had modern scientific methods been then available, this should have settled the question once for all.

Through the courtesy of Mr. Roughead, I have seen a reproduction of the press photograph mentioned by him in the second paragraph quoted from his Introduction. It was submitted by me to Dr. Heindl. His opinion in a letter in German to me, dated 23rd March, 1934, is that what has been taken for " the imprint of a hand—possibly bloody " is just the representation of dust or of some reflection on the mahogany or other back of the chair; and, in any event, the state of the photograph is such that it could have been of no use in the question of fingerprint identification.[9]

In the paragraph quoted from Mr. Roughead's Introduction, it is stated erroneously that fingerprint tests were not known at the time. In Chapter XXIV I have collected practically all the fingerprint capital cases anywhere, and all the minor ones in England, prior to the date of the murder of Mary Gilchrist. The Deptford murder trial, in particular, in 1905, had a very wide publicity. Many cases of burglary and theft were proved between 1901 and December, 1908, by fingerprint evidence not only in and around London, but also in or around such centres as Birmingham and Bradford. Not only London but some provincial cities had a fingerprint bureau.

So far back as 1902 and in the then standard Scottish medico-legal treatise of Professor Glaister, the subject-matter of fingerprint identification was specially dealt with as of value in the detection of crime. This distinguished man lectured in Glasgow in December, 1906, upon this very topic. *The Glasgow Herald* of 18th December, 1906, does not mention the presence of the Superintendent of the Criminal Investigation Department, or of any of his official staff, on the platform or elsewhere on the occasion of this public address.

All this widespread knowledge of fingerprints and the importance of its practical application in the investigation of the murder of Mary Gilchrist seems to have entirely escaped the consideration of the Glasgow Police, the Procurator-Fiscal, the Law Officers of the Crown, and the medical jurists specially called in to assist. How or why this should have been so is puzzling. It is a most remarkable and very regrettable instance of official and professional somnolence. All the police and other officials with the medical men concerned in investigation of the murder have passed away.

It is very different to-day with the City of Glasgow Police under the able direction of its present Chief-Constable, Captain P. J. Sillitoe. The Fingerprint Bureau instituted by him is under the charge of Detective-Lieutenant Bertie J. Hammond. Many convictions of criminals in Glasgow have been obtained by means of fingerprint identification.

The services of Detective-Lieutenant Hammond were notably and successfully enlisted in 1935 by the Perth Police in a murder, rape, and theft charge, and in the same year by the Lancastrian Police in the Ruxton murders.

The Scottish Police lost a great opportunity over the

Gilchrist murder case. If finger-impressions of her assailant had been obtained, I agree with Mr. Roughead that their use then "should have settled the question once for all."

What tragic consequences to Slater and to other individuals[10] ensued through the strange failure to search for fingerprints?

NOTES

[1] Then 15 Queen's Terrace.

[2] This detective officer was, I believe, an enthusiastic advocate of fingerprint identification; but, at the time, if he suggested its use to his superiors, the aid of New Scotland Yard would have been necessary. Might reluctance by the Glasgow Police to seek this aid be the reason for omission? The estate of Miss Gilchrist was given up in January, 1909, as amounting in all to £12,000 odd. She left a will, dated 28th May, 1908, with a codicil, dated 20th November, 1908.

[3] See Government Paper, Cd. 7482, issued 27th June, 1914.

[4] 1928. S.C. (J.) 94.

[5] *Moorov* v. *H.M. Advocate*, 1930 S.C. (J.) 68, *per* Lord Justice-General Clyde at p. 75. See Wigmore's "Principles of Judicial Proof," *supra*, pp. 134 *et* 988.

[6] Third edition, 1929. William Hodge & Company, Edinburgh. Glasgow, and London.

[7] See Herschel's dedication to Henry of his "The Origin of Finger Printing" referred to in Chap. XXI.

[8] "Forensic Medicine," *supra*, fifth edition, 1936, by Professor Sydney Smith. See pp. 57, 59, *et* 126.

[9] The reference to this photograph by Herr L. Engelhart, Munich, in his "Der Mordprozess Slater," in "Archiv für Kriminologie," p. 170, should be modified by this opinion of Dr. Heindl, one of the collaborators of this Berlin journal. Herr Engelhart calls attention to the omission to search for fingerprints in view of previous cases in England which he mentions.

[10] Mr. Roughead clearly indicates the "other individuals."

XXVI

DENNIS GUNN : NEW ZEALAND MURDER TRIAL : FINGERPRINT INCIDENTS : 1920

In May, 1920, a five days' trial, remarkable for three unusually interesting fingerprint points, one dramatically so, was held at Auckland, New Zealand. The King, as the indictment ran, charged Dennis Gunn, a labourer, before Mr. Justice Chapman and a jury, with the murder on 13th March previous of Augustus Edward Braithwaite, Postmaster, Ponsonby, Auckland, by shooting him with a revolver. A separate charge against him of burgling Post-Office premises was held back to await the result of the murder trial. Both charges, according to Scots practice, would have been combined in one indictment. The accused pleaded not guilty in this trial, stated an alibi, and led evidence of witnesses in support of it.

Fingerprints were found on three Post-Office cash-boxes. On the day after the murder, twenty-four people were treated as suspects. From information reaching the police authorities that the accused had been seen loitering about the Post Office on the crime date, his fingerprints, taken as a military defaulter in June, 1918, were examined. These corresponded to some of those on the cash-boxes. All other suspects were then regarded as cleared. On 17th March, 1920, the accused was arrested.

Part of the burgled property was found on 20th March in some bramble-bushes not far from where Gunn lived. A bag also was found there, containing three revolvers. Of these, one had been recently fired and cleaned. It bore a fingerprint. That fingerprint corresponded to one of the prints on the accused's military fingerprint form and to a fingerprint on one of the cash-boxes. The inference from these was clearly that Gunn had committed both the murder and the burglary. Some forty points of resemblance were proved in the trial in regard to one of the cash-box impressions, with fifteen and nine in regard to others. The pistol impression tallied in eleven points. There was a permanent whitlow or scar indicated also on the revolver pattern. The accused's 1918 and 1920 prints revealed that scar.[1]

All other fingermarks on the cash-boxes had been duly eliminated and accounted for.

A left-palm print had been found on one of the cash-boxes. The Crown had nothing with which to compare it. Apparently, the accused's palmar prints had not been taken on his arrest. After he had been formally charged, the Crown did not take these.

The accused went into the witness-box. In cross-examination he was asked to give a print of his left hand. The accused deferred to his counsel. His counsel could not advise him to agree. The accused then replied to further questioning that in any event, with or without counsel's advice, he would not agree, as, he said, the Crown experts would swear, if he did so, that the cash-box palm print was his. In charging the jury, Mr. Justice Chapman, in a very helpful address, observed that they would have no doubt how an innocent man normally might have responded to such an opportunity, suggesting at the same time that such a point should not be unduly stressed against the accused.[2]

The jury unanimously convicted the accused of the murder. Sentence of death was pronounced. Gunn then admitted the burglary, and blamed other two men for the actual shooting of the Postmaster; and said that at their instigation he hid the bag with the revolvers among the blackberries. On full police investigation, these men were cleared of all complicity in his crimes. Gunn later allowed his left-palm print to be taken. It was found to correspond to the cash-box palm print. Beyond doubt in this trial, the Crown " ultimately " relied for a verdict of guilty solely upon the fingerprint evidence. Gunn was executed.

Immediately prior to the trial and on his arrival from New South Wales, Mr. John Alexander Fowler, Inspector in charge of the Finger Print Branch in Sydney, was invited by Crown counsel to submit to a test of his experience and skill as a fingerprint expert at a joint meeting with the defence counsel. The selection of the test was left to the defence counsel, and he decided upon what was regarded as a severe experiment. Choosing the accused's fingerprint as photographically enlarged from the revolver fingerprint impression, with less than half a fingerprint to work from, the accused's counsel placed a set of the accused's fingerprints in a bundle of " a thousand others," made up of one hundred and one sets (natural size), of serial prints, each set representing ten distinct and separate fingermarks. After examining the impression from the revolver, Inspector Fowler within half-an-hour found the companion print. Then he examined the remainder merely to ascertain if another print of the same finger was in the bundle. His whole search was completed inside two hours. The defence made no attack in the trial on the Inspector's success in this test.

The last point of relevant interest in this case was that the defence alleged that fingermarks could be forged. Such forgery is a favourite device with detective-novel writers. A " forged " fingerprint had actually been prepared for defence purposes. Defence counsel, however, refrained at the trial from asking Inspector Fowler and Mr. Edmund Walter Dinnie, Senior Sergeant in charge of the Criminal Registration Branch in Wellington, the other fingerprint expert adduced by the Crown, to distinguish fabricated prints from genuine prints. On this point, the case revealed the exceptional skill of both these officers. Their evidence, based upon experiments unconnected with Gunn's charge, proved the facility with which forged fingerprints can be detected. Forgery in such circumstances implies that the intended victim, as they explained, must himself be a party to the fraud. I know of no fingerprint case in which the topic of forgery is so well and fully discussed.[3]

In view of all these interesting points, this case does not seem to have obtained the wide publicity it deserves for the instruction and assistance of students of criminology and legal medicine. The Government Report of the trial, published in 1921, contains plates or cards of the various finger and palm prints of Gunn in collation with those found on the cash-boxes and the revolver.[4] The Report also shows that the cases of *Castleton* and *Parker*, fully dealt with in Chapter XXX, were referred to by counsel in their closing speeches. The trial judge did not allude to these cases or to any decisions in charging the jury. Obviously he regarded the admissibility of fingerprint evidence as well established, and left its value entirely to the jury for their consideration.

NOTES

[1] In " Kim," Kipling tells " Mahbub felt in his belt, wetted his thumb on a cake of Chinese ink, and dabbed the impression on a piece of soft native paper. From Balkh to Bombay, men know that rough-ridged print with the old scar running diagonally across it." 1919 edition, p. 193. London. Macmillan & Co., Ltd.

[2] See *Zahuri Sahu* v. *King Emperor*, 1927. Ind.L.R. 6 Pat. 623. Here the High Court of Appeal in Patna upheld a conviction for uttering a hand-note as genuine. The accused had refused to allow his thumb-impression to be taken for comparison. The Court decided that an inference adverse to him could be drawn from his refusal. This seems common sense. The case is also noted in Butterworth's " Encyclopædia of the General Acts and Codes of India " under " Evidence," p. 663.

[3] On this topic see " Modern Criminal Investigation," *supra*, p. 126, 1936. The position of the pores is a factor that militates against forgery. In regard to the use of gloves, Dr. Locard expresses the view that these are " un péril surtout imaginaire." See " La Preuve par les Empreintes Digitales," *supra*, p. 257. Finger-impressions can be developed from the inside of gloves. See " Modern Criminal Investigation," *supra*, p. 125. See Faulds's article on " Poroscopy " in *Nature* of August, 1913. Vol. XCI, p. 635, and cf. " Fingerprints," *supra*, p. 166. 1936. F. Brewester. Calcutta. It is suggested in novels and elsewhere that fingerprints can be duplicated, whereby the ends of justice may be defeated. Fingerprint impressions made on plasticine or other similar substance and transferred therefrom to glass or other smooth surface do not result in true duplicates; glass, mirror, or other transfers show reversed impressions : papillary ridges become furrows; and furrows appear as ridges. See " The Forging of Finger-prints," &c., by Lt.-Col. Henry Smith, C.I.E., Indian Medical Service (Retired), in the Transactions of The Medico-Legal

Society, 1931, Vol. XXIV, p. 88. The author of this paper refers to his experiments in making " duplicates " of fingerprints " in the early years of this century." Experts can detect reversed fingerprint impressions of the description in question. Dr. R. Austin Freeman's detective novels are noticed by Lord Atkin in his observations as President of The Medico-Legal Society upon Lt.-Col. Henry Smith's paper, *supra*, p. 95. It is regrettable that, in some foreign countries, it should be suspected the police may resort to a "frame-up." If successful, their success must be attributed to the want of expert assistance on behalf of the victims in the exposure of such criminal methods. Mere statements about the possibility of "duplicating" fingerprints are of no value unless they can be subjected to cross-examination. Juries, as a rule, cannot appreciate the intricacies of any class of expert evidence. Generally, they must rely upon the skill, experience, reputation and, above all, the probity of experts. Mr. Justice Humphreys, as President of The Medico-Legal Society, recently observed in his Presidential address that he surmised the readiness of juries to accept as conclusive the evidence of fingerprint experts was due not so much to their own discovery on the photographs produced "of the 16 ridge characteristics spoken to by the witness," as to the uncontradicted evidence that the examination of hundreds of thousands of fingerprints over a series of years "has failed to discover a single case of identical prints being made by the fingers of two separate persons." See *The Medico-Legal and Criminological Review*, 1938, Vol. VI, p. 15 at p. 23. Cf. case at Croydon Quarter Sessions, London, on 20th January, 1938, and alluded to in *The Times* ("Points from Letters" Column) of 28th January, 1938.

4 The Report is published in Wellington by Marks, Government Printer. Copies of it ought to be in some of our British Libraries. Very few copies seem now available. A copy is now in the National Library of Scotland. I am indebted to Mr. D. J. Cummings, Commissioner of Police for New Zealand, Wellington, for the perusal of the Report and for his having had all the facts in this Chap. checked for me. He gifted the National Library's copy of the Report.

XXVII

UDEY CHAND: MURDERED HINDU: IDENTIFICATION BY FINGERPRINT SIGNATURE: 1924

" THE DELHI TRUNK CRIME " case illustrates in the most striking way the usefulness in the East of finger signatures to documents in the investigation of crime responsibility.

On the evening of 1st October, 1924, Udey Chand, a Hindu, was robbed and murdered by two of his low associates, Janeshar Das and Inayat Ullah, in the house of Das in Delhi. Chand, a single man and of dissolute life, was a very skilled goldsmith, partial himself to wearing jewellery. Das and Ullah beguiled him to the house of Das by leaving a message for him that day of an assignation arranged for him there. His murder, with the disposal of his body and the removal of the jewellery he wore, had been all deliberately planned. They had purchased earlier in the day a large galvanized steel trunk of Delhi manufacture with a Benares lock. After draining his corpse of nearly all its blood, removing all garments, covering the face with a bit of an old shirt, and tying the neck and knees together with the torn part of a laundry-marked *dhoti* or under garment belonging to Das, they placed the corpse in this trunk. With it, both men entered at Delhi the Punjab night mail train for Calcutta. Das took a ticket for Cawnpore; Ullah had only a platform ticket. Both went a certain distance only, returning to Delhi by another train. The trunk was left in the compartment they vacated. Farther on its journey, other passengers entered the compartment, saw the trunk between the seats, and advised the guard. The Howrah Railway Police opened the trunk after arrival there of the train on 2nd October. The corpse was then decomposing. An autopsy was made. No bones were found to be broken. The body had been crushed into the trunk before stiffening. The throat was slashed almost from ear to ear and the stomach had been stabbed.

The corpse was first thought to be that of the husband of a Bulandshahr woman in the United Provinces. He had disappeared for some time. She thought he must have been murdered. She could not identify the photographed corpse when shown to her some ten or so days after the murder of Chand. Her description tallied with that of the body.

It fell from 24th October, 1924, to Inspector Govind Behari Lal, Allahabad, of the C.I.D. of the United

Provinces, to take up from the Howrah Police the further investigation of the crime. With the *post mortem* report before him and other information, he made such deductions as showed him to be a real " Monsieur Lecoq." The skill he displayed and the discreet inquiries he made in Amritsar and Delhi were very remarkable. By adroit methods he succeeded in tracing the tradesman who had sold the trunk to the murderers on 1st October, 1924. He made inquiries among Delhi *dhobis* or washermen, of whom there were about four thousand. But up to 6th December, 1924, no identification of the body or clue to the murderers could be secured. No alarm had been raised by the mother or other relations of Chand. According to them, he left home on the fatal evening with the intention of going to Amritsar. They had expected his return any day.

Discussing the perplexities of the case that 6th December, Inspector Lal was casually told by one of his subordinates that Chand, a friend of this officer, had been away since the Jumna October floods. Inspector Lal was aware that the Delhi mail train in which the trunk was found was the last to get through before these floods breached the line. Lal questioned the constable, and found that his description of Chand resembled that of the corpse. Following up this clue, Chand's mother and relations were shown the photograph of the corpse. They saw strong resemblances but could not absolutely identify. An impression of one of Chand's thumbprints had been secured by the Howrah Police. Lal inquired whether it could be compared with any deed Chand might have executed. A lease of his business bazaar was discovered. The thumbprint impressed thereon agreed with the corpse thumbprint. Thus, conclusively, it was proved that the corpse was that of Chand.

175

Lal concluded that Chand had been murdered by his associates and these he gradually traced within a week from 6th December to be Das and Ullah. By a clever ruse of Lal, an acquaintance of Das visited him and got one of his shirts. Lal was delighted to find that its laundry-mark tallied exactly with the similar mark on the *dhoti* fragment tied up with the corpse. The house of Das was then searched, and other articles of clothing with the same laundry-mark were found. Traces of blood were found in one of his rooms. Then Ullah was involved. His house was searched with incriminating results. Das and Ullah were arrested on 13th December. Das then falsely implicated someone else as guilty of Chand's murder. Ullah made a full confession. Das thereafter confessed. Chand's jewellery had been sold or melted down. Some articles were recovered and identified by his relatives.

Das and Ullah were arraigned for murder before the Sessions Judge at Delhi on 1st July, 1925, and they were found guilty and sentenced to death. They appealed to the High Court of Judicature of the Punjab at Lahore. Their appeals were rejected on 23rd October, 1925. No point was raised over the fingerprint identification. Both men were hanged.

Doubtless this crime might have been traced to Das and Ullah without resort to the fingerprint signature of Chand on the lease of his shop. But the prosecution might have failed through the impossibility of personal recognition of Chand's corpse. So far as bodily identification was concerned, the case was virtually in the situation that Faulds forecasted in his *Nature* Letter of 1880 of there being nothing left but the hands of the victim. It was this fingerprint signature in correspondence with his corpse thumbprint that solved the crime.

I have been indebted to the article, entitled "The Delhi Trunk Crime," by Mr. E. M. Rogers, C.I.D.,

PLATE VII—LEFT THUMB IMPRESSIONS

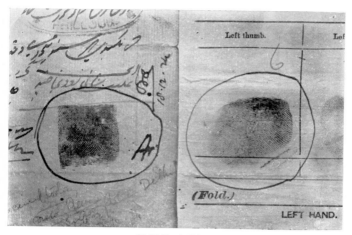

Delhi Trunk Crime

On lease, 1912   Dead body, 1924

Allahabad, in *The Police Journal*, Vol. VII, p. 369, 1934, for facts of the case I have extracted from it. I came upon this crime and Mr. Rogers's most interesting article upon it by mere chance when perusing for other purposes all the volumes of *The Police Journal*. Mr. J. A. Scott, Senior Superintendent of Police, Delhi, recovered for me after considerable trouble copies of (1) photo of the left thumb-print of the victim as taken on 4th October, 1924, by the Calcutta Police; (2) photo of his left thumb impression upon the stamped lease executed by him on 22nd December, 1912; and (3) photo of his corpse and of the steel trunk as taken on 4th October, 1924, by the Calcutta Police.[1] Plate VII shows photos Nos. 1 and 2 as produced at the trial. The Registrar of the High Court at Lahore favoured me with the correct names of the criminals. Chand's case was an instance of a crime substantially brought to justice by a fingerprint signature made to a deed in much the same way as the Chinese lady had done in executing her deed of sale in 1839. I refer to Chapters XIV and XXIX.

NOTE

[1] The photo of the corpse on account of the adipocere and otherwise repulsive condition of the body is not suitable for reproduction.

XXVIII

RUXTON MURDERS AND " CORPSE " FINGERPRINTS : 1935[1]

ONE of the most revolting crimes in the annals of British jurisprudence is that known as the Ruxton murders. Some of the remains of the victims were found in Scotland. The discovery of the murderer was due to Scottish detectives, taking, probably for the first time, the major part in the investigation of murders committed in England.

Isabella Kerr, belonging to Edinburgh, married to a Dutchman and divorced, was the reputed wife of Buck Ruxton, of Parsee parentage. He was a graduate in medicine of the University of Bombay.[2] Prior to the murder in September, 1935, of Mrs. Ruxton and a maid-servant, Mary Jane Rogerson, Ruxton and his wife had lived together for some years, and at that time they were residing at No. 2 Dalton Square, Lancaster, England, with their three young children, the eldest just six. Ruxton had his surgery there. Mary Rogerson, the maid in their service, by all accounts was a very respectable young woman. Her parents lived in Morecambe.

On Saturday afternoon, 14th September, 1935, Mrs. Ruxton drove in her husband's motor-car to Blackpool, some twenty miles away, to visit two sisters there. She saw and left them late the same evening to return home. No one, save Ruxton and possibly the children, ever saw her alive again. The maid was last seen somewhat early at the Lancaster house that Saturday evening. Ruxton was then indisputably at home. No one, except Ruxton and possibly the children, after that time ever saw her alive. Ruxton admitted that both his wife and the maid were in his house that night. He represented to the Police that, much to his surprise, they went away together on the following (Sunday) morning. He gave very disquieting and inconsistent or contradictory explanations to different people of their continued absence from home. The maid's parents became anxious, and in a few days they went to the Lancaster Police.

On 29th September, 1935, the third Sunday after the disappearance of the women, a woman was walking a mile or two out from Moffat, Dumfriesshire, over a hundred miles away from Lancaster. She stopped at a road bridge, crossing a small stream, known as Gardenholme Linn, on a main road to Edinburgh and near the Devil's

Beef Tub. Looking over the bridge, she saw in the ravine something that attracted her attention. It seemed to be a human hand and arm. She went back and told her brother. With a friend, he went to the spot. They discovered human remains in a ghastly state, wrapped in separate bundles; one in newspaper and the other in bed-sheeting. Local police were informed. They summoned the aid of Glasgow City Police, and some of its experienced officers travelled to Moffat and made investigations. They took possession of the dismembered and mutilated remains lying about the banks of that part of the stream running into Annan Water, some five hundred yards from the road bridge. Later, elsewhere in the neighbourhood, other remains were also found.

Beyond dispute, these remains were portions of the bodies of Mrs. Ruxton and her maid. Some forty-three pieces of soft tissue so found could not afterwards be fitted satisfactorily to either body. Some parts of both bodies were never found. Distinguished anatomists, pathologists, and medical forensic jurists, connected with Edinburgh and Glasgow Universities, with the aid of a very skilled Scottish surgeon-dentist, examined the remains and assembled some seventy separate parts, as far as they could, as applicable to one or other of the bodies. By 11th October, 1935, the doctors were able to affirm positively that the remains were those of the bodies of two females. The bodies were reconstituted. Photographs of the skulls with known photographs of the victims superimposed " featured " in the trial of Ruxton.[3]

In the meantime, Ruxton had been interviewed by the Lancaster Police. On 13th October, 1935, Ruxton was arrested and charged with the murder of Mary Rogerson. There then appeared, it is understood, to be more evidence for the identification of her " corpse " than for that of her mistress. On 5th November, 1935, Ruxton

was also charged with the murder of his wife. Ultimately, in March, 1936, he stood a trial of eleven days
at Manchester Winter Assizes, under an indictment for
the murder of his wife alone. It is understood he was
also served with a separate count or indictment for the
murder of the maid. But, of course, it was unnecessary
to have Ruxton tried on that count or indictment. It
remains undisposed of on the file of the Assizes. In our
Scottish practice, Ruxton would have been indicted
under one and the same indictment for both murders.
The last penalty of the law would have ensued irrespective of both murders being held as proved by a jury.
A Scottish jury would have required to have been satisfied only of one or the other. In the circumstances,
however, of Ruxton's case, any differentiation would
have been out of the question. Perhaps, in result,
English procedure is not really different.

On 13th March, 1936, the jury unanimously found
Ruxton guilty of the murder of his wife. Virtually,
Ruxton was convicted of both murders. The death sentence was pronounced. After a hopeless appeal against
his conviction had been summarily dismissed by the
Criminal Appeal Court, sitting in London, Ruxton was
executed on 12th May, 1936.[4]

There can be no doubt that the lives of both women
were taken in the early morning hours of Sunday, 15th
September, 1935. The unfortunate maid may have tried
to save her mistress. Those early morning hours must
have been employed by Ruxton in dismembering and
dissecting their bodies in such a way, as he believed, as
would defy all identification after he disposed of them.
Evidence was led at the trial that, for some days after
that Sunday, Ruxton locked the doors of two bedrooms
usually kept open. He seems to have been much engaged
during those few days in draining off blood, burning up
flesh, clothes, and other things, occasioning some

unpleasant smell and not a little talk. On the night of Monday, 16th September, 1935, he went in a motor-car with some bundles and disposed of them by pitching them into the Gardenholme Linn and thereabout; and on Thursday, 19th September, 1935, he disposed of more somewhere else. Probably he hoped that they would never be discovered; or that, if found, they would have become so decomposed as to be impossible of identification. By withdrawing all blood in the bathroom of his house before he removed the parts, the paper and other material in which he wrapped them disclosed no blood stains. He had striven to cut out or away any characteristic marks on the bodies as far as he could in a discriminating process of dissection. I cannot think that Ruxton had any knowledge of English Criminal Law and thus consciously relied to any extent upon the necessity in the usual case of arraigning a person for murder within a year and day of its commission. He may have trusted to the non-discovery of the remains, or in any case of their non-identification within that period as rendering him safe from prosecution. Be this as it may, Ruxton made great efforts to remove from his house all traces of his dreadful work. These were unavailing. Some of the rooms of the house, with a bathroom and the inside stairs, resembled even at the time of his arrest something very like an abattoir.

Ruxton pleaded not guilty. Not only during the preliminary Magisterial Inquiry but in his long trial he made many protestations of innocence and complaints of injustice. Perhaps he hoped that in his condemnation the jury would not be unanimous.[5] The evidence, however, was so strong that his hope was vain. Except by his own evidence in the witness-box, no medical testimony was offered on his behalf in dissent from that of the medical and other experts adduced by the prosecution. I understand that Professor John Glaister, of Glasgow

University, for himself and his colleagues in investigations, desired that the fullest opportunity should be given in the interest of the accused to medical and other experts to test all their results. I believe the experts called in for the defence did so.

If neither the body of Ruxton's wife nor that of the maid could have been found, there was, according to the Criminal Law of England (and I know of nothing to the contrary in our own Scottish Criminal Law), ample circumstantial evidence otherwise available for his conviction of both murders.

The one redeeming feature of the costly prosecution was the last words of the unfortunate man upon the announcement of his doom by the jury's verdict, thanking everybody " for the patience and fairness of my trial."

My interest in Ruxton's case rests solely in the very remarkable manner in which fingerprint evidence was obtained and, partially coming into his prosecution, contributed to his conviction. In its relation to the accused, as far as I am aware, the trial of Ruxton is totally different from any other case in the records of any country. With the fingerprints of Ruxton, except in a very minor degree, the case was not really concerned. His fingerprints, taken after his arrest, were used only for comparison with his fingerprint-impressions found upon paint-tins, to show that he had been working with white and black paint in obliterating some of his nefarious work. He had never before done tradesmen's jobs. His wife's finger-impressions, again, were not available. He had cut off her finger tips at the third or top joint and all her toes. The fingerprint-impressions of the maid were, however, available, and these were alone of material importance. With her murder he was not formally tried. The fingerprints of the maid, as far as spoken to in the evidence, were of her left hand only. Comparison was made of her finger-impressions, left when alive in the murderer's house, with prints of her finger-tips taken from her left dismembered hand and arm as found near Moffat.

On 1st October, 1935, the services of Detective-Lieutenant Bertie James Hammond, in charge of the Finger Print and Photographic Bureau of the City Police, Glasgow, were requisitioned. He went to Gardenholme Linn on that date and photographed the bridge and the ravine.

This Officer deponed at the trial of Ruxton that he had had more than twelve years' experience of finger-print work, and had examined up to that time nearly half-a-million fingerprints of criminals, together with thousands of fingerprints of other persons. In the case of those other parties, examination was necessary to exclude their participation in crimes or offences under investigation.

For the trial needs, finger and palmar prints of both hands of Mary Rogerson were taken for comparison with impressions found in Ruxton's house. Some of these were taken by the Finger Print Department of the Edinburgh City Police. Her left hand was first discovered on 29th September, 1935, and, then, several weeks later, her right hand.

The body of Mary Rogerson, as reconstructed by the medical experts for the purposes of the trial, was treated as " Corpse " or Body No. 1. That of Mrs. Ruxton similarly figured as Body No. 2. Hammond made a thorough examination of Ruxton's house, finding finger-impressions of both hands of Ruxton, the maid, and others on various articles or places.

Immediately after the right hand of Body No. 1 had been found on 4th November, 1935, and taken to Edinburgh University, Hammond photographed that hand, of which the upper skin or epidermis had disappeared.

Only the under skin or dermis was left. He found that its ridge-lineations agreed with those of Mary Rogerson's impressions on a bottle in the cellar of Ruxton's house and on a wash-hand basin in her bedroom there. She had assisted the doctor in giving out medicine from his dispensary. In these Hammond obtained sixteen points of agreement as regards the bottle impression and nine referable to that on the wash-hand basin. Professors Glaister and Brash in their work on the " Medico-Legal Aspects of the Ruxton Case " show (Fig. 98)[6] a comparison of the bottle fingerprint with the dermis and with the sixteen points of agreement. No reference to these fingerprints will be found in the account of Ruxton's trial in the *Notable British Trials* series.[7] I deal later in this Chapter fully with these right-hand fingerprints of Body No. 1.

Here I miss out the wife, for, while her impressions might be guessed as amongst those found in the house, there were no impressions from her remains available with which to compare those discovered in the house.

In particular, and dealing at this stage only with Hammond's evidence as made use of in the trial, he found referable to the left hand of Mary Rogerson the following : —

(1) A palmar impression on the leaf of a wooden table in a cellar used for dispensing purposes :

(2) A forefinger-impression on a medicine-bottle in a wicker basket in another cellar :

(3) A forefinger-impression on another medicine-bottle also in a cellar :

(4) A middle-finger-impression on a vinegar-bottle in the kitchen cupboard :

(5) A middle-finger-impression on a plate in the same cupboard :

(6) A palmar impression on the door of the bathroom :

(7) A thumb-impression on a decanter on a sideboard in the dining-room:

   Note.—This thumb-impression was shown for comparison with papillary ridges photographed direct from left thumb of Body No. 1.

(8) Another thumb-impression on the same decanter:

(9) A middle-finger-impression on a plate in a sitting-room cupboard:

(10) A " ring "-finger-impression on another plate in the same cupboard: and

(11) A middle-finger-impression on a plate in the middle cabinet in the drawing-room.

Of all such articles Hammond took possession and had them duly marked. The " chance impressions " thereon were photographed under his supervision. At Edinburgh University, where the remains of the maid lay for examination by the medical experts, Hammond himself also photographed the papillary ridges of the maid's left thumb. Palmar impressions Nos. (1) and (6) corresponded. Forefinger-impressions Nos. (2) and (3) did so. Likewise middle-finger-impressions, Nos. (4), (5), (9) and (11). So also thumb-impressions Nos. (7) and (8). Of the " ring "-finger, there was only one impression, No. (10), made out. In the " dead " hand, imprints of all four left fingers and the thumb were available. In Ruxton's house, impressions of the palm and digits of the maid's left hand were found as follows: Three palmar, five thumb, two forefinger, eleven middle-finger, five " ring "-finger, and five little-finger.

Assuming a knowledge of all the finger and palmar impressions of one hand of any individual, one cannot tell the state of the other hand. Given one finger of a hand, no expert can tell what the formations of the other fingers are. From these facts, the extraordinary variety in the structure of papillary ridges in human hands may be imagined.

At the trial of Ruxton, Hammond stated that, as a fingerprint expert, he would be satisfied in certain cases of establishing identity between fingerprint-impressions found in places or on articles in comparison with those of the actual fingers of anyone by getting a minimum of eight points in agreement in papillary-ridge characteristics. It is the practice in Scotland, as I may interpolate, to require in most cases definite assurance of identity in at least sixteen points of agreement. Getting that length, one need not progress to all remaining points of agreement; they must be there. Beyond that, for all practical purposes, it is unnecessary to go. To do so would make charts more complex than spiders' webs.[8] The prosecution produced, as one infers from the list already specified, eleven exhibits altogether of finger-impressions of Mary Rogerson, taken from the accused's house, of which two were palmar and the rest digital. Each exhibit was referable to particular and different rooms or places in the house. Altogether, about sixty prints of the maid's left palm or finger-impressions were found. All these were easily identifiable with impressions obtained from the dead left palm and fingers of Body No. 1.

Hammond was able to state to the Court that he did find, in the case of Body No. 1, sixteen, if not seventeen, similarities in the ridge-characteristics in several instances on a comparison of the left finger-tips of that body, the maid's, with those found upon the household materials. In the case of the table-leaf, he found twenty such points of resemblance. Illustrations of the dead finger-pads showed various blank spaces, due to shrinkage of tissue after death. But, superimposing the household impressions upon the dead fingerprints would have shown these gaps completely filled up.

All points of agreement, whether sixteen or more, Hammond stated, were found in sequence. " Sequence " signifies that the ridge-characteristics in all cases were exactly alike in regard to shape and position in each ridge compared, starting, as is usual, from their inner-most, recurring ridge, termed the core or inner terminus, to the delta or outer terminus.[9]

Thus, from Hammond's fingerprint evidence, the deduction drawn by him for acceptance by the jury was clearly that there was a very close, and, indeed, positive, connexion between the remains of the two female bodies found together in the same spot or neighbourhood, and the domicile of Ruxton. His house was certainly a place where Body No. 1, when living, had been a constant occupant. The " reconstruction " evidence of the medical men, strong as it was for the prosecution, could not be supported by reference to any fingerprint evidence in the case of Body No. 2. The third finger-joints of both hands of Mrs. Ruxton had been cut away. Accord-ingly, no *data* were available from dead Body No. 2 with which to compare her marks upon household articles. It seems strange that Ruxton should not have similarly treated the fingers of the maid. He could not, and, in any event, did not, think of every precaution. Their absence in the wife's case, however, was really a point against Ruxton. Many fingerprint-impressions were dis-covered in the house other than those of Ruxton, his wife, and the maid; these in most cases were associated with persons known to have been visitors to the house or working in it. The exceptions, after such elimination, pointed to their being the fingerprints of Mrs. Ruxton.

Hammond, the only fingerprint expert tendered by the prosecution, was accepted by the Court as sufficient on that branch of the case. The very distinguished counsel for the prisoner, Mr. Norman Birkett, M.P., K.C., elicited in his cross-examination that Hammond had photographed many fingerprint-impressions found by him on household furniture and furnishings of Ruxton's house, spoken to by him in exhibits made, as well as on articles not produced at the trial. Elimination prints, Hammond stated, were taken of all living persons having access to Ruxton's house, and comparison was made with all prints found. That had been done for the purpose of excluding fingerprint-impressions of all other people having access to Ruxton's house and surgery as in any way connected with the murders. Mr. Birkett handsomely acknowledged that this part of Hammond's investigation had been done with great care. The fingermarks of a maid servant, who had left Ruxton's service some three years before the murders, were found on a dish!

The evidence of Hammond was not challenged. In our Scottish practice two experts are always adduced in fingerprint cases; perhaps unnecessarily, in view now of the accepted, conclusive nature of such scientific evidence. One expert alone might be deemed on technical grounds as uncorroborated, and, therefore, according to the Scottish system of Criminal Law procedure, as insufficient evidence. Lord Sands's forecast of the future sufficiency of simple production and proof of the compared fingerprints may in time be ruled by Act of Adjournal or otherwise as all that is necessary by Scots Law in fingerprint evidence.[10]

The significance of the prisoner's fingerprints found upon paint-tins or other articles in his premises was not material to his conviction. Certain parts of his house where blood was traced in large quantities were referred to at the trial. Ruxton had been seen working with black and white paint in patching up places. His " arrest " imprints were identical with those on the paint-tins. It was not disputed that he was at home at all times material to the charge against him, and that he had been handling various articles upon which blood was found, some undoubtedly his own. For the presence of such blood, certain explanations were made by him.

The signal value of Hammond's evidence on finger-prints lay in its establishing beyond any reasonable doubt that the remains found near Moffat and reconstructed as Body No. 1 were those or part of those of Mary Rogerson. Unknown to, or, if known, unappreciated by, the prisoner, she had left fingermarks behind her all over the house; in particular on the table-leaf, wine-decanter, and other articles in the eleven exhibits shown by the Prosecution to the jury. Ruxton's mind had not been alert to such a possibility and to the need for drastic scouring of his house and all its contents. It is difficult to believe that Ruxton thought at all of identifi-cation by finger-impression marks in the case of either woman. It occurred to me as more likely that he had cut off the tips of his wife's fingers and her toes because of some peculiarities known to him about them. In revising this Chapter for me, Mr. Hammond informed me it had been discovered that Mrs. Ruxton carefully manicured her nails. The reason for the mutilation of her fingers, therefore, becomes obvious. · It destroyed a very significant sex-pointer: a " Marie Roget " indica-tion to identity. Ruxton, with all his knowledge as a medical man, failed, however, to frustrate the extra-ordinarily skilful ingenuity of the medical men in their reconstruction of the bodies, fitting in so marvellously with shoes the women wore, and accounting for other matters, such as a bunion, crumpled toes, birth, vaccina-tion, operation, and other scar-marks to which, in the respective peculiarities of wife and maid, general evidence was directed at the trial. The wife had a bunion and bent toes; the maid, *inter alia*, a birthmark and four vaccination marks.

I have examined the closing speeches of Counsel for the Crown and for the Defence. Practically, the only reference to fingerprints in the address of the late Mr. Jackson, K.C., for the prosecution was a brief reference to the left hand of the maid—

> You may have noticed how my learned friend (Mr. Birkett) endeavoured time after time, but without success, to get the learned medical men that I called to admit that there might be some doubt about the left hand of Mary Rogerson. Professor Glaister and the other medical gentlemen said they had no doubt at all that the two arms with the hands attached to them were a pair.
>
> You might well wonder why my learned friend (Mr. Birkett) was so anxious to throw doubt on that left hand, Members of the jury, it is simple, *because the left hand was the only one from which they got any finger-prints*, the palm and the fingers of that hand,[11] and if my friend could have thrown doubt on those finger-prints of that hand, it might have gone a long way to put a doubt in your minds; but if you are satisfied, as I ask you to be on that evidence, which is absolutely clear and is not contradicted, then you get a very strange set of circumstances; for, the finger-prints of that left hand of the body, which we say is Mary Rogerson's, are found in all sorts of places in the house of Dr. Ruxton. You have heard of the infallibility of the finger-print system; but if those finger-prints in the house tally with the finger-prints of the left hand of body No. 1, can you have the slightest doubt of the identification of Mary Rogerson?

Mr. Birkett, I suppose, with studied discretion, made no reference at all to fingerprint evidence in his final address. That evidence was so deadly as to be unchallengeable: hence, silence on that topic.

Mr. Justice Singleton, in this, his first, important criminal trial, charged the jury in an address, striking in its simple, telling style, and convincing in its subtle persuasiveness. Dealing near its close with Hammond's evidence, he said—

> Now, members of the jury, you have had certain other

evidence in this case, about which I ought to say a word, namely, the finger-print evidence. I do not know whether you have had experience before as jurors or of finger-prints. I thought it desirable that the officer (Hammond) who produced those prints should tell you something about them. He told you how many points are thought generally by him or by others to point to a conclusive result. Was it eight? he said, were often taken as enough, but he liked more? You saw in the three instances, to which reference was made, how many there were from a plate, a decanter—and something else, a table. I am not sure which you looked at. But there you had indicated to you the different points. When you look back at that for yourselves, with that officer in the box, have you any doubt that, in so far as these things can tell the ordinary one of us anything, they were amazingly alike? If you find, in the three you looked at, ten or fifteen points picked out like that—and, in one instance, the officer said there were more that he had not marked—if you find points of similarity on Body No. 1, which is said to be Mary Rogerson's body as reconstructed, and the mark on the table, or the decanter or plate at 2, Dalton Square, does it help you? If there could be doubt, I say, *if* there could be doubt—does that resolve it beyond any possibility of doubt? It is not for me to express an opinion on the value of evidence, but I cannot help thinking that some of you may think that these finger-print impressions, from the point of view of establishing identity, may be more helpful than superimposed photographs (i.e., of Bodies Nos. 1 and 2).[12]

The learned Judge clearly indicated by this passage that, in his own mind, the fingerprint evidence of the Scottish fingerprint expert was the most, if not the absolutely, conclusive proof in satisfying the jury of the identity of the remains of Body No. 1 with those of the maid, and so also, inferentially, of the identity of the other remains as those of her mistress.

The scientific work of the medical men (very brilliant and unique in, at least, one of its phases, in the reconstruction of the disarticulated bodies and in the use of life-size photographs of the heads and faces of the victims for superimposition upon the skulls produced) did not reach certainty in identification. The learned Judge in the course of the examination of Professor Brash, of the Anatomy Chair in the University of Edinburgh, assessed his evidence thus, addressing the Jury—

" In the result, Professor Brash says very truly: ' These may be the bodies of Mrs. Ruxton and Mary Rogerson.' If his results had been otherwise, he would have said quite clearly ' It cannot be,' and then (turning to the Professor), ' Am I right in this? You do get in both cases an amazing similarity in any event? ' ' That is so! ' answered the Professor."[13]

Without in the least detracting from the value and weight of the medical evidence, it can, I think, be said that the fingerprint evidence as adduced beyond all doubt turned into absolute certainties the reasoned conjectures of the medical men that the remains of the two bodies before them were those of the wife of the accused and of the servant. Had it been impossible to obtain any fingerprint evidence, the cumulative weight of the medical evidence, including the fine work of a distinguished Scottish dental-surgeon, was so strong as to compel the conviction that the reassembled parts respectively pertained to the wife of Ruxton and to the maid.

The arrest, prosecution, and conviction of Ruxton ensued mainly from the investigations of Scottish police and of Scottish University medical men.[14]

New Scotland Yard, so far as evidence in Court was concerned, did not come into the case. That, no doubt, was due to the discovery in Scotland of the remains of the two victims and of the association therewith of Scottish detectives. The investigations of these detectives were brilliantly conducted.

Professors Glaister and Brash, in their " Medico-Legal Aspects of the Ruxton Case," deal exhaustively with all

PLATE VIII—RUXTON MURDERS, 1935

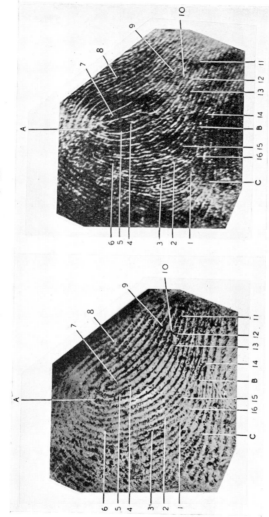

Chart B—Chance impression on bottle in
Ruxton's house

Chart A—Dermal print obtained
from dead hand

Impressions of right thumb of Mary Rogerson

branches of the evidence. Their treatise is conspicuous in the acknowledgment of the importance of the finger-print evidence. Numerous imprints found in the house by Detective-Lieutenant Hammond, as these authors state, were " positively identified " as the fingerprints of both hands and the palmar impressions of the left hand of Body No. 1, Mary Rogerson's.[15] They affirm that this evidence completed " one of the strongest links in the circumstantial chain "[16]; was, indeed, " the most crucial part of the evidence which connected the remains found at Moffat with No. 2 Dalton Square, Lancaster "; and, " taken with other facts, they placed the identity of Body No. 1 beyond doubt."[17]

With regard to the prints taken by Detective-Lieutenant Hammond from the " dermis, corium or true skin " of the right hand of Mary Rogerson and identified by him as agreeing with the imprints of her right hand found by him on articles in Ruxton's house, Professors Glaister and Brash record the submission of these finger-impressions " to several American fingerprint experts," and add that it was not found necessary to use this evidence about the right hand, " although information regarding the identity of digital imprints from a right hand at Dalton Square was supplied to the Defence."[18] Finally, in their book, the distinguished Professors note the observations by Mr. Justice Singleton in his charge to the jury with regard to the paramount importance, in his opinion, of the fingerprint testimony of the Scottish detective and fingerprint expert.[19]

On reading the proceedings at the trial of Ruxton, I was surprised to find that, although both forearms and hands of Body No. 1 (Mary Rogerson) were exhibited to the jury, neither Mr. Justice Singleton nor any of the jury had inquired how the right hand and arm stood in regard to fingerprints. It seemed so natural to raise this question. " It is worth remembering," as Professor

Sydney Smith observes in his " Forensic Medicine," that " prints can be obtained from the dermis after the skin has been lost in putrefied and drowned bodies." See Fifth Edition, p. 60, 1936.

The right forearm and hand of Mary Rogerson were found near Moffat, as already stated, on 4th November, 1935, seven weeks after the discovery of the portions of both bodies at Gardenholme Linn. Her right forearm and hand, from such exposure, were in a very bad condition. The epidermis was missing from all digits and the palm. But the derma (under, latent, or true skin) was almost complete, except for one or two places on the " ring "-finger. The tip of the middle finger was missing, and the little finger was too decomposed for photographing. Technically, the papillary ridges, due to maggots, were in a " crenated " state. Vermin had also been at work. In these circumstances, it was very skilful work on the part of Hammond to succeed in getting satisfactory " dermal " fingerprints. I know of no previously recorded case where identification of the criminal has been established on impressions that have been taken from the *derma* of a murdered person.

No exhaustive search was made at the beginning of the investigations for right-hand impressions of Mary Rogerson. Right-hand impressions, however, on a few articles, as already enumerated, were taken at the outset, in case the right hand should be found before the trial began.

On 7th November, 1935, the Chief-Constable of Lancaster, in charge of the case against Ruxton, was informed that the thumb of the right hand found at Moffat had been positively identified as that of the maid.

I have ascertained that on 14th January, 1936, by letter of that date and with the authority and approval of his Chief, Captain Sillitoe, Hammond submitted to Mr. John Edgar Hoover, LL.D., LL.M., Vice-Chairman of the International Police Association, and Director of the Federal Bureau of Investigation, United States Department of Justice, Washington, D.C., three sets of photographs, explaining that one of the prints was taken from the *derma* of a right thumb and one from the impression found on a household article. I understand this course was adopted in view of some difference of opinion between experts in London and Glasgow. The Washington Director was requested to place them before three of his fingerprint experts for their examination and report on any points of agreement found by them. He was not informed of the conflicting opinions already formed on these prints. The Washington Bureau is the best equipped in the world. Such a *derma* print and the comparative impression, if genuine, are self-demonstrative and conclusive.[20]

By letter dated 31st January, 1936, and received by Captain Sillitoe in Glasgow on 14th February, 1936, as I have been informed by him, Dr. Hoover advised Captain Sillitoe that an examination had been made, and that his three experts were unanimous in their opinion that the latent fingerprint was identical with the impression taken from the *derma* of the right thumb. Photographic charts were subsequently forwarded in substantiation of the opinion of these experts. These charts were enlarged two-and-a-half times the size of the photographs as submitted from Glasgow. In the result, these charts showed sixteen points of agreement, and, of these, thirteen had been already indicated in the sixteen points marked on the Glasgow charts. There were, therefore, in all, nineteen points of agreement marked as found between the Glasgow expert and the three Washington experts. The American experts started from a point different from that selected by Hammond, and so accounted for the extra three points. Messrs. Glaister and Brash refer to

195

these " American charts " in their work and there record
that the " American finger-print experts . . . agreed with
Lieutenant Hammond's conclusions." Ruxton does not
appear to have disagreed with any of that expert's results.
Messrs. Glaister and Brash also state in their book that
information was given to the Defence in regard to the
identity of digital imprints from the right hand. I
believe the Defence called for production of all nega-
tives taken of fingerprints and these were accordingly in
Hammond's care at the trial.

All the fingerprints of both hands of Mary Rogerson
as obtained for the prosecution were inspected in Edinburgh by the Lancaster solicitor for Ruxton, along with
his medical and other experts, at meetings in Edinburgh
University on 18th and 19th January, 1936, when the
medical-jurists for the Crown demonstrated their " reconstruction " of the two bodies.

It can, therefore, now be understood why no question
was raised at the Trial on behalf of Ruxton in regard
to the existence or absence of either epidermal or dermal
fingerprints dealing with the right hand of Body No. 1.
It would have been dangerous, if not disastrous, for the
defence to have cross-examined Hammond upon that
subject. Hammond was asked by Mr. Birkett only
whether he had taken " chance impressions " of the right
hand as found on articles in Ruxton's house in comparison with the alleged left hand of the maid.
Hammond answered affirmatively. There Ruxton's
Counsel left the matter!

By permission of Captain Sillitoe, copies of some of
the finger-impressions in Ruxton's trial were made for me
from material in the possession of the Glasgow Finger
Print Bureau. Illustrations of the imprints of the left
thumb of Mary Rogerson as found on a decanter on
Ruxton's dining-room sideboard and of the impression as
taken from her left thumb after death are given in the

published account of Ruxton's trial in the "Notable British Trials" series, and also in the elaborate work of Professors Glaister and Brash. These need not be reproduced here. The illustration on Plate No. VIII shows the imprints—Chart B.—of the maid's right thumb as found on a bottle in a cellar of Ruxton's house, and Chart A.—of the derm of her thumb reversed and photographed from her dead hand. Both charts, composite to save space, show (1) the sixteen points marked originally on Hammond's charts, with (2) the three additional points A., B., and C., noted by the Washington experts. Their charts, which also exhibited sixteen points, started from a point different from Hammond's and did not disclose points 10, 11, and 12 in Hammond's chart. Thus, nineteen points of agreement were revealed from a comparison of both Glasgow and Washington charts.[21] All links in the chain of fingerprint evidence of both hands of Mary Rogerson were thus made complete, and absolutely conclusive. I feel that the Judge and the Jury would have been still more impressed if the position of the fingerprint evidence in regard to the right hand of Mary Rogerson had been also explained to them. The presentation in the trial of these results, as it appears to me, would have cut away any foundation for the somewhat lame suggestion made by the defence that the left hand of Body No. 1 (ring or no ring mark) was not that of Mary Rogerson. Hammond's results, as the forensic jurists in the case agree and declare in their "Medico-Legal Aspects," proved beyond all dispute that the two hands of Body No. 1 were a pair, and were those of Mary Rogerson.[22]

"Guilty"—the verdict of the Jury was never in doubt. It may be said, therefore, that the fingerprint evidence based upon the derm of the right hand of the maid proved "unnecessary" to that result. If the derm print had been used, it would have certainly figured in the Crown evidence at the trial as both unprecedented and deadly in its telling significance.

Finally, this chapter, with its disclosures of amazing triumphs in fingerprint detection, may close with the query—To whom was all this due? Solely to Faulds. His " conception " alone made these achievements possible. Bertillon, Galton, Henry, and Herschel, jointly or individually, never had any such idea in their minds. No criminal fingerprint registers had the remotest bearing on Ruxton's case.

NOTES

[1] The typescript of this Chap. was revised for me prior to March, 1937, as to facts by officers of the Glasgow Police Force.

[2] In the Introduction to the " Trial of Buck Ruxton," 1937, Vol. 66 of " Notable British Trials " (p. xvii et p. 202), it is stated that Ruxton was a graduate of London University. That is incorrect. He was not on the roll of students of that University. Of this I have been officially notified. His own evidence does not conflict with my information. He simply stated, " I studied in London." His Indian name, as given in the Colonial List of the Medical Register for 1936, was Hakim Bakhtyar Rustonji Ratanji.

[3] In the summer of 1890, and at the Medical Theatre in Paris, behind the Morgue, then close to Nôtre Dame, in connexion with the University, I saw many autopsies conducted by M. Paul Brouardel, Dean of the Medical Faculty, and Professor of Legal Medicine of the University. The very worst cases I saw, some really bad, were mild in contrast with the experiences of the medical men in Ruxton's case. Some appreciation of these and their difficulties in re-arranging each body may be had from perusal of " Medico-Legal Aspects of the Ruxton Case," with the plates illustrating this work. I refer later to this work in the text of this Chap.

[4] The *News of the World*, in its weekly Sunday issue of 17th May, 1936, announced a " confession " by Ruxton of both murders. It was never authenticated officially.

[5] In England, a jury of twelve must return a unanimous verdict of " Guilty "; or " Not Guilty "; or be discharged as disagreeing. In Scotland a jury of fifteen can return unanimously, or by a simple majority, one of three verdicts : " Guilty "; " Not Guilty "; or " Not Proven."

[6] " Medico-Legal Aspects of the Ruxton Case," p. 136. 1936. Edinburgh. E. & S. Livingstone.

[7] Vol. 66. 1937. Edinburgh. William Hodge & Co., Ltd.

[8] Wentworth and Wilder in " Personal Identification," *supra*, p. 279, give an illustration with eighty-two points in agreement. In the French case noted in Note 8 to Chap. XXIV, a sequence of one hundred points is recorded. Of course, in some cases where there are puntos caracteristicos, or " individualizing features," the agree-

ment *quoad* these rarities may be so striking as to make the expert satisfied with eight or even fewer points. In such cases, poroscopic evidence may aid greatly and especially may this be the case in smudged or partial impressions. In regard to palmar prints, twenty points of agreement are generally considered sufficient.

9 Hammond informs me that the patterns or types of the right and left thumbs of Mary Rogerson fell under the class of ulnar loops.

10 See *Hamilton*, 1934, S.C.(J.) 1, cited in Chap. XXX.

11 The italics are mine. " Exhibited (or Produced) for the purposes of the trial " would have been accurate. The " derm " fingerprints of the right hand, not adduced in evidence, are dealt with later in this Chap. Mr. Jackson's speech begins on p. 293 of " Notable British Trials—Buck Ruxton," referred to in next note. The particular passage is on p. 294.

12 Through the courtesy of William Hodge & Company, Limited, the publishers of the " Notable British Trials " series, I was furnished with copies of the professional shorthand notes, taken for the Crown, of Hammond's evidence, speeches of Counsel, and of the Judge's charge. Ruxton's case, as one of the " Notable British Trials," is Vol. 66, 1937. In the long Introduction of over seventy pages to the " Trial " by the Editors, one legal, and the other medical, the only reference made to fingerprint evidence is that on page lxxix, where the Editors state : " The only part of the evidence on the reconstruction of the bodies which was seriously challenged by the defence was the allocation of the left forearm of Body No. 1 to that Body. The reason for this will be obvious when the evidence is read, as it was from this hand that fingerprints were obtained corresponding to those found at Dalton Square."

13 See " Trial," *supra*, p. 185.

14 While I speak of Scottish police and Scottish University men, I should not omit to recognize that Captain P. J. Sillitoe, the Chief-Constable of Glasgow City Police, and his Officer Hammond, belong to England. Of the University Professors, Brash is Scottish ; Sydney Smith is Australian ; Glaister is Scottish. Messrs. Glaister and Brash in their " Medico-Legal Aspects," *supra*, of the trial acknowledge the fingerprint expert and photographic services rendered by the Edinburgh City Police, mentioning specially in this connexion Detective-Constables Norman MacKenzie and Thomas S. Scobie. See pp. 127 *et* 165.

15 *Ibid.*, 108 *et* 110.

16 *Ibid.*, 127.

17 *Ibid.*, p. 137.

18 *Ibid.*, p. 139.

19 See Chap. XXX. I understand that a fingerprint expert with some connexion formerly with New Scotland Yard was consulted on behalf of the defence, and was present at the trial when Hammond gave evidence. He had seen, as I understand, the right-hand fingerprints.

20 See " The Finger Print Instructor." Frederick Kuhne. 1917. New York. Munn & Co. Inc.

21 Captain Sillitoe, in addressing the International Police Conference at Montreal on 26th November, 1937, mentioned the assistance the

Glasgow Finger Print Department had received from the three finger-print experts of the Washington Federal Finger Print Bureau with regard to the derm right-hand thumbprint of Mary Rogerson, and with the results as stated in the text.

22 See " Medico-Legal Aspects of the Ruxton Case," *supra*, Table XI, p. 108. I understand Professor Sydney Smith dealt in Egypt with the identification of a dead body from an impression taken from a finger of which the outer skin was missing. Lt.-Col. Henry Smith, C.I.E., Indian Medical Service (Retired), on 27th February, 1930, read a paper before The Medico-Legal Society, London, in the course of which he mentioned the case of the body of a native in India that had been in water during hot weather for probably a week. The upper skin of hands and feet had been cast. He was able to dry and replace that of the hands. Tying a ligature round the fingers at the first joint and then distending with a hypodermic syringe, and inking the fingers, he got good prints. The body was thus identified as that of a man whose fingerprint was on the discharge sheet of the Swat Canal Construction, three hundred miles away from the place where his body was found. The man had been robbed and murdered by two fellow workmen. They were traced, tried and convicted of his murder. See Transactions of The Medico-Legal Society, 1931. Vol. XXIV, p. 87.

XXIX

THE CHINESE AND FINGERMARKS

In the last paragraph of his Letter in 1880 to *Nature*, Faulds said—

> It need not surprise us to find that the Chinese have been before us in this as in other matters. I shall be glad to find that it is really so, as it would only serve to confirm the utility of the method, and the facts which may thus have been accumulated would be a rich anthro-pological mine for patient observers.[1]

It is evident from Herschel's postscript to his Letter in 1880 to *Nature* that he doubted this suggestion of Faulds upon the possible Chinese origin of fingerprints for identification purposes. Herschel then believed, as he continued to the last to believe, that he had himself independently discovered, and for the first time, the permanent nature of finger and thumb marks and their use in personal identification. Ultimately, he granted that Faulds had also independently made the same discovery.

Faulds narrates that the examination of old Japanese pottery led to his study of finger characteristics.[1] Finger-prints of very ancient potters on their clay wares have been revealed by recent excavation in the East; the work of different potters three thousand years ago could be plainly identified and assorted.[2] Thumbprints on clay seals are proved to have been in existence in China at least some two hundred years B.C. This use of finger-impressions on seals clearly indicates their significance for identification purposes.[3]

There does not seem to be the slightest doubt that the Chinese used finger-impressions from very early times for the purpose of identification in connexion with the execution of documents. But the difficulty is to find any direct authority for this statement in any early Chinese book. So far as I can ascertain, there is no specific Chinese reference to the practice of a date before the Christian era. It may be that very early Chinese literature dealing with this matter was destroyed. Frequent devastation of great libraries occurred in the civil commotions of the opening centuries of the Christian era. For any evidence of Chinese customs upon this matter we must rely mainly on the records of personal observations by foreign travellers and the works of foreign historians. I do not think that Laufer's optimistic hope that some early legal Chinese documents might shed light on the subject has yet materialized. Unfortunately, I did not apply to the Chinese Embassy in London until after trouble had arisen in the East. While the Embassy was willing to help, it was then impossible.

The first notice of any kind relates, I think, to docu-ments of the eighth century A.D. Sir Aurel Stein, in "Ancient Khotan,"[4] narrates, *inter alia*, that he discovered in the course of his travels and investigations among sand-buried cities in Eastern Turkestan three Chinese documents, dated round about A.D. 782. These documents, all contracts of loan, he submitted to Professor Edouard Chavannes (1865-1918), of Paris, whom he describes as " the leading authority on all Chinese sources of information concerning the history and geography of Central Asia." One, which, though mutilated, is entire and dated A.D. 782, Professor Chavannes, in Appendix A to Sir Aurel Stein's work, notes that, as in all three documents, it ends with the formula: —

> " Les deux parties ont toutes deux trouvé cela juste et clair et y ont apposé l'empreinte de leurs doigts pour servir de marque."[5]

Here apparently we have for the first time a clear reference to the use of finger-impressions. Professor Chavannes explains that this private contract was so framed in case of bad faith on the part of individuals to it. The borrower's wife and daughter, aged 35 and 13 years respectively, acted as witnesses. These witnesses also attached their finger-impressions. Professor Chavannes by his description suggests that the purpose of these finger-impressions was the preservation of evidence of identity.

Dr. Lionel Giles (a son of Herbert Allen Giles (1845-1935), the very distinguished sinologist), Keeper of Oriental Printed Books and MSS. in the British Museum, in a recent article in the *Bulletin of Oriental Studies* (Univ. of London) upon " Dated Chinese Manuscripts in the Stein Collection," describes in detail each of these three loan contracts.[6] These documents belong to the period of the T'ang dynasty. which began in A.D. 618 and ended in A.D. 905. Probably that was the most illustrious period of more than one Augustan age in the long history of China.

In reference to the one noticed as particularly dealt with by Professor Chavannes, No. S. 5871, of A.D. 782, Dr. Giles states that he is of opinion that the fingermarks shown upon it are blobs and of no use for identification purposes.[6] By arrangement with Dr. Giles, I had the privilege of inspecting these old documents. From the information Dr. Giles gives about them in his article, we find their intense human interest. They are older by some six hundred years than Scottish estate title deeds I had through my hands many years ago. To the eye of the layman, the fingermarks upon the one that is entire do resemble blobs. With the magnifying glass, it is diffi- cult to discern finger-ridge lineations. The marks seem to have been made more by the tips than by the bulbs or pads of the fingers. I do not think, however, that it would be reasonable to infer from the examination of this particular document that all fingermarks upon writings of the period in question were so blobbed as to make identification impossible. Dr. Giles does not himself so generalize. In view of the opinions of other sinologues, including that of Dr. Giles's father, I cannot think that fingermarks generally were made just as crosses or other marks have been and are made by illiterates. The crosses of illiterates are not usually attested by the crosses of illiterate witnesses. It is a peculiarity of these old Chinese documents that the witnesses also placed their fingermarks. It is not with- out interest to find the writer of the obituary of Henry in *The Times* of 21st February, 1931, stating: " For centuries finger-prints have been regarded as incontro- vertible signatures to documents of value."

Laufer cites Kia Kung-yen, a writer of the T'ang period, as noting an ancient practice of notching wooden tallies in the execution of contracts. That Chinese writer observes that " The significance of these notches is the same as that of the finger prints (hua chi) of the present time."[7]   Laufer states this Chinaman so wrote about A.D. 650.   Contracts were then inscribed upon wooden blocks.   Rag paper, as Laufer explains, had not then been invented by the Chinese.   Laufer records his opinion that fingerprints, as inferred from the reference to them by the Chinese writer, were utilized during the T'ang dynasty and were so employed for the express purpose of establishing the identity of the persons making the fingerprints and, I add, thus obliging themselves contractually.   We may assume that the use of fingerprints in this way did not begin with the T'ang era, and that the origin of this use is lost in the mists of very early times.

We are mostly indebted to French writers of last century for translating original works in Arabic or Persian.   It is through their translations, sometimes rendered in English, that so much is known about Ancient China in reference to fingerprints.

Clearer light on our subject seems to be gained from the observations of Soleiman,[8] an Arabian merchant who travelled in China about A.D. 851.   Trade then between Arabia and China was very flourishing.   This merchant seems, from the notes he made, to have been a very accurate observer.   His journeys were recounted anonymously.

From a French translation[9] by Joseph Toussaint Reinaud (1795-1867), Oriental scholar, of an anonymous work on Travel in India and China by Arabs and Persians in the ninth century, covering the account of Soleiman's travels, I cite first the following passage as rendered in English by Laufer in his 1912 *Smithsonian* article.   It is as follows:—

> The Chinese respect justice in their transactions and in judicial proceedings.   When anybody lends a sum of money to another, he writes a bill to this

effect. The debtor, on his part, drafts a bill and marks it with two of his fingers united, the middle finger and the index. The two bills are joined together and folded, some characters being written on the spot separating them; then, they are unfolded and the lender receives the bill by which the borrower acknowledges his debt.[10]

I have submitted Reinaud's rendering of the Arabic to Dr. A. S. Tritton, Reader in Arabic, London University School of Oriental Studies. Reinaud appends a copy of the Arabic to his translation. There is no copy of the original Arabic in this country. Paris has possessed such a copy since 1673. It is now housed in La Bibliothèque Nationale. Dr. Tritton is of opinion that, while Reinaud's version is substantially correct and good in comparison with the Arabic as found in Reinaud's work, some of his renderings cannot be supported by the Arabic text.

I doubt if Laufer fully understood what Reinaud here translated. I may not do justice to the remainder of Reinaud's translation from which Laufer made this excerpt. It has to be kept in view, as Dr. Tritton has guardedly informed me, that Reinaud, as well as other writers, including myself, may have read into the Arabic text or the translations of it what is not literally found in the text or translations but ought to be rightly implied. Reinaud's translation is, however, most interesting, and read, with reference to his " Note (91)," it seems clear what this highly observant merchant saw in China about this matter.

According to Reinaud's version, and freely translating, Soleiman proceeds—

If later, the borrower denies his obligation, they (presumably, he means, I think, the judges) say to him: " Produce the document you got from the lender." (This may refer, I suggest, to a release or discharge.) Should he pretend that he has none, and deny that he ever wrote any voucher accompanied with his signature and his mark and (after, as I may say, an Irish manner) assert that in any event the document has disappeared, he is then challenged: " Put in writing that you have no concern with the lender's claim "; and at the same time he is warned (again, presumably, by the Court) that " If your creditor can prove you to be a liar, you will get twenty blows of the bastinado on your back and be subject to a fine nearly equal to 2000 dinars."[11] Twenty blows can kill a man. Nobody in China ever makes this written declaration from fear of losing both life and fortune. We have never seen anyone who would agree to make such a written statement. The Chinese in all their relations comply with the law : no one is dispossessed of his right; they have no resort to witnesses or oaths.

Reinaud, in his " Note (91)," states that the Arab text is obscure. According to an old Chinese authority, which he cites in that Note, private agreements in ancient China were executed in duplicate upon the same tablet, or, later, paper. Then the block or sheet of paper was divided. Hence, may be, I suggest, the origin of the parchment indenture or bilateral deed as known in early English law. It was split down the indent or tooth-marked centre. With this explanation of Reinaud, the observations of the Arabian merchant can be better understood. The documents, under the hands of the borrower and lender respectively, were written on the same sheet of paper with the borrower's two-fingered mark, as stated, placed upon his writ and across the indent. Then the sheet was split. The lender retained the borrower's acknowledgment, and had thus a double security in (1) the fingermarks upon it and (2) its exactly fitting the part he delivered to the borrower, narrating the terms of the loan.

It is not, therefore, surprising that in those early periods dishonest debtors in China refused to comply with the challenge of their creditors to put in writing their denial of indebtedness. With the finger-marked paper of a debtor in their hands, creditors had an irrefutable proof in its comparison with the finger-impressions of the debtor.

M. George Sarton, the Belgian Orientalist, in his " Introduction to the Origin of History," citing this account of the merchant Arab, merely says : " Sulaiman records the use of finger prints by the Chinese," adding in a note on the authority of Laufer: " The Chinese had been using finger impressions for the purpose of identification at least since the beginning of the T'ang dynasty."[12] M. Sarton cites Laufer's 1912 *Smithsonian* Article in proof of this. Laufer there cites Sulaiman, as I have said. He did not there refer to Stein's " Ancient Khotan." In fact, it was Laufer's article of 1912 that led me to look at his authorities for myself as found in French translations from Arabic or Persian.

Coming to the fourteenth century, there is the notable Persian historical work of Rashid (1247-1318), written about A.D. 1303. Rashid (Fadl Allah or Fazl-Ullah prefixed and Ed-din or Ud-din suffixed) was a Wazir of the Persian empire, noted for his knowledge, experience and integrity.[13] His " Cyclopaedic History " is of great authority in the East. Laufer cited in his 1917 *Science* article a passage from Rashid's work as rendered in English by Colonel Sir Henry Yule (1820-89), a famous Scot, in his " Cathay " and from the revised edition of that book published in 1914.[14] The passage is the same as it appears in the first edition published by Yule in 1866. I do not quote the whole passage. I omit the reference it makes to ambassadors and foreign merchants arriving in Persia and to orders in Council and passports and the verification of acts of Council by the " finger signatures " of those present at Council boards. The particular part of the passage to which I attach importance is as follows : —

> It is usual in Cathay, when any contract is entered into, for the outline of the fingers of the parties to be traced upon the document. For experience shows that no two individuals have fingers precisely alike. The hand of the contracting party is set upon the back of the paper containing the deed, and lines are then traced round his fingers up to the knuckles, in order that if ever one of them should deny his obligation this tracing may be compared with his fingers and he may thus be convicted.[15]

I have had Yule's rendering of the whole passage checked for me with the Persian as found in the E. W. Gibb Memorial Series, edited by M. E. Blochet and published in 1911.[16] No original copy of Rashid's work is in Britain. So far as the part I cite is concerned, Mr. N. C. Sainsbury, M.A., one of the Assistant Keepers of Oriental Printed Books and MSS. in the British Museum, finds that it is substantially correct, subject to the deletion of the words " up to the knuckles," and to the rendering of " fingers " as " finger-divisions " or " finger-joints."[17] Yule states that he based his translation on the French rendering made by Heinrich Julius Klaproth (1783-1835) in an article in *Nouveau Journal Asiatique* of 1833.[18]

I suggest that there must have been some misunderstanding, however, on the part of Rashid as to what the Chinese practice really was. Rashid got, Yule records, his information from a Mongol Prince, an envoy of the Great Khan to the Persian Court and after he had become Prime Minister. He was a man of exceptionally brilliant attainments and of untiring energy, writing his famous " History " at lightning speed amidst many other occupations. His reference to finger divisions or jointures is not happy. I cannot find that impressions of the fingers, as Rashid indicates, were traced or placed upon the backs of documents. The observations of Sulaiman, the Arab merchant, appear to have been more accurate. Professor Yetts, London, whom I have consulted, agrees that what Rashid was explaining was probably the " split " or indented contract mentioned by Sulaiman. The idea of tracings being made round the fingers does not seem a feasible method of achieving identification. I cannot find any other reference to a method so described. No extant document, so far as I know, exemplifies it.

The most striking fact is, however, that Rashid, who was a physician by profession, passing much of his life in that capacity at the Court of various Persian Khans, and, indeed, rising, it is related, to his high position on account of his medical skill, should have recorded in his " History " that " experience shows that no two individuals have fingers precisely alike." The passage from Rashid appears to me to be the earliest known recorded recognition anywhere of this fact. I do not recall in relation to this matter any writer who has already drawn attention to the medical side of Rashid. It is natural to assume that Rashid would not record this statement made to him on Chinese authority without looking at his own hands and fingers and so satisfying himself of its truth. Laufer well remarks that

" it is striking that we do not find in any author a clear description of it (fingerprint system) and its application. The physicians, in their exposition of the anatomy of the human body, do not allude to it, and it is certain that it was not anatomical or

o

medical studies which called it into existence. It formed part of the domain of folk lore, but not of scholarly erudition."[19]

Its significance lies in the idea of permanency or persistency in fingermark lineations being obviously implied. Outline tracings of finger-joints could never give conclusive identity tests.

M. Henri Cordier, of Paris, French Orientalist, who revised Yule's "Collection of Mediæval Notices of China" published in 1914, states that the passage in question "is a peremptory proof of the antiquity of the use of finger prints by the Chinese."[20] Laufer in his 1917 *Science* article called attention to this decisive opinion of M. Cordier. It seems indisputable that the French savant is right. "Most certainly," concluded Laufer in that 1917 *Science* article, "the idea underlying Chinese finger-prints was principally that of identification, as expressly stated by Rashid-eddin and all Chinese informants."

On all matters of Chinese interest, Giles (Herbert Allen) is a distinguished authority. His practical acquaintance with China and her language was exceptional. His various works on Chinese topics, including his Dictionaries, are classics. Many of these were published in China; some before he became Cambridge University Professor of Chinese.

In his *Adversaria Sinica*, No. 6, p. 183, published at Shanghai in 1908, dealing with Phrenology, Physiognomy, and Palmistry, Giles states—

> In conclusion it should always be remembered that the wonderful system of identification by . . .[21] finger-prints, which is forcing the modern burglar to carry on his trade with gloved hands, was borrowed straight from China, where it has been in vogue for many centuries. Title-deeds, and other legal instruments, are still often found to bear, in addition to signatures, the finger-prints of

the parties concerned; sometimes, indeed, the imprint of the whole hand.[22]

Giles appears to make his contention for the use in ancient China of fingerprints for criminal identification absolutely indisputable by the narration of the story with which he ends in his *Adversaria* the notes in question.

Here it is—

> In a small volume of the 12th Century, entitled . . . Omissions from History, we read that a favourite concubine of the Emperor . . . Ming Huang (A.D. 713-756), "a slave to beauty," having several times dreamed that she was invited by some man to take wine with him on the sly, spoke about it to the Emperor. "This is the work of a magician," said His Majesty; "next time you go, take care to leave behind you some record." That very night she had the same dream; and accordingly she seized the opportunity of putting her hand on an ink slab and then pressing it on a screen. When she awaked, she described what had happened; and, on a secret examination being made, the imprint of her hand was actually found in the Dawn-in-the-East Pavilion outside the Palace. The magician, however, was nowhere to be seen.

From the general drift of Laufer's *Smithsonian* article, 1912, he would apparently treat this anecdote as an illustration rather of palmar impressions than of finger-impressions. That would surely, however, include fingertips and bulbs. Apart from fingertips, American Police in different parts of the United States, as I understand, now frequently rely upon palmar impressions, when they are available, in the restricted sense of without the fingers, just in the same way as they do with fingerprints.[23] Registers of both are kept.

Let it be, however, as Laufer seems to suggest. The idea of the hand, or of some part of it, seems encrusted in the tale of Giles as likely to be of use for criminal identification. It is, of course, unfortunate, that the sorcerer was never discovered. Apparently, he was not one who had been previously found out and convicted as a misdemeanant. The Emperor cannot have installed in his palace any register, black or white, of the fingermarks of his entourage. Such a register would have been invaluable in the destruction of intrigues!

Laufer supplies a rather lovely, though fanciful, story about this favourite of Ming Huang, giving her name as Yang Kuei-fei. It is even more pointedly relevant to this Chapter than the anecdote taken from Giles's *Adversaria*. It gives her a lasting niche in fingerprint history. It is said, as mentioned by Laufer in a footnote to his *Smithsonian* paper,[24] that the Honourable Lady Yang[25] once touched, with her delicate rouge-tipped fingers, some peony petals. In the following year, and after the shrub had been transplanted, the red traces of her fingertips were seen on the opening blooms!

From Chinese sources, Dr. Heindl cites an instance in the twelfth century A.D. of two murderesses being compelled to have their fingers blackened and impressions taken of them. I suppose this would be done with a view to their conviction. Dr. Heindl does not go so far as to say that he finds criminal fingerprint black-lists were in operation in the twelfth century.[26]

What a pity Herschel did not submit " The Origin of Finger-Prints " to some expert in the historical literature of the East before he published that brochure in 1917! Placed in possession of the ancient history of fingerprints, he would still have been able to say, with Faulds, that he had been instrumental in introducing fingerprints as an aid to modern criminal investigation.

With regard to the modern history of China, apart from the practice as stated by Meadows in his article in the China Branch of the Royal Asiatic Society's Transactions of 1847 and fully dealt with by me in Chapter XIV, the position is far from clear. Laufer's article[27] brought to my notice the article of Meadows and the

Chinese land contract of 1839 with the thumbprint upon
it of Mrs. Ch'ên. He notes that in recent times the
fingerprints of foundlings are taken on their reception
into any of the asylums established all over China and
also of illiterates in their execution of contracts.[28]
Thanks to Galton's reference I culled from *Science*[29] of
1886, a statement by Mr. Joseph F. James, writing from
Miami University upon " Thumb Marks," as follows:—

> The Chinese take advantage of all this to identify
> their important criminals, at least in some parts of
> the Empire. We photograph their faces: they take
> impressions from their thumbs. These are stored away
> and if the delinquents should ever again fall into the
> hands of the police, at once afford the means of com-
> parison.

This certainly suggests in the infant stage the existence
of a C.I.D. It is thought, however, that the passage
goes too far. I refer elsewhere to the introduction in
1913 by Vucetich to China of his system of fingerprint
registration. Galton called attention to this contribution
of Mr. James as early as 1888 (see Chapter XIII). Yet
in 1890 Galton regarded the association of the Chinese
with fingerprints " as proof of identity " as " an
egregious error "! (see Chapter XII).

Laufer, who travelled widely in China and Tibet, and
is reputed " one of the foremost authorities on the
art and antiquities of China," with " unrivalled knowledge " of its antiquities,[30] recorded his opinion that
" crime had never assumed vast proportions in China,
that detection and capture were comparatively easy, and
that anything like a criminal science was not required
for a patriarchal organization of government."[31]

It does not appear, however, that Laufer was right in
expressing this view in 1912, repeated in 1917, that the
process of fingerprint identification was not applied by
the Chinese in ancient times for the detection of

criminals. While not suggesting that the Chinese had then anything like our present-day systems of registration and classification, there appears, as we have seen, to be good authority for affirming that the Chinese of fairly-remote times did track criminals by their fingerprints, i.e., their " chance impressions " left behind them on the scenes of their misdeeds.

In stating that our fingerprint system " was borrowed straight from China," Giles, in his sinological enthusiasm, went too far. Only very indirectly could such a proposition be regarded as true. Further, his suggestion that the system was in vogue in China in recent centuries is not strictly accurate. It never was seen in China at any time upon the scale and to the extent now exemplified all over the world, including Japan. Upon Japan's indebtedness to China in so many ways, Giles, in his writings, likes to expatiate.

Much, certainly, is to be said for the influence of Eastern ways and customs, among which Faulds and Herschel respectively found themselves, in directing their attention independently to the marvellous nature of our fingertips. But, allowing for all this environment, we should never have had our modern system of criminal identification without the observations of these men as original investigators, Faulds having the greater title to distinction as a scientific observer and worker. All fingerprint writers concede that Faulds and Herschel were unaware prior to 1880 of the ancient literature of China on the subject of fingerprints. Galton, despite his perusal in 1888 of *Science* for 1886, or, in any event, incredulous, was also unaware in his criticism of the position of the Chinese in that branch of knowledge. It is difficult to understand such careless assumption of knowledge on the part of so great a scientist.

Galton scouted the very idea of the Chinese having

ever known of the use of fingerprints in criminal detection, and even doubted the existence of any knowledge on their part of finger-characteristics. On this latter point, he recanted. He could discern no identification purpose or value in the use made by the Chinese of their finger-impressions as signatures to deeds. These finger-impressions Sir Arthur Keith terms " unmistakable signatures " :[32] others have called them " unforgeable." But to Galton they were no more than " daubs " or " smudges." What, if this had been true, was the good of the Chinese resorting to this method in the execution of their contracts, he never seems to have considered. How far wrong he went in the particular instance he cited for his contention, adverse to the Chinese, in his " Finger Prints " book has been shown in Chapter XIV.[33]

Herschel, with the support of Galton's unwarranted views, in time went the ridiculous length of stating, or, at least, of implying, in his surprising innocence, that it was through him that the Chinese and the Japanese gained their knowledge of fingerprints ! Temptation to take to himself the credit of first discovery was certainly great. Faulds himself succumbed to it. In his " Guide to Finger-Print Identification," published in 1905, departing from his original thought, Faulds expressed his scepticism about fingerprint identification being known to the Chinese of distant periods.[34]

It is impossible to tell how Galton would have reacted to the Chinese historical facts and legends recounted in this Chapter. The legends must have had some foundation in fact. Galton would be about 77 years of age when Giles's *Adversaria Sinica*, No. 6, was published. Possibly it never came under his notice. He never seems to have made inquiries of Chinese *literati* or of other Orientalists.

It really does not matter whether Faulds or Herschel

had any glimmering of how fingerprints in the sphere of identification stood anciently in the East, or what was the state of their knowledge as to the use there in their own time of fingerprints for the purpose of identification other than criminal. Consciously or not, they evolved out of their Eastern environment their respective ideas and conceptions and applied these to the institution of fingerprint criminal registers and to the tracing of criminals. No one would withhold the credit due to them on this ground for developments that were, in truth, original.

The very fact that finger or thumb tip marks are acknowledged to have been used in ancient times all over the East as signatures to deeds and otherwise might have suggested to Europeans that ancient Orientals must have perceived that there was something distinctive and enduring in all finger and thumb patterns for identification purposes, so accounting for their widespread use in the East. Reasons for variations in such marks and their permanence might not have been apparent. The East accepted the facts as it found them.

Laufer's 1912 *Smithsonian* article is a most valuable contribution to fingerprint history. It is very remarkable, however, for a singular omission. In a paper so erudite and so seemingly exhaustive, no notice of Faulds is taken. How Faulds could be passed over in any authoritative history of the subject is puzzling. I can only surmise that Laufer read the publications of Galton and Henry and, perhaps, the letters of Herschel in *Nature* of 1880 and 1894 and that he had probably read the " Review " by Galton in *Nature* of 1905 of the " Guide to Finger-Print Identification," published by Faulds in September of that year. Perusing that " Review " and accepting the *ipse dixit* of Galton, Laufer might easily assume that anything Faulds had found out or written on the subject was of no value.

216

Perhaps he had not then consulted Yule's "Cathay" in the edition revised by Professor Cordier and published in 1907, and so missed the Professor's interesting "Note (2)," in which Faulds and Herschel were particularly noticed: Faulds with credit; not so, Herschel.[35] Certainly, Laufer, in his article, was most complimentary to Galton, Henry and Herschel. His article, however, was published five years before the announcement in *Nature* of 1917, by Herschel, of his admission that Faulds, *pace* Galton, had made a discovery beyond his "conception."[36]

NOTES.

[1] See Chap. IV; but see "Guide," *supra*, p. 29.

[2] See anonymous contribution upon the Palestinian excavations of Dr. William F. Bade in *The Scientific American*, 1935, Vol. 152, p. 4. Referred to in Note 3 to Chap. IV.

[3] See Laufer's 1912 *Smithsonian* article, *supra*, and his Plate 4. They may have had also, per Laufer, a magical or spiritual meaning.

[4] Vol. 1. 1907. London. Oxford University Press.

[5] Appendix A, p. 527. See Plate CXV, Vol. II. Dr. Lionel Giles states that some 7000 documents were recovered by Sir Aurel Stein from the great hoard in Tunhuang : 380 bore dates : 50 were legal in character. See "Dated Chinese Manuscripts in the Stein Collection" : *Bulletin of The School of Oriental Studies* (Univ. of London). 1935. Vol. VII, p. 1. London. Luzac & Co.

[6] See *Bulletin of The School of Oriental Studies, supra*, 1937. Vol. IX, Part I, p. 21. Dr. Giles reproduces two of the three loan contracts in Plate I as frontispiece to his third paper. 1937. Vol. IX. Fingermarks are there shown. It is noteworthy that Dr. Heindl in his "Daktyloskopie," p. 20, states that "Even in relation to crime the Chinese of this period seem already to have taken dactylography as within the scope of their deliberations."

[7] See Laufer's 1912 *Smithsonian* article, *supra*, p. 643.

[8] Sometimes rendered as Salomon, Soleyman, Solomon, Sulaiman, Suleiman, &c.

[9] "Relation des Voyages faits par les Arabes et les Persanes dans le IXe siècle," Vol. I, p. 42. 1845. Paris.

[10] See Laufer's 1912 *Smithsonian* article, *supra*, p. 643.

[11] An Arab gold coin of the value of twelve shillings as estimated by Etienne Marc Quatremère (1782-1857), a distinguished Orientalist.

[12] Vol. I, 571. 1927. Baltimore. Williams & Wilkins Co.

[13] Yule in his "Cathay," *supra*, Vol. III, 108, suggests that Rashid's character cannot have been so high as is claimed for him by some writers, notably Quatremère. He denounced, Yule observes, too

many State officials during his Wazirate. In the end he met a cruel death. It was from Quatremère's writings that I found more detailed reference to Rashid's life as a physician. Yule also refers to this. See Quatremèré's " Mémoire " of the life and works of Rashid, p. viii, prefixed to his translation of Rashid's " History of the Mongols." 1936. Paris. Royal Press.

[14] See " Cathay," *supra*, Vol. III, 123. The long Note (2) by M. Cordier on this passage, commencing, as it does, by a reference to Faulds and his letter to *Nature* of 28th October, 1880, is extremely interesting. Laufer quoted part of it in his 1917 *Science* article. Yule considers Rashid used Mahomedan names for Chinese titles.

[15] This passage as translated into French by Abraham C. D'Ohsson, Tome II, p. 637, published at Amsterdam in 1852 by Muller, does not substantially vary from that of Yule in English. For " outline," contour is used and for " fingers " " finger divisions " or " finger joints." The phrase " des traits a l'endroit des jointures de ces doigts " is employed : D'Ohsson adds " afin si jamais il niait son obligation, on put comparer ses doigts avec les contours et le convaincre par cette preuve." Klaproth in his translation uses the expression " placer l'impression " of the fingers. This seems to convey the right meaning whether put on the front or back of a deed.

[16] The title of Rashid's work is given here as " Djami El-Tevarikh (Histoire Générale du Monde) par Fadl Allah Rashid Ed-din." 1911. London. Luzac & Co. M. Blochet's notes do not deal with the subject.

[17] Mr. Sainsbury informed me that the statement as to the meaning of " finger-signature " in the prior paragraph does not appear in the original. It seems to have been inadvertently interpolated by Yule in place of his making a note about it.

[18] Tome XI, 357. Paris.

[19] See Laufer's 1912 *Smithsonian* article, *supra*, p. 641.

[20] Yule published his first edition in 1866 under the title of " Cathay and the Way Thither."

[21] The . . . indicate my omission of Chinese ideographs as unnecessary to be reproduced. So, likewise in the tale quoted later from Giles.

[22] See Chap. XIV and Plate III for an illustration of a Chinese land contract.

[23] See the American mail stage murder case of *Kuhl*, noted in Chap. XXX. Laufer assures us that thumbprints preceded the use of palmar impressions.

[24] See p. 646 of Report.

[25] I am indebted to Mr. Basil Gray, B.A., Assistant Keeper, British Museum, for this English rendering of her Chinese name. She was the ruin of the Emperor. She was strangled at the instigation of rebel soldiers. Dr. Laurence Binyon referred me to Giles's " Chinese Literature," 1901, pp. 168 *et seq.* The reader may also consult Giles's " Chinese Biographical Dictionary."

[26] See " Daktyloskopie," *supra*, p. 19. Probably all the instances given by Giles, Heindl, and Laufer are extracted from " P'ei wên yün fu," an encyclopædic Chinese work, cited by Laufer at p. 646 of his 1912 *Smithsonian* article.

[27] See Laufer's 1912 *Smithsonian* article, *supra*, p. 634.

[28] *Ibid.*, *supra*, p. 638.

[29] 1886. Vol. VIII, p. 212.

[30] See his obituary notice in *Nature*, Vol. 134, under date, 13th October, 1934. I surmise it was not written by Giles. He did not agree with the view that Laufer's knowledge of the Chinese language was unrivalled.

[31] See Laufer's 1912 *Smithsonian* article, *supra*, p. 642. See Chap. XXI.

[32] "The Human Body," p. 199. 1912. London. Williams & Norgate.

[33] In his letter to *Science*, 1886, Vol. VIII, p. 166, Walter B. Hough states : " Chinese sailors shipping on junks are made to sign with five fingers in order to get a more certain identification." I was recently informed by a retired captain of the mercantile marine service that Chinese crews in British ships sailing in Eastern seas have cards with their thumbmarks. See Chap. XII from which it will be seen that Galton was aware in 1888 of Mr. Hough's letter.

[34] See " Guide," *supra*, pp. 31 *et seq.* : " Dactylography," *supra*, p. 11.

[35] Laufer did quote afterwards from this " Note " of Professor Cordier in his 1917 *Science* article over the pretentious " discovery " claim made by Herschel in " The Origin of Finger-Printing." Laufer probably never noticed Herschel's " Remarks " in *Nature* of January, 1917, before his article to *Science* was published in the following May.

[36] Laufer in his 1912 *Smithsonian* article deals with finger-tip painting by the Chinese. I have deemed this subject irrelevant to the theme of my book. I hope in another place to deal with the subject and to give illustrations of finger-tip sketches by Chinese artists. It may, perhaps, be noted as singular that I have found no evidence of these artists at any time impressing their paintings or sketches, originals or copies, with their thumbprints.

XXX

EVIDENTIAL ADMISSIBILITY AND VALUE[1] OF FINGERPRINTS

THERE was never any serious doubt about the admissibility of fingerprint evidence from the time its scientific importance, as based upon the life-long character of fingertip-lineations and their absolute variance in every person, was realized. It is not essentially different from evidence of uncovered footprints, except that its identity value is very much higher. Boot or shoe prints are of much less value. Photographs, properly proved, taken by a concealed trap camera with silent automatic action of a burglar while he is moving about the premises he is burgling, it is thought, would not be rejected by any court. The inference would clearly be that he had been on the premises and had set the camera in motion by touching some secret spring. Probably, either in conjunction with such a device or independently of it, a silent recorder of the conversations of criminals has also been or may be installed in mercantile or other establishments. By means of invisible-ray traps and other devices the movements and speech of malefactors might be proved. No actual cases of the kind so far have occurred. The admissibility of evidence of the identity of criminals gained by such means could not be in doubt. But, while photographic prints or slides and recorded voices are artificial, the evidence of finger-impressions is the natural inference of presence at some particular spot of the maker. The acceptance by judges and juries of evidence of identity obtained by any means, natural or artificial, must simply depend upon adequate, satisfactory proof. Juries in England, in the early stages of fingerprint identification, had fewer qualms in its acceptance than some eminent judges.[2] Now, its value may be said to be definitely appreciated by everyone.

The earliest reference to fingerprints in any legal report or legislative enactment appears to be that contained in the Act of 1899 amending the Indian Evidence Act, 1872, passed by the Government of India. Section 45 of the Act of 1872 runs as follows:—

> When the Court has to form an opinion upon a point of foreign law, or of science or art, or as to the identity of hand writing or finger impressions, the opinions upon that point of persons specially

skilled in such foreign law, science or art, hand writing or finger impressions are relevant facts.

Such persons are called experts.[3]

I believe that the case of Kangali Charan narrated in Chapter XVII was largely instrumental for this amendment. While no one would cite the opinion of the native trial judge in that case as of any legal assistance in other causes, it will always remain as the record of extremely curious dialectics on the part of a judge with assessors obviously clear in their duty of convicting an accused of theft, while on the same evidence acquitting him of the murder that the accused was charged with committing at the same time as the theft. I should say they were " compelled " to acquit because the native Government Prosecutor withdrew the murder charge. Charan was formally acquitted of the murder charge and must be held as innocent of the murder. Fortunately, the opinions of the trial judge, of his native assessors, and of the High Court at Calcutta in a futile appeal by the accused against his conviction for theft are now permanently to be found in a British Law Journal.[4]

The significance of finger-impressions being found on articles in or about the place where a crime has been committed is that this is tantamount to an admission by the criminal, and, in any event, to proof, that he was actually there and did commit the crime with which he is charged. If such finger-impressions are competently proved, the question of guilt is demonstrated and settled against the accused. "All proof," as Lord Justice-General Clyde said in delivering the leading opinion in the Scottish case of *Hamilton* v. *H.M. Advocate*[5] in 1933,

> depends at bottom on presumption; even the evidence of two credible and uncontradicted witnesses, who speak to the same occurrence, is *probatio probata*,

221

not because it is impossible that they should both be mistaken, but because of the high presumption that what two credible witnesses say happened in their presence did actually happen.

In England it was decided in November, 1909, by the Criminal Appeal Court, consisting of Lord Chief Justice Alverstone and Justices Darling and Bucknill, in the case of *Castleton*, that the court or a jury might accept evidence of fingerprints as the sole ground of identification.[6]

Herbert Castleton had been sentenced to three years' penal servitude by a Yorkshire Court of Quarter Sessions. The only evidence against him was that of fingerprints on a candle left behind him in the burgled premises. He did not give evidence on his own behalf. No evidence at all was led for him. It was suggested for him, however, in the appeal, that, as an associate of thieves, the fingerprints might have been put on the candle by Castleton, and then used by somebody else. The court, however, held that suggestion was disposed of by the jury's deciding the case against him on the evidence before them.

Mr. Justice Darling is reported as asking counsel for the prisoner: "Can the prisoner find anybody whose fingerprints are exactly like his?" It is assumed the learned judge was aware, from his knowledge of the subject, that the answer to his query was negative. It is, of course, no part of an accused's duty to prove his innocence affirmatively. He could not be expected to search the whole world for the desired duplicate; and, even if he had found someone, e.g., in Alaska, who could not possibly have been at the time in the vicinity of the burgled premises, the duplicate might not have availed him. But, if a prisoner is proved by eye-witnesses, fingerprints, or other competent evidence to have been on the scene of a crime at the relevant time, the burden is then upon him to explain his presence consistent with innocence. If he offers no evidence in explanation, the result is damning. Mr. Justice Darling's query in the appeal was, therefore, pertinent. The report of the appeal does not narrate the number of points of agreement between the candle imprints and those taken of the prisoner's fingers on arrest.[7]

The Supreme Court of Victoria in April, 1912, held (Madden, C.J., dissenting) in *Rex* v. *Parker*[8] that the identity between the fingerprint of an accused and that found upon an article might be sufficient evidence to justify a jury in finding that the fingerprint on the article was made by the accused. *Castleton's* case was cited with *The Journal of Criminal Law and Criminology* for March, 1911, p. 848, in which the United States case of *People* v. *Jennings*, afterwards referred to, was noted. The accused, Edward Parker, had broken into premises in Melbourne and removed the contents of a safe, to the value of £500. A member of the warehouse firm had locked up the premises early on a Saturday, intending to go back the same afternoon, and had procured two bottles of stone ginger beer against that return. He did not go back till the Monday. He had left the bottles unopened on the office table. Returning on the Monday, he discovered the burglary, and saw one of the bottles standing open on the floor a few feet from the table. He left this bottle untouched until detectives arrived. Parker was arrested on suspicion, and his fingerprints were taken. The bottle bore the impression of his left middle finger. It showed also a scar that appeared on that finger. The detectives deponed that, apart from the scar, the prisoner's finger must have impressed the bottle. Fingerprints of the warehouse partner, and of the boy who brought the bottles to the office, were put in evidence. The detectives stated there was no similarity between them and that on the bottle. The jury convicted the prisoner. He appealed from the Court of General Sessions at Melbourne to the Supreme Court of Victoria.

Madden, C.J., in dissenting, rightly characterized the case of *Castleton* as an unsatisfactory judgment from its want of reasoned assistance. It was the only English case cited against the prisoner. The Chief Justice said he could take no notice of Mr. Justice Darling's question as it was in his opinion, " not seriously meant." He thought that the fingerprint evidence was insufficient to convict Parker. Hodges and Cussen, JJ., disagreeing with the Chief Justice, held the evidence sufficient. Hodges, J., said he knew of no rule of law that required the evidence to be corroborated by any other class of evidence. Cussen, J., expressed the view that mathematical demonstrations were not called for in such cases. All that is necessary is that the jury should have no reasonable doubt. Experts are " simply convenient helpers of the Court." Cussen, J., also added:

> It now seems that this much is established—that there is a very high degree of probability that a fingerprint corresponding with that of the prisoner was made by his finger, and evidence of this kind has the additional advantage that it is made by something that is permanently attached to the prisoner, generally speaking, at all events.

The High Court of Australia unanimously refused special leave to the prisoner to appeal to that tribunal. In commenting upon this Victorian case, an anonymous writer on " The Conclusiveness of Finger Print Evidence," in *The Law Times* of 14th October, 1933, vol. 176, p. 287, observed that a fingerprint " is in reality an unforgeable signature."[9]

The leading decision in the United States of America on the admissibility of fingerprint evidence was given in 1911 in the State of Illinois. It is the case of *People* v. *Jennings*.[10] Thomas Jennings, an ex-convict negro, was convicted of murder in 1910. He shot his victim in Chicago. Strong circumstantial evidence of identification by witnesses, apart from fingerprint evidence, was adduced to the jury. Experts spoke to photographs of fingerprints found on a newly-painted porch-railing of the victim's home, and to their comparison with enlarged fingerprints of the accused. Thirty-three points of identity were demonstrated. The accused objected to the reception of fingerprint evidence as incompetent at common law. No Statute authorized it. The objection was repelled. The fingerprint evidence clinched the guilt of the prisoner. The County Court conviction was upheld by the Supreme Court of Illinois. The English case of *Castleton* was cited by Carter, C.J., in his lucid and interesting leading opinion. Other cases in the States followed.

In a case in 1918 of *State* v. *Kuhl et al*,[11] the admissibility of palmprints was raised in an appeal by B. E. Kuhl, convicted of the murder of Fred M. Searcey, a Government mail-stage driver, in Elko County, Nevada, and mainly on the evidence of experts as to the impression of part of his bloody left palm found on an envelope recovered from one of the rifled mailbags. Citing *Castleton*, *Jennings*, and other authorities, and after an elaborate and almost completely exhaustive review of all known literature printed in English on the subject of finger and palmprints, not excluding Faulds, and including " Mark Twain," " the beloved author," the Nevada Appeal Court came easily to the conclusion that palmprints were on the same plane as fingerprints for evidential purposes,

> evolving the indisputable conclusion that there is but one physiological basis underlying this method of identification ; that the phenomenon by which identity is thus established exists, not only on the bulbs of the finger tips, but is continuous and co-existing on all parts and

P 225

in all sections and sub-divisions of the palmar surface of the human hand.

So, this Court held—

> The evidence of these experts as to the identity of the palm-print of the defendant with that found upon the blood-smeared envelope taken from the rifled mail sack was a proper subject for the consideration of the Jury. The weight to be given to this testimony was for the Jury to determine; (adding) whether they (experts) give their best judgment or belief or testify positively as to their conclusion, the fact remains that it is for the Jury to determine the weight to be given to their testimony.

The Supreme Court of Nevada in this case also rejected various objections to the use of projectoscopes or other apparatus used to illustrate expert evidence.

The only fault to be found with the review of fingerprint literature in the Nevada case, which would hardly find any place in the opinions of British judges, is that M'Carran, C.J., does not seem to have gone to the root, at least, the modern root, of the discovery of criminals by this finger or palmprint method. No one would find or suspect out of all the mass of writers cited, including Faulds himself, that Faulds was the very man who had made possible the discovery of this mailbag robbery miscreant.

The Scottish case in 1933 of *Hamilton*[12] can now be noticed with more detail.

Lord Justice-General Clyde, holding the competency of fingerprint evidence as implicitly established by the English judges in 1909 in *Castleton*, and as apparently not open to question in the Scottish Criminal Courts, proceeded to say—

> If it (fingerprint evidence) is believed, it constitutes real evidence of the presence of the accused at the scene of the crime in something the same way as a fragment

226

of clothing (left behind by the criminal) or his bootmark might be. . . . The value of finger-print evidence depends on the reliance which can be placed on the result of expert investigation and experience—in an immense number of cases examined over a very extended period of years—to the effect that identity is never found to exist between the skin ridges on two different persons' fingers. This is what leads the experts to claim infallibility for the finger-mark method. I deprecate the use of the word " infallibility " in this connexion at all. What the experts obviously mean is, not absolute, but practical infallibility—that is to say, a presumption of truth, the reliability of which may be accepted, not because it is irrebuttable in its own nature, but because long and extensive experience is shown to provide no instance in which it has ever been successfully rebutted. . . . Accordingly, the strength of the link provided by the finger-print depends on the degree of reliability which—on the evidence presented to them—the Jury thought should be attributed to the finger-print method as applied by the police and the experts in the present case. They evidently thought the presumptions in favour of its reliability so high as to warrant the circumstantial inference that the [accused] was the criminal, or one of the criminals, who broke into the shop.

There was nothing in the present case (i.e., *Hamilton's*), his Lordship observed, to support or, indeed, to suggest, any possibility of the fingermarks having been made on the surface of the bottle by the accused, or by anyone else, at any time other than that at which the crime was committed. Lord Sands, one of the other judges in the case, sounded a note of caution against any jury's being bound to accept fingerprint evidence, and expert evidence connected with it, in every case as conclusive. It is a question for the jury, said Lord Sands, in the particular case, and, in order to disturb their verdict, it would be necessary to conclude that it was not a view which a jury might reasonably have taken.

The facts of this Scottish case, as put by Lord Justice-

General Clyde, were that, between the closing of a shop in Glasgow on a Saturday night and its opening on Monday morning, the shop was broken into, a safe blown up, and some money abstracted. The accused was arrested very shortly after the shopbreaking was discovered, and his fingerprints were then taken. There was nothing else to connect him with the crime, except the fact of his living in the neighbourhood of the shop. The only evidence led with the object of his identification as the criminal or as one of the criminals, (such a crime generally involving two or more in its participation,) was a fingermark on a raspberry-wine bottle in the shop. That bottle had been left wrapped up in paper on the Saturday night. On the Monday morning it was found with the paper removed, the cork out, and part of the contents away. On the surface of the bottle there were certain fingermarks. One was so clear and distinct as to enable a photograph of it to be taken and then enlarged.

The identity of the fingerprint with that of the accused as taken on his arrest was proved by two New Scotland Yard experts. They deponed that they found sixteen recognized points of comparison, and that there was complete identity between the fingermark on the bottle and the print of one of the accused's fingers. Such an extent and degree of comparison, in their opinion, accordingly was more than sufficient to warrant the inference of identity. This method of identification, they deponed, had been widely followed in Britain and elsewhere for many years. No case of identity in the ridges of the skin of the fingers of two different persons had been discovered. The method of identification, the experts declared, had never once proved to be unreliable. The accused led no evidence. The jury found the accused guilty. His conviction was upheld by the Scottish Criminal Appeal Court. Faulds was right, it is thought, in insisting generally upon more intense comparison than eleven or twelve points of agreement as presented in the trial of the *Strattons* for murder in 1905.

The Scottish Court of Criminal Appeal was doubtless influenced in *Hamilton's* case by the citation of the English judgment. The opinion of Lord Justice-General Clyde is a reasoned and convincing argument for the acceptance of such evidence. The short, unreasoned, statement by the Lord Chief Justice in *Castleton's* case, that the court was "clearly of opinion that this application must be dismissed," gave no help. No very strenuous case seems to have been made for Castleton in the English appeal. It was otherwise in the Scottish case. The American cases and the Australian decision to which we have referred were not cited to the Scottish judges.

An alibi might in certain circumstances be conclusive against the acceptance of fingerprint evidence; but, generally, unless seemingly iron-cased in proof, the defence of an alibi is a dangerous line against fingerprint proofs. An unintelligent jury, of course, may be bluffed by spurious testimony of an alibi.

So far as known to the writer, there is no case on record of any conviction obtained by the use of finger-print evidence being set aside or of any prisoner being set free on account of the person convicted or imprisoned satisfying any court or Government of his innocence. Generally, persons so convicted make no protest against their condemnation. This is silent corroboration of the virtue of such evidence.

I am indebted to Mr. Frederick Kuhne, an American author, for calling my attention to the difference in the evidential weight of expert evidence on fingerprints over that on handwriting.[13] Many mistakes have been made in Britain, not to mention the United States and other countries, by experts, sometimes highly skilled, in handwriting. Handwriting can be successfully forged and falsely attributed to another by the forger. The fraud may not be detected if its exposure cannot be achieved otherwise than by comparison of the calligraphy of admittedly genuine letters or other documents with the letter or document challenged as spurious. Examination, chemical or other, may condemn false documents through the date or otherwise of the ink or paper used and some- times of the stamps employed.[14]

So, with marks by crosses or otherwise made by illiterates in the execution of deeds. These crosses may be counterfeited by dishonest persons. Witnesses may be procured to swear falsely that they saw the crosses made by the persons purporting to have executed con- tracts in this way. Parties again may sign by marks and afterwards deny their marks. Attesting witnesses may support their denial. In many countries from time immemorial documents have been authenticated by illiterates with their marks and such execution has been usually attested by one or more subscribing witnesses whose names, occupations and abodes have been generally recorded either after their signatures or in the *testimonia* of the deeds so executed. It may be that in many instances the early Chinese made imperfect marks or blobs with their fingertips or pads that showed no clear lineations and such marks or blobs would be, of course, of no use as means of identifying the individuals who made them. Authentication in all such cases would depend for reliable proof upon the credit of the testifying witnesses.

It is wholly otherwise with fingerprint signatures. No witnesses are essential. For convenience it is better to have them in rendering oral proof easy of a party's having attached his fingerprint. To leave evidence to be supplied as, say, in the case of a testament until after the death of the testator who had impressed his finger- mark in the presence of no witness, might be fatal.

While a fingermark cannot be fabricated, at least successfully, any person may be forced by duress or by cunning or other deceit to impress a deed with his fingerprint in the same way as he might be compelled or induced to apply his signature or mark or even his most exclusive seal. The discovery of, and relief from, all such crimes must be left to the common law of the country they infringe. It should always be kept in view that in forgery cases connected with cheques, blackmailing letters or other writings, latent fingerprints, when chemically developed, may lead to the identification of forgers. See " Forensic Chemistry and Scientific Criminal Investigation," 1935, p. 183, Third Edition by A. Lucas, O.B.E., F.I.C.

The identification of fingerprints is now so well recognized that controversy apart from their production, exhibition, and explanation by experts, cannot arise. Although evidence was given for the Crown and the defence in the trial of the Stratton Brothers in 1905 for murder,[15] fingerprint testimony was then in this country in its infancy and its absolute conclusiveness was not recognized. Moreover, fewer than sixteen points of identity, in that case, apparently, could only be obtained by comparison with an impression, found on the empty tray of a cashbox, with that of the finger-impression of one of the brothers. Certainly, that was a point for reflection as to its unsatisfactoriness in that particular case. Nowadays, it is no use putting forward the comparison of fingerprints unless they are demonstrably clear and can be carried as a rule in sequence at least to sixteen points of agreement. In these circumstances, as the American writer well observes: " The testimony of a finger-print expert is not subject to contradiction by another finger-print expert." In other words, given the assumption made, there can be, in any fingerprint case, no two opinions contradicting each other.[16]

Commenting on the fingerprint system in 1911, Faulds observed : —

> " It is essentially English and every accused person in the dock is as able as a judge, or counsel, or official witness, to test its validity." See " Finger Prints," *Scientific American Supplement*, 18th November, 1911, Vol. LXXII, p. 326.

In other than criminal cases, of course, there are many ways in which fingermarks may be available as evidence of identity. For example, dead bodies have been so identified. Numerous cases occurred in Argentina after Vucetich set up in 1891 his fingerprint bureau in La Plata. Unaware of these cases, writers to *The Times* in 1926 mentioned cases occurring long after Vucetich had been successful in such identification.[17] Instances are recorded in *The Times* of 28th June, 1926, through a letter written to the Editor by the late Professor Harvey Littlejohn, then Professor of Medical Jurisprudence in Edinburgh, and appearing in its issue of 25th June, 1926. One was stated as occurring in London in 1910, and the other in 1911 at Amritsar, in India. Professor Littlejohn thought his experience in 1926 was the first case of identification of an unknown man found dead. He suggested to the police in Edinburgh to have his fingerprint-impressions taken and sent to New Scotland Yard. By return of post came the information from London that the dead man, who had been discovered in a quarry, had been convicted in Edinburgh Sheriff Court of stealing hens. He had received fourteen days' imprisonment. New Scotland Yard, in addition to the recorded fingerprints, sent a photograph of the man, confirming his identity set up by the fingerprints. Faulds records the case of a Deal farrier found badly mutilated on the railway at Slough before 1912, and identified by the taking of his fingerprints and their comparison with prints at New Scotland Yard. The *Ruxton* case, specially dealt with in Chapter XXVIII, in regard to this last matter is highly illuminating. There, fingerprint-impressions taken from the dismembered left hand of the dead woman, Mary Rogerson, materially contributed to the conviction of the accused for the murder of her mistress, his wife, and inferentially of herself at the same time. The derm print impressions from her dismembered right hand, as explained in that Chapter, did not come before the jury.

Recall how Faulds in his *Nature* Letter of 1880 observed—

" Other cases might occur in medico-legal investigation, as when the hands only of some mutilated victim were found."

Professor Schlaginhaufen, in 1905, first pointed out the value of that observation.[18]

NOTES

[1] " Evidential Value " is here used in a legal sense, and not in the scientific meaning employed by Galton in his " Finger Prints." See Chap. XIV.

[2] See Chap. XXIV for instances in England and Scotland.

[3] Indian Acts, 1873-1900. Calcutta. Thacker, Spink & Co., and Government Printing Office.

[4] See *The Juridical Review*, Vol. XLIX, p. 417. 1937. Edinburgh. Wm. Green & Son, Ltd.

[5] 1934 S.C. (J.) 1.

[6] 1909, 3 Cr.App.R. 74. The Chief Justice (Sir Robert Stout) of the Supreme Court of New Zealand at Wellington on 4th May, 1905, convicted John Clancy of housebreaking and theft committed on 23rd February, 1905, upon evidence that the impression of his third right finger corresponded to the impression of that finger registered by Auckland gaol authorities. This case is claimed by New Zealand police as the first conviction recorded on evidence of a single print.

[7] The Chief Constable of Bradford City Police states that Castleton committed his offence in Huddersfield, and that Superintendent Talbot was the Bradford officer who secured the candle imprint. *The Bradford Telegraph* of 13th November, 1909, reported that Alverstone, L.C.J., in giving the judgment of the Court, observed that it was the

first case which had come before the Court in which a conviction had rested on fingerprints alone, and that he had taken great interest in it and had carefully examined the evidence. He relied absolutely upon the evidence of Superintendent Talbot, and particularly his evidence upon a middle finger of the accused. No appeal seems to have been taken against the competency of the fingerprint evidence. Leave to appeal further was refused.

[8] 1912 V.L.R. 152.

[9] Cf. " Mark Twain's " "Pudd'nhead Wilson," *supra*, p. 231.

[10] 252 Ill. 534 : 96 N.E. 1077.

[11] 42 Nev. 185 : 175 Pac. 190.

[12] 1934 S.C. (J.) 1.

[13] See " The Finger Print Instructor," p. iv of Introduction. Frederick Kuhne. 1917. New York. Munn & Co., Inc.

[14] See " Documents and their Scientific Examination," 1935. London. Charles Griffin & Co., Limited. Dr. Mitchell was Cantor Lecturer on " Inks."

[15] 142 C.C.C. Sess. Papers, p. 958.

[16] When identity points are truly indisputable, the cross-examiner will wisely " sit-still," *per* Brewester on " Fingerprints," *supra*, p. 108. Cf. the singular procedure of the native Indian judge (a barrister) and his two native assessors in the case of Kangali Charan, dealt with in Chap. XVII, but on this point only in my article on that case in *The Juridical Review* as cited in Note 4.

[17] " Dactylography," *supra*, p. 115. *The F.B.I. Law Enforcement Bulletin* for October, 1936, illustrates the unidentified ten-finger impressions from the " badly decomposed body " of an unknown man, found naked, in a clump of bushes in Eaton Canyon, California, and supposed to have been lying there for any time up to five months, together with photographs of his ten fingers taken (both before and after distention) by the process explained in the *Bulletin*. I believe the corpse was identified through this publication of these fingerprints.

[18] See Chap. XXXIII for full reference to Professor Schlaginhaufen's tribute to Faulds.

XXXI

BRITISH GOVERNMENT INQUIRIES INTO FINGERPRINTS

On 4th October, 1894, the Report was published of the Committee upon the Identification of Habitual Criminals. This Committee was appointed on 21st October, 1893, by the Right Honourable Henry H. Asquith, K.C. (later Lord Oxford and Asquith), as Secretary of State for the Home Department. It was composed of Charles Edward Troup, of the Home Office, as Chairman; Major Arthur

Griffiths, Inspector of Prisons; and Melville Leslie Macnaghten, Chief-Constable of the Metropolitan Police Force. The directions, *inter alia*, to this Committee were to inquire into (1) the existing methods of registering and identifying habitual criminals in England; (2) the Bertillon system; and (3) the suggested system of identification by means of a record of fingermarks; and to report whether either of such (2) and (3) methods could with advantage be adopted either in substitution for or to supplement the existing methods.

According to the Report[1] of this Committee, the " suggester " of the " finger " method was Galton, and it was, the Committee stated, then associated with his name! The Committee, as might have been expected from its composition, recommended the adoption of the " admirable " Bertillon system, with fingerprints as subsidiary, but that only to a very limited extent.

The Committee were clearly dominated by Galton and his then known views. The only finger expert or investigator called before them by the Committee was Galton. The Committee were well aware of Faulds and his work. Faulds felt deeply his exclusion.

In his evidence before the Committee Galton correctly credited Herschel with first suggesting and to some extent practically applying fingerprint-impressions in India in the identification of convicted or habitual criminals. Galton, as Faulds had done in 1880, expressed his views upon this method " as incomparably better than *per* recognition or by photo." No allusion of any kind appears from the Report to have been made to Faulds. It is right to say that, as the inquiry was limited in its scope, the far-reaching speculations and conclusions of Faulds, apart from his suggested registration of criminal fingermarks, were literally outside it. Galton satisfied the Committee upon the lifelong persistence of finger-patterns. Upon this point Faulds could have enlightened the Committee by reference to countless cases of drastic interference with cuticles, including his own, of very much more weight and importance scientifically than the accidental burning of a finger of one of Galton's laboratory assistants.

It is understood that, some time in 1894, Faulds saw Troup, the Chairman of the Committee, but with the Galton-Herschel atmosphere, in which Troup was then enveloped, Faulds could make little or no impression upon him.[2]

An Inquiry, some years after the Troup Inquiry, was ordered by the Government, known as the Belper Committee, for investigating the best method of effecting criminal identification. There does not appear to be any trace of the Report of this Committee being published. Faulds was not associated with this Committee in any way. It is understood that the Committee, presided over by Lord Belper, reported to the Government that the anthropometric method should not be employed, and advised the sole adoption of the fingerprint system according to the ten fingers in serial order.[3] Faulds first proposed that method.[4] It is in current use. Scotland Yard Finger Bureau was set up in July, 1901.

In 1902 the Right Honourable W. St. John F. Brodrick, as Secretary of State for War, appointed a Committee to inquire into fingerprints with regard to their use in the Army for the purpose of preventing recruits re-enlisting under false names, and of identifying deserters.

It is satisfactory to record that Faulds was the only expert invited to give evidence before this Committee. He did so on 9th May, 1902. No report of the proceedings seems to have been made public. Faulds relates that he was able to clear away many difficulties and misconceptions, with which the subject in official minds had become involved. He then explained, as I understand, that his plan was to have on record all the ten fingers in serial order. One important feature in his view was the maintenance of an index of single fingers. Single fingers (left on crime scenes) could thus be matched with their counterparts, if they existed, in the indexed collection.[5]

Faulds's claims so made were modestly and correctly asserted, and, by independent authorities, they have been since upheld.

NOTES

[1] Report, pp. 7, 27, *et* 29.

[2] Faulds met Troup afterwards at the Home Office. See " Dactylography," *supra*, p. 114.

[3] Henry in " Classification and Uses of Finger Prints," *supra*, states, p. 14 (seventh edition), that in consequence of the Belper Committee's Report the anthropometric system was " superseded under the orders " of the Home Secretary. See Annual Report for 1901 by Henry as Commissioner of The Metropolitan Police, H.M.S.O.

[4] See " Manual of Practical Dactylography," *supra*, p. 63.

[5] See " Guide," *supra*, pp. 6 *et* 44 : " Manual of Practical Dactylography," *supra*, p. 63. The Director of Publications, H.M.S.O., informs me that the Office is unable to trace Reports of the Belper and Brodrick Committees " as issued to this Office for sale."

XXXII

APPEALS TO BRITISH GOVERNMENT FOR FAULDS

IT cannot be surprising, after perusal of the preceding Chapters, that Faulds never made any headway in getting his due and fair recognition from the Government.

Several friends, among others, Lord Rowallan, his maternal cousin, tried to secure some Government recognition for Faulds.[1] Colonel John Ward, as his Member of Parliament for Stoke-on-Trent, raised the matter in the House of Commons. On 19th April, 1910, the Right Honourable Winston Churchill, as Home Secretary, stated in answer to Colonel Ward's question—

" Several communications from Mr. Faulds have

reached the Home Office; but I cannot find that he has any claim on the (Home Office) Department for recognition. So far as the Home Office is concerned, I am informed that the adoption of the Finger Print System in 1894 (*sic* for 1901) was entirely due to the labours of Mr., now Sir, Francis Galton.''[2]

This statesman, in so replying, could rely, of course, only upon his subordinates, in the absence of personal investigation by himself. It is granted that their information would be supplied to him in all good faith. But investigators removed from all Departmental or Administrative grooves and influences have since viewed Faulds's position very differently. The judgment of Dr. Heindl, as a criminologist of cosmopolitan repute, with all his vast knowledge and experience of fingerprints and fingerprint systems particularly in German cities, indicates the true place of Faulds in a way that Mr. Churchill's subordinates were unable to see. Dr. Heindl is not alone. Herschel himself, by his admission some seven years later, put the pre-eminent place of Faulds in fingerprints beyond all dispute.

This short Chapter closes upon a pleasant note. After one of his later interviews with Government officials, who had obviously learned more about him, Faulds informed his family that he had been promised by them an appointment in Scotland in the event of the fingerprint system developing there under Government regulation. It was the expression of hope, never realized, but nevertheless comforting to Faulds.

NOTES

[1] See Note 1 to Chap. VI, *supra.*
[2] Hansard, 1910, Vol. 16, p. 1874.

XXXIII

BRITISH, AMERICAN, AND FOREIGN TRIBUTES TO FAULDS

So far as I can trace, Dr. Otto Schlaginhaufen, of Zurich, was the first person of outstanding reputation in any country to appreciate Faulds. Without bias of any kind he treated of his services to anthropology as well as to criminology. I do not recall any passage in the writings of Galton in which he praised Faulds as an ethnologist, or took any particular notice of him in this regard.

Schlaginhaufen in 1905, then a young doctor of twenty-six and an assistant in the Anthropological Institute of Zurich University, of which since 1911 he has been Professor of Anthropology, published a remarkable article on "The Skin Formation of Primates." It appeared in *Gegenbauer's Morphologisches Jahrbuch* for August, 1905. By a coincidence Faulds was then passing through the press his "Guide to Finger-Print Identification." It was published in September, 1905. Faulds was not aware at that time of Schlaginhaufen's now world-famous article.

By October, 1905, Galton had noticed Schlaginhaufen's article. He refers to it in his "Review" in *Nature* of the "Guide" of Faulds, but for the purpose only of depreciating the bibliography supplied by Schlaginhaufen. Galton declared that that bibliography was incomplete; he said it did not include Tabor, a photographer of San Francisco: on the same footing Galton might have said Thompson, an American geologist, was also omitted. He had referred to both in his "Finger Prints."[1]

Galton, in this reference to Tabor, grasped at a straw. His criticism of Schlaginhaufen's bibliography was petty and misdirected. Tabor never published any book or pamphlet about anthropology or fingerprints.[2] Galton's innuendo plainly was that Faulds's pronouncements had been anticipated by Tabor and that Schlaginhaufen was ignorant of this " fact." Tabor and Thompson did not figure in any way prior to 1882. Galton made no other reference in his " Review " of Faulds's " Guide " to Schlaginhaufen. Schlaginhaufen in his article mentioned Galton, his place as an anthropologist, and his work in the development of Fingerprint systems.

The accompanying Plate IX is a photostat of the whole of Schlaginhaufen's passage with his relative note in which he assigns a place to Faulds and Herschel respectively.[3] No one perusing Galton's " Review " would infer that Schlaginhaufen had even mentioned Faulds.

Here is a free translation of Schlaginhaufen's tribute to Faulds and Herschel—

> A new period in research concerning papillary lines begins with an announcement by Faulds ('80), viz., one which brings skin formation into the use of criminal anthropology and juridical medicine. The publication is the forerunner of an extensive literature, which finds its way into regular periodicals and even into the daily press, and consequently can here receive only a limited consideration. By means of finger imprints shown on prehistoric Japanese pottery Faulds was led to the study of skin formation. He extended it to the apes, and had further opportunities of examining Japanese as well as English. He proved correctly that a careful study of corresponding impressions by lemurs shed light on genetic relationships. Further, we find here, for the first time, finger-prints used for identification, even although the author had not discovered the proof, arising from this, of the unchangeability of skin formation. The material for this was soon forthcoming from Herschel ('80) and the exact proof a little later from Galton ('91a). Faulds ('80, 605) makes further reference to the inheritance of papillary lines and brings this into juridical medical questions; e.g., finding value for this in the identification of mutilated corpses. " If unknown previously, heredity might enable an expert to determine the relatives with considerable probability in many cases,

PLATE IX—OTTO SCHLAGINHAUFEN

Das Hautleistensystem der Primatenplanta usw.

Mit einer Mitteilung von FAULDS ['80] beginnt eine neue Periode der Erforschung der Papillarlinien, nämlich diejenige, die die Hautleisten ·in den Dienst der kriminellen Anthropologie und der gerichtlichen Medizin zieht. Die Publikation ist die Vorläuferin einer großen Literatur, die sich bis in die populären Zeitschriften, ja in die Tagespresse hinein erstreckt und hier deshalb nur bis zu einer gewissen Grenze Berücksichtigung finden kann. Durch Fingereindrücke, die sich auf prähistorischen, in Japan gefundenen Töpferwaren zeigten, wurde FAULDS auf das Studium der Hautleisten geführt. Er dehnte es auf die Affen aus und .hatte ferner Gelegenheit, außer Engländern auch Japaner zu untersuchen. Mit Recht weist er darauf hin, daß ein sorgfältiges Studium der entsprechenden Gebilde bei den Lemuren Licht in die genetischen Verhältnisse werfen würde. Ferner finden wir hier zum erstenmal die Fingerabdrücke in ihrer Bedeutung für die Identifikation gewürdigt, ohne daß der Autor jedoch die dazu erforderlichen Beweise der Unveränderlichkeit der Hautleisten erbracht hätte. Das Material dazu lieferte indessen bald darauf HERSCHEL ['80], die genauen Beweise etwas später GALTON ['91 a]. Im weiteren tut FAULDS ['80, 605] der Vererbung der Papillarlinien Erwähnung und mißt ihr in gerichtlich-medizinischen Fragen, z. B. bei der Identifikation verstümmelter Leichen etwelchen Wert bei: ›If unknown previously, heredity might enable an expert to determine the relatives with considerable probability in many cases, and with absolute precision in some.‹ In Indien wandte HERSCHEL ['80] zur Wiedererkennung der Individuen die Fingerabdrücke beim Militär, bei Dienststellen und im Gefängnis an und gelangte so in den Besitz von ·Abdrücken, zu denen er die nach Verlauf von mehr als 20 Jahren von den nämlichen Individuen gewonnenen Vergleichsabdrücke ebenfalls aufweisen konnte. Betreffend die Rassen- und Sexualdifferenzen mag folgende Bemerkung HERSCHELS ['80, 76] von Interesse sein: ›The difference between the general character of the rugae of Hindoos and of Europeäs iǹ as apparent as that between male and female signatures, but 'my inspection of several thousands has not led me to think that it will ever be practically safe to say of any single person's signature that it is a woman's, or a Hindoo's, or not a male European's [1].‹

[1] Die beiden eben besprochenen Autoren (FAULDS ['94, 548], HERSCHEL ['94, 77]) haben sich später um die Priorität gestritten. Zeitlich erschien die Publikation FAULDS' früher; aber HERSCHEL wies durch die Veröffentlichung· eines halbofiziellen Briefes nach, daß er sich schon 1877 mit dem Gegenstand beschäftigt habe. Jedenfalls sind beide Beobachter unabhängig voneinander auf die gleiche Idee gekommen, und wenn auch die Materialien, die HERSCHEL lieferte, für die kriminelle Anthropologie speziell von größerer Bedeutung waren, so hat FAULDS doch in seiner ersten Mitteilung die Erforschung der Hautleisten von einem höheren Gesichtspunkt aus erfaßt und ihr in einem umfassenderen Plan den Weg vorgezeichnet.

On Faulds and Herschel, 1905

and with absolute precision in some." In India, Herschel ('80) turned to the recognition of finger prints of individuals amongst army men, civilians and prisoners, and in this way acquired prints, by which and by means of similar prints he was able to identify the same individuals more than twenty years later. The following remarks of Herschel ('80, 76) may be of interest in connection with social or sexual differences : " The difference between the general character of the rugæ of Hindoos and of Europeans is as apparent as that between male and female signatures, but my inspection of several thousands has not led me to think that it will ever be practically safe to say of any single person's signature that it is a woman's or a Hindoo's, or not a male Europeans."[1]

And this is a free translation of Schlaginhaufen's footnote " 1 "—

1. The two authors who have just been discussed, Faulds ('94, 548) and Herschel ('94, 77), later quarrelled as to priority. As far as actual time goes, Faulds's publication appeared earlier : but Herschel proves, through the publishing of a semi-official letter, that he had been busy with this matter since 1877. Anyhow, both observers arrived at the same idea quite irrespective of each other, and, if the materials which Herschel produced were specially important to criminal anthropology, then Faulds had grasped in his first intimation the research of skin-formation from a higher point of view and had shown the way in his all-embracing plan.

In 1905 Schlaginhaufen's interests, as they have since remained, lay in ethnical directions. Not being a criminologist or a medical jurist, he seems to place, by the passage and note quoted, greater stress than facts warranted upon the value to criminology of Herschel's services in comparison with those of Faulds. Eminent criminologists and medical jurists have since 1905 ranked those services of Faulds on the medico-legal side higher than Herschel's. There can be no doubt in the mind of anyone to-day that the major contribution of Faulds to crime detective methods was of first importance. It transcended his suggestion and that of Herschel of finger-print criminal registers. Exception might be taken to some of Schlaginhaufen's observations about Herschel as not wholly accurate; but it would seem somewhat ungenerous to elaborate objections to them in view of the impartiality with which Schlaginhaufen treated his subject.

Yet, when Schlaginhaufen's passage and note are care-fully examined, one may deduce, even upon the state-ments of Schlaginhaufen himself, that the services ren-dered by Faulds to criminology were in fact greater than those of Herschel. Observe that Schlaginhaufen singles out for special attention the suggestions of Faulds in regard to the identification of mutilated bodies, provided, as Faulds had said in his 1880 *Nature* Letter, a hand remains intact. How strange that fifty-five years after Faulds's *Nature* Letter of 1880 this major conception of Faulds should materialize so dramatically in the trial and conviction of Ruxton, the murderer, despite the ghastly treatment and dissection of his two victims! See Chapter XXVIII.

Needless to say, Schlaginhaufen's tribute to Faulds greatly pleased Faulds when he discovered it.[4]

The Law Times of 28th October, 1905, is, I believe, the first of all the legal, scientific, or other journals published in Britain to call attention to the work of Faulds as meritorious. It was, too, the first publication of the kind in this country in which a note of distrust was sounded, inferentially at least, of adverse opinions that had been expressed over the discoveries and labours of Faulds. In its very favourable review of Faulds's " Guide " in that October issue, it was observed—

" Credit where credit is due. Mr. Henry Faulds'

claims to honourable mention in connection with the system of identification by finger-prints have been strangely overlooked."

" Strangely "! How apt and suggestive!

The present Editor of *The Law Times* courteously gave me the name of the late Tighe Hopkins, a leader writer of the then existing *The Daily Chronicle*, London, as the contributor of its review. The article was initialled "T. H."[5] I have referred already to this writer in Chapter XIV.

Hopkins also reviewed Faulds's " Guide " for *The Daily Chronicle* in its issue of 30th September, 1905, somewhat more pointedly than he did for *The Law Times*. In his newspaper contribution, this passage occurs—

Hitherto, however, one person who plays an important part in the history of this system has missed the justice that is his due. As long ago as 1880, Mr. Faulds addressed to *Nature* a letter suggesting the identification of important criminals by using, in serial order, the imprints from the last phalanx of the ten fingers. He explained how prints could be made, showed the general character of certain patterns of fingers, and made it clear enough that the system which he outlined would sooner or later become of extreme importance in legal cases. That letter to *Nature* contained the first proposal to use this method of identification in jurisprudence. The claim put in for Sir William Herschel does not touch Mr. Faulds'. Sir William had been taking " sign-manuals " by finger impressions in India; but the first systematic plan, and the first that was communicated to the English Press, was the one that is outlined in this treatise. Further, what Mr. Faulds advanced in 1880 is what has been officially adopted, namely, the record for old criminals of each of the ten fingers in serial order.[6]

So far as I can learn, Hopkins did not know Faulds personally. His name should be permanently remembered as one who, so far back as 1905, evidently thought Faulds had not been recognized as he deserved to be.

Taylor, in his " Principles and Practice of Medical Jurisprudence," the standard English work, did not deal with Fingerprint Identification. The science was not known in his time. But the editor of the sixth edition of that work, which was published in 1910, did include it. Then it was discussed under the heading of " Thumb Marks," and, to boot, by the way, of " Galton's Thumb Marks "! Another instance of misdirected credit! Faulds had in his 1880 *Nature* Letter used the expressions " Finger Marks " and " Thumb Patterns." The heading should rather have been " Faulds's " or " Faulds's and Herschel's Finger and Thumb Marks." Faulds was not mentioned in that or the seventh edition. But in the eighth and ninth editions of 1928 and 1934, respectively, as edited by Professor Sydney Smith of the Chair of Medical Jurisprudence in the University of Edinburgh (the latter edition in collaboration with Mr. W. G. H. Cook, Barrister), this statement is made—

> " The honour of first proposing this method, which has revolutionised personal identification, must be divided between two Englishmen (again! *sic*) : Dr. Henry Faulds and Sir William Herschel."[7]

And in the ninth edition the further statement is made—

> " Faulds first publicly described the method in a letter to *Nature*, published on October 28th, 1880, and there can be no doubt that at that time he was fully aware of the importance of taking prints of the ten fingers in identification, and he also discussed the possibility of chance impressions and of mutilated parts."[8]

In making the suggestions about identification from " chance impressions " and from mutilated remains,

Faulds was more revolutionary and " revolutionizing "
than Professor Sydney Smith's emendation on the eighth
and ninth editions of Taylor indicated.

In his own treatise on " Forensic Medicine," first published in 1925, Professor Sydney Smith, having probed
further, states almost too cautiously that " Faulds . . .
appears to have first grasped the importance of the skin
ridges as an aid to identification."

In the fifth and 1936 edition of this treatise the Professor has the following passage : —

> " Although Herschel took finger prints for official
> purposes in India as far back as 1858, he did not
> attempt to classify prints."

Then the Professor repeats Faulds's having " first
grasped the importance of the skin ridges," still qualifying his statement with the cautious " appears." Who
in this was before Faulds? Was it Galton? Certainly
not. Was it Henry? Certainly not. Was it, then,
Herschel? Herschel has confessed that he did not think
of the " skin ridges " as leading to identification of
" chance impressions " and of mutilated remains.

Professor Sydney Smith has gone further than any
other British forensic jurisprudent in making independent inquiries over Faulds. It seems, as is generally
agreed, erroneous to suggest that Herschel used the same
method of finger-impressions for all the purposes proposed
by Faulds.[9]

The late Dr. John Glaister, Professor of Medical Jurisprudence in Glasgow University, was the first British
Medico-Legalist, as Faulds has observed, to treat of the subject of fingerprint identification, doing so in the first
edition, published in 1902, of his " Medical Jurisprudence, Toxicology, and Public Health." It was only in
his second edition, however, of 1910, that he mentioned
Faulds as one who had " claimed " to have first pub-

lished in *Nature* of 1880 facts about fingerprints, giving at the same time fair extracts from Faulds's *Nature* Letter and also citing his " Guide." On this matter, the subsequent editions of his work remain the same, including the last and fifth, published in 1931 in collaboration with Professor John Glaister, his son and successor in his Chair.[10] With fuller investigation into the subject, it is to be hoped that, in future editions of the medico-legal treatises under consideration, such disparaging expressions as " appears to have " and " claimed " will disappear.

Unqualified acceptance of the claims of Faulds has been made in the United States. It is pleasing to see how Faulds and his work are notably presented in the first edition of " Personal Identification," published at Chicago in 1918 by Mr. Bert Wentworth, formerly Police-Commissioner of Dover, New Hampshire, and the late Harris Hawthorne Wilder (1864-1928), Ph.D., Professor of Zoology in Smith College. The eleventh chapter, p. 351, is devoted to " Present Use of Friction-Ridge Identification : Possibilities for the Future." In this Chapter, after quoting from Faulds's Letter of 1880 in *Nature* as their text for that Chapter, they say—

> It is not a little singular that the one who was the first in modern times to suggest in print the use of finger prints for identification purposes, saw, at the same time, a wider application of a system so based than did his contemporaries. Yet, as shown in the previous chapter, Dr. Faulds, in the same short letter in which he suggested the use of finger prints for the usual form of identification, mentioned also, in addition to certain directions of thought important to the biologist and ethnologist, the identification of severed members, and the tracing of relationship by the continuance, through heredity, of characteristic configuration.

> While in the suggestions of Faulds there are some that seem at present to be rather visionary, there are others, notably the identification of a criminal by accidental

finger impressions left at the scene of the crime, which have been abundantly verified. By the introduction of the entire palm and the sole into the system, the identification of a man, not only by a severed member, but at times by even a small fragment of friction skin, becomes a possibility soon to be realized. Later research into the heredity of the finger patterns does not furnish sufficiently positive results to promise much; yet, when dealing with the larger and more striking features of the palms and soles, certain heredity characters often appear with marked distinctness, and may be of use in furnishing good presumptive evidence either for or against near relationship.

. . . .

As soon as the system was incorporated, however, there appeared an unexpected application, namely, that of tracing the agent of a crime by accidental finger marks left on the spot, especially those to be found on glass, polished furniture, and other smooth surfaces. The remarkable results of this discovery, resulting in the conviction of the criminal in numberless cases where otherwise there would have been no definite clue, are now so much matters of common knowledge that there exists a popular error to the effect that this is the sole, or at least the chief, use of the finger-print system, while the purpose for which it was originally advocated is more or less forgotten.

The eleventh chapter of their work remains with regard to Faulds in the same state in the second edition, published by Mr. Bert Wentworth in 1932, Professor Wilder having died in the interval. Strange to say, all mention of Faulds is omitted from the prefaces to both editions. Surely, an inadvertent oversight!

Dr. John Edgar Hoover, Vice-Chairman of the International Police Association and Director of the Federal Bureau of Criminal Investigation in Washington, D.C., U.S.A., of the widest knowledge, theoretical and practical, in fingerprints, recently recorded his opinion of the value of the researches of Faulds in a manner that contrasts greatly with the belittling views of Galton.

Faulds's experiments in Japan, according to Dr. Hoover,
"definitely established that the varieties of individual fingerprint-patterns were very great; that the
patterns remained constant throughout life; and that
even after the removal of the ridges by the use of
pumice stone and acid the patterns invariably grew
out again 'with unimpeachable fidelity' to their
originals."[11]

In Chapter XIV I have quoted the opinion of Dr.
Ainsworth Mitchell to the same effect.

Several of the publications on fingerprints that I have
seen are adorned with portraits of Galton, Henry, and
Herschel or of one or other. For example, Wentworth-
Wilder put Henry in their frontispiece. Faulds so far
has not thus been honoured.

Lastly, out of chronological order, but, perhaps, first
in importance, I come to Dr. Heindl. His "Daktyloskopie," a *magnum opus*, which was first published in
1921, the third edition being issued in 1927, does justice
to Faulds. Various citations from his work have been
made by me in previous Chapters. But here, without
further elaboration, I may cite Dr. Heindl's opinion to
the effect that the discovery—or, let me say, to be perhaps historically correct—the rediscovery by Faulds of
fingerprint identification in criminal administration and
his principal suggestion for its introduction in its medico-
legal aspect to Western civilization is "*absolut
originell*," observing, as Dr. Heindl does, at the same
time that Faulds was both a physiologist and a theorist,
influencing by his 1880 *Nature* Letter the later development of criminal dactylography.[12]

Somewhat after the discriminating tenor of the review
in *The Law Times* of 1905, Dr. Heindl further states—

"The first author of modern times who has published his opinions on Finger-Print Inspection is the

Englishman (*sic*) Faulds. He has been far too little regarded and his utterances mostly passed over until now."[13] (1921-7.)

Hopkins had said almost these very words twenty-two years previously. How suggestive! Passed over! By whom? Englishmen? Yes. His contemporaries! Galton, Henry, and for long, Herschel! No wonder many were led to do likewise. The high officials of New Scotland Yard appeared to have completely lost sight of Faulds. With a scalpel of unusual temper, Galton dissected him, and in dissection found nothing of value! How very regrettable that Galton's admiration for Herschel should have so warped his judgment. I cannot but believe that, if the Herschelian cataract had been removed from his eyes, Galton would deeply have regretted his treatment of Faulds, and, with his high sense of honour, that he would have made handsome amends by trying to repair as much as he could all the damage he had done to Faulds.

NOTES

[1] See Chap. XIV.

[2] Faulds noticed this flaw in Galton's "Review." See "Dactylography," *supra*, p. 27. Neither Tabor nor Thomson published any book. Consequently, no reference to either in any bibliography was appropriate. Probably they got their ideas from the Letters of Faulds and Herschel in *Nature* of 1880.

[3] The photostat has been prepared from pp. 5845 of Vol. XXXIII of *Gegenbauer's Jahrbuch*.

[4] See "Dactylography," *supra*, p. 24. So far as this Chap. has gone, the distinguished Professor read the typed manuscript. On 25th January, 1937, he wrote me in German, *inter alia*, that he had done so with vivid participation, and was pleased to see with how great an objectivity and justice I had treated the importance of Faulds, observing that, in my doing so, it was a satisfaction to him to find the historical part of his early work cited by me so fully.

[5] Vol. CXIX, p. 561.

[6] See Chap. XIV, *supra*. Hopkins published in 1913 his "Wards of the State," and his chapter on "Finger Prints" in that book seems to be based on his article on "Crime and the Finger Print" in *Cassell's Family Magazine* of May, 1902, referred to in Chap. XIV. He must have overlooked his contributions to *The Law Times* and *The Daily Chronicle* in 1905 as he does not refer to Faulds in "Wards of the State."

7 p. 124 in eighth edition and p. 117 in ninth edition. Wentworth-Wilder on " Personal Identification," *supra*, p. 335, agree; but also style Faulds and Herschel as " both Englishmen." Faulds died (for purposes of fisc and succession), domiciled in England. He was, and he regarded himself always as, a Scot.

8 p. 117. Faulds's " Dactylography " is alone cited among the authorities.

9 Faulds frequently refers to their different methods.

10 It is singular, however, that Dr. Heindl's " Daktyloskopie " does not seem to have come under the notice of Professors Sydney Smith and Glaister. There is no reference in their very exhaustive treatises to Dr. Heindl or to his great treatise, described as " unique in the literature of identification," by Messrs. Söderman & O'Connell in their " Modern Criminal Investigation," *supra*, p. 57, Note 10.

11 See Dr. Hoover's article on " Criminal Identification," in *The American Journal of Police Science*, Vol. II, p. 11, 1931. Chicago North Western University Press. I find, however, no reference to Faulds in the latest edition of the *Encyclopædia Britannica*, published now as an American work, under the article on " Finger Prints," contributed by Dr. Hoover. In this respect the article on " Criminal Investigation " by Mr. August Vollmer, Chief of Police, Berkeley, California, differs. Faulds was cited among the authorities mentioned in the article on " Finger Prints " in the previous edition. *Enciclopedia Italiana* (Rome. 1934-36) does not mention Faulds.

12 " Daktyloskopie," p. 52. The third edition was published in 1927. In his copious bibliography Dr. Heindl includes Faulds's article in *Nature* of 1917 on the " Permanence of Finger Patterns," but the " Remarks " of Herschel, appended thereto, are not included in the writings of Herschel in that bibliography.

13 " Daktyloskopie," *supra*, p. 54.

XXXIV

CONCLUSION

IT is a remarkable fact in the history of the modern development of fingerprints, in so far as Britain is concerned, that fingerprints have never been applied in any general and extensive way. In India, the registration system has been applied to matters other than strictly criminal. Notably, in the United States of America, fingerprints are taken of individuals at birth; for purposes of life assurance; in authentication of wills, bank cheques and deposits; in pawnbroking transactions; in connexion with emigration, passports; for army and navy recruiting; and so forth. Fraud detection is not necessarily the motive of this wide application. It is done in many cases where no question of criminality is expected to arise. In the Great War the officers and men of the American Navy, if not also the Army, were supplied with Monel metal identification tags attached by chain to neck or wrist. Upon one side of these tags were their names, numbers, and birth and enlistment dates: upon the other side an etched impression of their right-hand index fingers. Except in very great heat, these tags did not melt. Neither salt water nor acids affected them. There is nothing to prevent anyone from getting an impression of his right index finger or thumb made and placed on a card for identity purposes. Through the friendly offices of the Glasgow Fingerprint Bureau, the finger-impression of a very young child was recently taken and transferred to a small silver disc placed in a locket. I know of no previous instance of a similar kind. In fact, there is no limit to the application of fingermarks for authenticity and identity purposes.[1]

The Government of the Argentine Republic is, perhaps, the most advanced anywhere in its very extensive application of fingerprints beyond the sphere of criminal administration and investigation. Fingerprints there figure in the domain of civil life in all its manifold aspects. Vucetich, as we have seen in the Chapter devoted to his life and work, was early seized with all the possibilities of fingerprints in identification. Under his persistent advocacy, the Argentine Government gave legislative effect to his practical suggestions. Many countries beyond those of South America have made regulations after his views. Dr. Reyna Almandos, the Director of the Museo Vucetich, presses with zeal and skill the logical sequence of the reforming policy of Vucetich in the institution of a national identification record of every person. There are not wanting distinguished advocates of this great reform in the United States, and elsewhere. In Britain, Professor Sydney Smith, to whose works I have referred in Chapters XVI and XXXIII as appreciating Faulds, states in " Forensic Medicine," p. 61—

" It is obvious that finger print identification can only be of value when prints are available for comparison, and I have advocated the system of taking prints of every child born, either at the time of [birth] registration or at vaccination. If this were carried out, we should have in less than a century a record of every person in the country. If the labour involved in classification were too great, the prints would still be of the utmost value in deciding the identity of children claimed by two groups of parents, or of people who claim to be heirs to property; in fact, the existence of such a record would be of definite value even if the prints were unclassified."[2]

British people seem, however, reluctant to apply methods suited, as many probably think, to dark and more or less primitive races. No doubt also, despite the ever-increasing bureaucratic hunger for statistics of all kinds, the necessity of a vast collection of fingerprints with its elaborate classification deters this country from making extensive applications of registered fingermarks.[3] It is otherwise in the United States. In some of the States, fingermarks do not satisfy Police Authorities. Palmar and plantar impressions are also taken or advocated.[4]

The great outstanding fact remains that in the present day the high importance of finger-impressions in this and other countries relates not so much to their use in the speedy and certain identification of previous or habitual criminals as in bringing wrongdoers by their chance impressions to justice. Such a mode of discovering crime was never mooted in modern times until Faulds thought of it; not merely as a happy guess but as the result of serious tests and experiments. In this wide sense, Faulds was beyond doubt the true pioneer of Police Fingerprint Bureaux as now set up all over the world, including Japan in 1922, where he received his inspiration.

Faulds was never well off. Rarely is a Christian missionary, medical or otherwise, a man of means.

In writing of the life of Faulds and his association with fingerprints, I put myself very early in communication with his daughters, Misses Agnes Cameron Faulds and Isabella Jane Faulds. They gave me much information about their father, and led me to search other likely means of obtaining material facts in regard to him as exhaustively and as correctly as I could.

I hope this book may lead to the highly-deserved recognition of the services of Faulds to the scientific investigation of crime. What better recognition of these services could there be than that material provision, such as Faulds never received, should be graciously made for his daughters?

NOTES.

[1] Mr. Frederick Kuhne in " The Single Finger Print Instructor," *supra*, pp. 11 *et seq.*, records an amazing variety of cases to which fingerprint registration is applied in New York State. He is prophetic of their still further extended use. In " Science *versus* Crime," by Henry Morton Robinson (1937. London. G. Bell & Sons, Ltd.), the author says, p. 66, that there is " a strong and growing tendency " for the universal application of fingerprint registration in the United States." On 17th July, 1933, *The Scotsman* newspaper reported that Sydney University, Australia, in association with New South Wales Medical Board, had adopted a scheme to safeguard the public against impersonation by " quacks," whereby " the thumb prints and signature of a doctor " would be thenceforth affixed to his qualifying diploma. M. Marx Darmoy, Minister of the Interior, France, is stated by *Le Temps* of 16th December, 1937, to be in favour of a compulsory identity card with fingerprints for all French citizens over eighteen years of age and of all passports being accompanied by the finger-prints of the holders. In regard to Egypt, Dr. Locard says : " les

cartes remises aux prostituées portent une empreinte digitale du pouce " : and that cards of identity are there similarly issued to domestics and porters. See " L'Identification des Récidivistes," *supra*, p. 189. *Cf.* the apparently ancient practice in China in reference to prostitutes : " on prend son signalement et on marque le lieu de sa demeure; elle est inscrite au bureau des prostituées." " Relation Des Voyages," &c., *supra*, p. 70.

2 This passage will be found substantially the same in the first (1925) edition of the Professor's book.

3 In the House of Commons on 17th November, 1937, Mr. De la Bère asked the Home Secretary, whether he was prepared to consider a scheme for the national registration of fingerprints throughout the country, with a view to storing them, thus making it easier for the police to trace unknown persons suffering from loss of memory. With other people unidentified as the result of accident or otherwise, there are said to be over 9000 persons in asylums, hospitals and other places in Britain. The answer of the Government, *per* Mr. Lloyd, was : " Finger prints undoubtedly afford an easy and certain means of establishing identity "; but he added that " the Home Secretary would not feel justified in considering the question of a national finger print registry for the purpose indicated, unless he were satisfied that there was a real and general desire for such a system." See Hansard, 1937, Vol. No. 17, p. 403. Mr. De la Bère again questioned the Government on 1st December, 1937, as to impressing passports with the right thumb of the holders. Such a step would protect travellers abroad and prevent the use of fraudulent passports. The Secretary of State for Foreign Affairs (Mr. Eden) gave this proposal no encouragement. See *Hansard*, 1937, Vol. 329, No. 27, p. 2046. An ideal registration system would embrace digital, palmar and plantar prints and, perhaps, other characteristic points. One very interesting letter, dated 23rd February, 1938, received by me from Mr. Bert Wentworth, tells of his giving evidence at the age of 81 in a Massachusetts murder trial in September, 1937, as an expert in footprints as well as in finger and palm prints. The case concerned a bloody print of the sole of the alleged murderer's left foot.

4 Laufer appears to have fallen into a serious error in dogmatically asserting that " a mere impression of the palm can never lead to the identification of an individual." See his 1912 *Smithsonian* article, *supra*, p. 634. The illustrations in the cases of Gunn, Kuhl and Ruxton prove conclusively that Laufer is wrong. Several convictions have been obtained in Glasgow upon palmar prints. In or about 1933, Detective-Lieutenant Hammond informs me that the impression of a portion of a palm was obtained by him. By its means the guilt of the criminal was established. The ten finger impressions of the offender as previously registered were distinct from his palmar impression. In his 1894 *Nature* Letter (see p. 71 *supra*), Faulds referred to the characteristic wrinkle points of the palm as observed by him in 1880. In this final note, the opportunity may be taken of confirming facts stated on p. 104 *supra* with regard to the Federal Bureau of Investigation, Washington, D.C., in so far as fingerprints in the United States are concerned, by referring to the broadcast to British listeners (of whom I was one) made by Dr. Hoover. It is recorded under the title of " Crime and the ' G ' Men " in *The Listener* of 11th May, 1938. It is there stated that Henry's finger-

CONCLUSION

print system has been reduced by the Fingerprint Department " to a comparatively simple procedure." The technique of fingerprints has not been dealt with in this book, except in a very general way. Many text books in different languages deal specially with technique. Faulds's books do so. But it is interesting to point out that in *The Listener's* account of Dr. Hoover's broadcast an illustration is given of the ingenious Hollerith machine in use by the Washington finger-print experts for the automatic sorting of fingerprint cards. It is understood that this machine has not yet been introduced in any British fingerprint bureau. I have also learned lately that Mr. W. Somerville Shanks, R.S.A., Glasgow, has combined with his signature or initials since 1886 a print—slightly rolled—of his right hand fore-finger on valuable books and other things he desired to make dis-tinctly personal. Neither he nor any artist known to him has superimposed a fingerprint on water colour drawings or oil paintings or used such as an artist proof signature. Mr. Shanks was a personal friend of the detective officer referred to in the second note to Chap. XXV. Mr. Shanks tells me that Galton corresponded with that officer. I have not, perhaps, emphasized in the text one qualification Faulds had for close research in his possession of wonderful sight and to which he alludes in his letter to *Nature* in 1894. See p. 71 *supra*. It has been suggested to me that my difficulty over the reference to the tracing of the contours of one's fingerprints dealt with on p. 209 of Chap. XXX might be resolved upon the supposition that both finger-impressions and contours are included within the tracing. Such a method would also definitely indicate the particular fingers traced. Lastly, I have not overlooked either Job xxvi, 7 : " He sealeth up the hand of every man," or Rev. xiii, 16 : " And he causeth all, both small and great, rich and poor, free and bond, to receive a mark in their right hand or in their foreheads." In these passages, some writers profess to find allusion to finger and palm marks.

BIBLIOGRAPHY.

Note.—The publications of Faulds and Herschel are first set out in this list and each respectively in chronological order. The publications of all other authors cited in the text follow under their names in alphabetical order. Parliamentary and other Government publications are detailed under " British Government Publications." Reports of trials and trials will be found under " Law Reports " and " Trials." Anonymous magazine, &c., articles are noted under " Anonymous " at the end of the list. Publications bearing on the subject matter of the book and consulted by the author are only included in this bibliography. It is not intended to be exhaustive of fingerprint literature.

FAULDS, HENRY

I. CONTRIBUTIONS TO SCIENTIFIC, &C., JOURNALS

(1) *Nature.* London. Macmillan & Co.

1880, Oct. 28.   The Skin Furrows of The Hand. Vol. XXII. 605.

1894, Oct. 4.   The Identification of Habitual Criminals by Finger Prints. Vol. L. 548.

1913, Aug. 21.   Poroscopy. The Scrutiny of Sweat Pores for Identification. Vol. XCI. 635.

1917, Jan. 18.   The Permanence of Finger Print Patterns. Vol. XCVIII. 388.

(2) *Sunlight.* Glasgow. M'Crone & Co.

1883, Oct. 15.   The Beautiful in Nature. Vol. I. 11.

1884, Feb. 15.   The Origin of Man. Vol. I. 235.

(3) *St. Thomas's Hospital Gazette.* London. J. J. Keliher & Co., Ltd.

1904, Jan. 13.   Dactyloscopy. Vol. XIV. 13.

(4) *Knowledge.* London. Knowledge Publishing Co.

1911, Apr.   Finger Prints. Vol. XXXIV. 136.

(5) *Scientific American Supplement.* New York. S.A.S. Office.

1911, Nov. 18.   History of Finger Prints : A chapter in their Use. Vol. LXXII. 326.

Faulds, Henry—*continued*.

II. Books

1885. Nine Years in Nipon. London. Alexander Gardiner.

1905. Guide to Finger Print Identification. Hanley. Wood, Mitchell & Co., Ltd.

1912. Dactylography. Halifax. Milner & Co.

1923. Manual of Practical Dactylography. London. " Police Review " Publishing Co., Ltd.

III. Pamphlets

1917. The Hidden Hand.

1926. Was Sir E. R. Henry the Originator of the Finger Print System ?

Note.—The publishers and places of publication of these pamphlets are not stated.

HERSCHEL, WILLIAM J.

I. Contributions to " Nature," *supra*

1880, Nov. 25. Skin Furrows of The Hand. Vol. XXIII. 76.

1894, Nov. 22. Finger Prints. Vol. LI. 77.

Note.—" Hooghly Letter," 1877, here printed.

1917. Jan. 18. Remarks on Faulds's Letter. Vol. XCVIII. 389.

Note.—Admission by Herschel is in these " Remarks."

II. Book

1916. The Origin of Finger Printing. London. Oxford University Press.

Abundo, G. d'.

1891. Contributo allo studio delle impronte digitali. Revista Generale Italiana di Clinica Medica. Vol. III. 254. Pisa.

Note.—The Director of the R. Biblioteca Universitaria di Pisa states that Herschel is briefly referred to and that there is no mention of Faulds in this article.

Almandos. See under Reyna Almandos, Luis.

Anonymous. See List at end of this Bibliography.

Bateson, Vaughan.

1906, May 5. Personal Identification by means of Finger Print Impressions. British Medical Journal. Vol. I. 1029. London. B.M.J.A. Office

BIBLIOGRAPHY

BATTLEY, Harry.

1930. Single Finger Prints. London. H.M.S.O.

1936-37. All About Finger Prints. Police Journal. Vols. IX and X. London. Philip Allan & Co., Ltd.

BEWICK, Thomas.

1805. History of British Birds. Newcastle. Edward Walker.

BILLINGS, John S.

1881, Aug. 13. Our Medical Literature. British Medical Journal. Vol. I. 262. London. B.M.J.A. Office.

BLOCHET, E. See under Rashid, Fadl Allah.

BRASH, James Couper. See under Glaister and Brash.

BREWESTER, F.

1937. Fingerprints. Calcutta. Eastern Law House.

BRITISH GOVERNMENT PUBLICATIONS.

1886-1902. (1) Annual Reports to Parliament of The Commissioner of Police of The Metropolis. H.M.S.O.

          (2) HANSARD.

1910.   Vol. 16. 1874. H.M.S.O.

1937.   Vol. 329. 403. H.M.S.O.

—   Vol. 329. 2046. H.M.S.O.

          (3) Report of Parliamentary Committee.

1894.   Asquith. Identification of Habitual Criminals. Vol. LXXII. H.M.S.O.

1904.   (4) Memorandum by New Scotland Yard on Henry's Finger Print System. H.M.S.O.

1914.   (5) Oscar Slater. Cd. 7482. H.M.S.O.

CHAVANNES, Edouard.

1914. Appendix A in " Ancient Khotan." See under Stein, Marc Aurel. *Re* Berthold Laufer's 1912 *Smithsonian* article. See T'oung Pao. Vol. 14. 490. Leide. Brill.

CLEMENS, Samuel Langhorne (" Mark Twain ").

1883. Life on The Mississippi. London. Chatto & Windus.

1894. Pudd'nhead Wilson. London. Chatto & Windus.

CORDIER, Henri.

1914. Notes in Revision of Yule's " Cathay." See under Yule, Henry.

CRIMINAL APPEAL REPORTS. See under Law Reports.

CROMWELL, Oliver U.

1907. Finger Print Photography. London. Elliot Stock.

CUMMING, John
  1935. A Contribution to Bibliography Dealing with Crime and Cognate Subjects, Third Edition. London. Metropolitan Police District Receiver.

DILNOT, George.
  1929. Scotland Yard. London. Geoffrey Bles.

DIXON, W. Macneile.
  1937. The Human Situation. London. Edward Arnold & Co.

D'OHSSON, Abraham C. See under Ohsson, D'.

ENCYCLOPÆDIAS. See General Index.

ENGELHART, L.
  1932. Der Mordprozess Slater. Archiv fur Kriminologie. Vol. 91. 166. Leipzig. Vogel.

FORGEOT, R.
  1891. Études Médico-légales des Empreintes. Archives de l'Anthropologie Criminelle. VI. 387. Paris.

FRÉCON, A.
  1889. Des Empreintes en Général. Lyon. A. Storck.
      Note.—M. Louis Baraduc, Procureur Général Honoraire, Bordeaux, informs me that there is no mention of Faulds in the papers of MM. Forgeot and Frécon.

GALTON, Francis.
      I. CONTRIBUTIONS TO SCIENTIFIC, &C., JOURNALS

      (1) *Royal Institution Proceedings.* London.

  1888, May 25. Personal Identification and Description. Vol. XII. 346.

      (2) *Royal Society Proceedings.* London.

  1890, Nov. 27. Patterns in Thumb and Finger Marks. Vol. 48. 455. See also Phil. Trans. (B.) 1891. Vol. 182. 1.
      Dec. 5. Co-relations and their Measurement. Vol. 45. 135.
  1891, Nov. 27. Method of Indexing Finger Marks. Vol. 49. 540.

      (3) *Nature.* London.

  1888, May 25. Personal Identification and Description. Vol. XXXVIII, 77 *et* 201.

  1890, Nov. 27. Patterns in Thumb and Finger Marks. Vol. XL. 455.

      Dec. 9. Patterns in Thumb and Finger Marks. Vol. XLIII. 192.

Galton, Francis—*continued.*

1891, June 11. Finger Print Indices. Vol. XLIV. 141.

    Nov. 27. Method of Fixing Finger Marks. Vol. XLIV. 141.

1893, July 6. Identification. Vol. XLVIII. 222.

    Oct. 19. Finger Prints in Indian Army. Vol. XLVIII. 595.

1896, Oct. 15. Signaletic Instructions. Vol. 54. 569.

1902, Oct. 16. Finger Print Evidence. Vol. LXVI. 606.

1905, Oct. 19. Review of Faulds's " Guide." Supplement to Vol. IV. 4.

    (3) *The Nineteenth Century.* London. Sampson, Low, Marston & Company, Limited.

1891, Aug. Identification by Finger Tips. Vol. 30. 303.

1900, July. Identification Offices in India and Egypt. Vol. 48. 118.

II. Books

1892. Finger Prints. London. Macmillan & Co.

1893. Decipherment of Blurred Finger Tips. Supplement Id.

1895. Finger Print Directories. Id.

1908. Memories of My Life. London. Methuen & Co.

Giles, Herbert Allen.

1898. Chinese Biographical Dictionary. London. Quaritch.

1901. History of Chinese Literature. London. Heinemann.

1908. Adversaria Sinica, No. 6. Shanghai.

1912. Chinese-English Dictionary. Second Edition. London. Quaritch.

Giles, Lionel.

1937. Dated Chinese Manuscripts in the Stein Collection. Bulletin of The School of Oriental Studies (Univ. of London). London. Luzac & Co.

Glaister, John (Father).

1902-31. Medical Jurisprudence, Toxicology and Public Health. Editions 1 to 5. Edinburgh. E. & S. Livingstone.

Glaister, John (Son), and Brash, James Couper.

1937. Medico-Legal Aspects of the Ruxton Case. Edinburgh. E. & S. Livingstone.

Hansard. See under British Government Publications.

Heindl, Robert.

1927. Daktyloskopie. Third Edition. Berlin. Walter De Gruyter & Co.

HENRY, Edward Richard.

  1899, Sept. 15. Finger Prints. The Times. London.

  — Sept. 23. Finger Prints. British Medical Journal. Vol. II,
  803. London.

  1900-37. Classification and Uses of Finger Prints. Eight Editions.
  London. H.M.S.O.

HERRERO, Antonio.

  1926. El Sistema Dactiloscopico Argentino. Buenos Aires

  1929. Breve Sintesis Historica de la Identificacion. La Plata.

HERRMAN, Louis.

  1931. Finger Patterns. American Journal of Police Science.
  Vol. II. 306. Chicago.

HOOVER, J. Edgar.

  1931. Criminal Identification. American Journal of Police
  Science. Vol. II. 8. Chicago.

HOPKINS, Tighe.

  1902, May. Crime and The Finger Print Cassell's Family
  Magazine. London.

  1905, Sept. 30. Review of Faulds's "Guide." The Daily
  Chronicle. London.

  1905, Oct. 28. Review of Faulds's "Guide." The Law Times.
  London.

  1913. Wards of the State. London. Herbert & Daniel.

HOUGH, Walter.

  1886, Aug. 20. Thumb Marks. Science. Vol. VIII. 166. New
  York. The Science Press.

HUMPHREYS, Mr. Justice.

  1938. Science and Justice. The Medico-Legal and Criminological
  Review. Vol. VI. 15. London. Bailliere, Tindal & Cox.

JAMES, Joseph F.

  1886, Sept. 3. Thumb Marks. Science, supra. Vol. VIII. 212.

KEITH, Arthur.

  1912. The Human Body. London. Williams & Norgate.

  1916, Dec. Review (Anonymous) of Herschel's "The Origin of
  Finger Printing." Nature. Vol. 98. 268.

KIPLING, Rudyard.

  1919. Kim. London. Macmillan & Co., Ltd.

KLAPROTH, Heinrich Julius.

1833. Description of China under Mongol Dynasty. Translated from Rashid-eddin. Nouveau Journal Asiatique. Vol. XI. 335. Paris.

KUHNE, Frederick.

1917. The Fingerprint Instructor. New York. Munn & Co. Inc.

LARSON, J. A.

1924. Single Finger Print System. New York and London. D. Appleton & Co.

LAUFER, Berthold.

1913. History of the Finger Print System. Annual Report for 1912 of the Smithsonian Institution. 631. Washington, D.C.

1917, May. Concerning The History of Finger Prints. Science. Vol. 45. 504. New York. The Science Press.

LAW REPORTS. See also under Trials.

American.

1911. People v. Jennings, 252 Ill. 534 : 96 N.E. 1077.

1918. State v. Kuhl *et al*, 42 Nev. 185 : 175 Pac. 190.

Australian.

1912. *Rex* v. Parker, V.L.R. 152.

English.

1905. Stratton (Alfred and Albert Ernest) Bros., 142 C.C.C. Session Papers 978.

1909. Castleton, 3 Cr.App.R. 74.

Indian.

1927. Sahu v. King Emperor, I.L.R. 6 Pat. 623.

Scottish: Session Cases (Justiciary). Edinburgh. William Hodge & Co., Ltd.

1933. Adair v. M'Garry, S.C.(J.) 72.

1934. Hamilton v. Lord Advocate, S.C.(J.) 1.

1930. Moorov v. Lord Advocate, S.C.(J.) 68.

1928. Slater, Oscar v. Lord Advocate, S.C.(J.) 94.

LOCARD, Edmond.

1909. L'Identification des Récidivistes. Paris. Maloine.

1910. Un Nouvel Essai de Classement Dactyloscopique. Archives d'Anthropologie Criminelle. Vol. XXV. 430. Lyons and Paris.

1911. La Preuve par les Empreintes Digitales dans trois affaires récentes. Archives d'Anthropologie Criminelle. Vol. XXVI. 254. Lyons and Paris.

LOCARD, Edmund—*continued*.

1936. Note sur L'Identification des Suspects. Revista de la Identificacion Y Ciencias Penales. Vol. 13. 23. La Plata.

LUCAS, A.

1935. Forensic Chemistry and Scientific Criminal Investigation. London. Edward Arnold & Co.

MAUGHAM, Lord.

1936 The Tichborne Case. London. Hodder & Stoughton.

MEADOWS, Thomas Taylor.

1847. Land Tenure in China. Transactions of the China Branch of The Royal Asiatic Society. 1. Hong Kong. The China Mail Office.

MINIKATA, Kumagusu.

1894, Dec. 18. Antiquity of Finger Prints. *Nature*. Vol. 51. 199.

Dec. 31. Finger Print Method. *Nature*. Vol. 51. 274.

MITCHELL, C. Ainsworth.

1911. Science and the Criminal. London. Sir Isaac Pitman & Sons, Ltd.

1923. The Expert Witness. Cambridge. W. Heffer & Sons, Ltd.

1930. Review : H. Battley's " Single Finger Prints." The Police Journal. Vol. 630. London.

1931. The Scientific Detective and the Expert Witness. Cambridge. W. Heffer & Sons, Ltd.

1935. Documents and Their Scientific Examination. London. Charles Griffin & Co., Limited.

NASMYTH, James.

1883. An Autobiography (S. Smiles). London. John Murray.

NEW OXFORD DICTIONARY. See Oxford English Dictionary.

O'CONNELL, John J. See under Söderman and O'Connell.

OHSSON, D', Abraham C.

1852. Histoire des Mongols. II. 637. Amsterdam. Müller.

OXFORD, (The) English Dictionary. Oxford. Clarendon Press. 1933.

PARLIAMENTARY PAPERS. See under British Government Publications.

QUATREMÈRE, Etienne. See under Rashid.

RASHID, Fadl Allah or Fazl Ullah.

1303. Djami El Tévarikh : A Cyclopædic History.

BIBLIOGRAPHY

TRANSLATIONS

(1) 1911. BLOCHET, E. E. W. Gibb Memorial Series. London. Luzac & Co.

(2) 1833. KLAPROTH, Heinrich Julius. See under Klaproth.

(3) 1852. OHSSON, D', Abraham C. See under Ohsson, D'.

(4) 1836. QUATREMÈRE, Etienne Marc. with Mémoire of Rashid. Paris. Royal Press.

REINAUD, Joseph Toussaint.

1845. Relation des Voyages faits par les Arabes et les Persans dans le IXᵉ siècle. 2 Vols. Paris. Royal Press.

REYNA ALMANDOS, Luis.

1909. Dactiloscopia Argentina : Su Historia é Influencia en la Legislación. La Plata. Joaquin Sesé.

— Origen del Vucetichismo. Buenos Aires. Alsina.

1912. Origen é Influencia Jurídico—Social del Sistema Dactiloscópico Argentino. La Plata.

1929. Ciencia Y Derecho de Identidad. La Plata.

1930. Herschel and Faulds : Precursores de la Dactiloscopia. Revista de la Identificación Y Ciencias Penales. Tomo VI. 240. La Plata.

1936. The Personal Number and The National Book of Personality. La Plata.

      Note.—See note under Juan Vucetich.

ROBINSON, Henry Morton.

1937. Science *versus* Crime. London. G. Bell & Sons, Ltd.

ROGERS, E. M.

1934. The Delhi Trunk Crime. The Police Journal. Vol. VIII. 369. London. Philip Allan & Co., Ltd.

ROUGHEAD, William. See under Trials.

SARTON, George.

1927. Introduction to the History of Science. Vol. I. 571. Baltimore. Williams & Wilkins Co.

SCHLAGINHAUFEN, Otto.

1905, Aug. The Skin Formation of Primates. Gegenbauers Morphologisches Jahrbuch. Zurich.

SILLITOE, P. J.

1937. Report to Glasgow Corporation for 1936. Glasgow. Robert Anderson & Sons, Ltd.

SMITH, Henry.

1931. The Forging of Finger-Prints, &c., Transactions Medico-Legal Society. Vol. XXIV. 87. Cambridge. W. Heffer & Sons, Ltd.

SMITH, Sydney (Alfred).

1925-36. Forensic Medicine. Editions 1 to 5. London. J. & A. Churchill.

SÖDERMAN, Harry. See under Soderman and O'Connell.

SÖDERMAN AND O'CONNELL.
1936. Modern Criminal Investigation. New York and London. Funk & Wagnalls Co.

SPEARMAN, Edmund R.
1894. "Known to the Police." Nineteenth Century. Vol. XXXVI. 356. London. Sampson, Low, Marston & Company, Limited.

STATUTES.
British Acts : Penal Servitude Act, 1891. Prevention of Crimes Act, 1871. H.M.S.O.
Note.—Cited in Adair v. M'Garry, 1933 S.C.(J.) 72.
Indian Acts, 1873-1900. Calcutta. Government Printing Office and Thacker, Spink & Co.

STEIN, (Marc) Aurel.
1907. Ancient Khotan. London. Oxford University Press.

TAYLOR, Alfred Swaine.
1934. Taylor's Principles and Practice of Medical Jurisprudence. 6th to 9th Editions. Edinburgh and London. J. & A. Churchill, Ltd.

THOT, Ladislao.
1934. " Criminalistica." Revista de la Identificación Y Ciencias Penales. Vol. X. La Plata.

TRIALS.
1937. Charan, Kangali. The Juridical Review. Vol. XLIX. 417. Edinburgh. Wm. Green & Son, Ltd.
1920. Gunn, Dennis. Report. Wellington. New Zealand. Marks, Government Printer.
1911. Jennings, Thomas. See under Law Reports.
1918. Kuhl, B. E. See under Law Reports.
1911. Parker, Edward. See under Law Reports.
1937. Ruxton, Buck. Notable British Trials. Edited by R. H. Blundell and G. Haswell Wilson. London, Edinburgh and Glasgow. William Hodge & Co., Ltd.
1929. Slater, Oscar. Notable British Trials. Edited by William Roughead. 3rd Edition. London, Edinburgh and Glasgow. William Hodge & Co., Ltd.
1906. Stratton Bros. See under Law Reports.
Note.—For other cases, see under Cases in General Index and Separate List of Cited Cases, p. 269.

Varigny, Henry de.
1891. Anthropologie : Galton's Finger Prints. Revue Scientifique. Vol. 47, 557. Paris.

Vucetich, Juan.
1896. Instrucciónes Generales para El Sistema de Filiación. 2nd Edition. La Plata. Solá, Sesé y Co.
1904. Dactiloscopia Comparada : El Nuevo Sistema Argentino. La Plata. Peuser.
1926. Mi Actuación Dactiloscópica (1916). Revista de Criminologia Psiquiatria Y Medicina Legal. Buenos Aires.
1929. Proyecto de Ley de Registro General de Identificación. Prologo by Dr. Reyna Almandos. La Plata.
1929. Conferencia sobre El Sistema Dactiloscópico (1901). La Plata.
1930. Historia Sintética de la Identificación (1920), with Introduction by Dr. Reyna Almandos. Revista de Identificación y Ciencias Penales. Tomo VI. 177, 355, 383; Tomo VII. 5. La Plata.

Note.—The Special Number (1926, Buenos Aires) of Revista de Identificación y Ciencias Penales, in memory of Vucetich, contains articles by Drs. Helvio Fernández and Reyna Almandos and others, and unpublished writings of Vucetich.

Vollmer, August.
1929. Investigation, Criminal. Encyclopædia Britannica. 14th Edition. Vol. 12 562.

Wentworth-Wilder (Bert Wentworth and Harris Hawthorne Wilder).
1932. Personal Identification. 2nd Edition. Chicago. Cooke.

Wigmore, John Henry.
1931. Principles of Judicial Proof. 2nd Edition. Boston. Little, Brown & Co.

Wills, William.
1912-37. Circumstantial Evidence. (7th Edition. 204.) Edited by Sir Alfred Wills. London. Butterworth & Co.

Wilton, George Wilton.
1937. Finger-Prints : The Case of Kangali Charan : 1898 : The Juridical Review. Vol. XLIX. 417. Edinburgh. W. Green & Son, Limited.

Note.—Reprinted in Revista de Identificación y Ciencias Penales. 1938. Tomo XV. 281.

1938, Jan. 8. Facsimile Discrepancies. Notes and Queries. Vol. 174. No. 2, 20. London. The Rolls House Publishing Co., Ltd.

YULE, Henry.
  1866. Cathay and The Way Thither. 1st Edition.
  1914. Cathay and The Way Thither. Revised by Henri Cordier. Vol. III. London. Hakluyt Society.

ANONYMOUS

1880, Dec. 7. Finger Prints. St. James's Gazette. London.

1883. Thumb Portraits. World of Wonders, 114. London and New York. Cassell & Co.

1905, Sept. 30. Review of Faulds's " Guide." The Daily Chronicle. London. See under Hopkins, Tighe.

1905, Oct. 28. Review of Faulds's " Guide." The Law Times. London. See under Hopkins, Tighe.

1909, Jan. The Metropolitan Police. The Times. London.

1916, Dec. Review of Herschel's " The Origin of Finger Printing." *Nature.* Vol. 98. 268. See under Keith, Arthur.

1933, Oct. Conclusiveness of Finger Print Evidence. The Law Times. London.

1935. Palestine Bade Explorations. Scientific American. Vol. 152. 4.

1936, Oct. Unidentified Body. F.I.B. Law Enforcement Bulletin. Vol. 5. No. 10, 23. Washington, D.C.

Note.—Since the completion of my text, Professor Glaister has edited and revised the 6th edition of his father's work. " Fingerprint Identification " has been rewritten. The origin of the system is not raised. Faulds's " Guide to Finger Print Identification " is one of the cited authorities.

G. W. W.

LIST OF CITED CASES.

Note.—See also under "Law Reports" and "Trials" in Bibliography.

(a) GEOGRAPHICAL

(b) ALPHABETICAL

Capital and Non-Capital Charges

GENERAL INDEX.

279

GLOVES
fps. found in, can be developed, 172.
views of Dr. Locard on, 172.

GOSH, HRIDAY NATH.
murder of, in Bengal, 88.

GOVERNMENT, BRITISH. See BRITISH GOVERNMENT.

GRAY, BASIL, B.A.
British Museum expert, referred to, 218.

GREGG, C. C.
Director of Chicago Field Museum, 62, 67.

GRIFFITHS, MAJOR ARTHUR, 234, 235.

" GUIDE TO FINGERPRINT IDENTIFICATION "
of F. published in 1905, 108.
    reviewed in *The Daily Chronicle*, 243.
       ,,   *The Law Times*, 242.
    reviewed by Galton in *Nature*, 109.

GUNN, DENNIS, case of, 168.
cross-examined as to palm print, 170.

HABITUAL CRIMINALS
Herschel registers fps. in India for, 9, 19.
    nothing to do with F.'s major claim, 9, 19.
suggestions by F. for fp. register of, 17.

HAMILTON, ROBERT, CASE OF, 5, 199, 221, 226.

HAMMOND, SUPERINTENDENT-DETECTIVE BERTIE J. See under POLICE.

" HAND, THE HIDDEN," Pamphlet by F., 139.

HANSARD. See under British Government Publications in B.
interpellation in House of Commons as to fp. registration, 254.
statement by Right Hon. Winston Churchill *re* F., 237.

HANDWRITING
superiority of fps. over, 229.
    in relation to forgery, 230.

HEINDL, ROBERT. See B.
author of " Daktyloskopie," unique work, 67, 250.
    affirms originality of F.'s discovery, 238, 248.
criticism of Herschel's claims, 75.
dactylography in regard to crime identification in ancient China, 217.
deals with Chinese nail markings, 47.
expresses opinion on F.'s system of classification, 83, 103.

T

INTERNATIONAL FINGERPRINT CODE
developed by Dr. Icard, 80.
  first instance of, 156.

INTERNATIONAL FINGERPRINT REGISTER
advocated by Vucetich, 85.

INTERNATIONAL MEDICAL CONGRESS, 40, 41.

ITALIAN-O : ITALY
no reference in Enciclopedia, to F., 250.

JACKSON, HARRY
Galton refers to case of, 50, 52, 156.

JACKSON, MR., K.C., 190, 199.

JAMES, JOSEPH F. See B,
letter by, in *Science*, 40, 213.
  Galton refers to, 46, 213.

JAPAN-ESE
  confessions of criminals, sealed by thumb nails, 17.
  F. begins first Scottish mission in, 26.
    edits magazine there, 26, 28.
    engravings of fps. procured by, 6, 8, 14, 17, 20.
    establishment by, of medical school in, 27.
    experiments at hospital, 18.
    illustration of tattooed employee referred to, 20.
    influence of, in, 27.
    lectures on physiology, &c., 27, 71, 248.
    " Nine years in Nipon," by, 28.
    Prince of, offer to, 27.
  institution in, of fp. bureau, 253.
  Minikata, K. See MINIKATA, KUMAGUSU.
  pottery, reference to, 1, 14, 16.
  trace fps. from Chinese, 119.

JENNINGS, THOMAS
case of, in U.S.A., 224, 225.

JOB. See BIBLE.

JOHNSON, HENRY. See List of Cases.
Laufer refers to case of, 102, 156.

JONES, MR. P. NORTON. See POLICE.

JORGENSON, HAKON, 108.

JOURNALS : MAGAZINES : REVIEWS
  1. Legal
      F.B.I. Law Enforcement Bulletin
        Note as to Unidentified Body, 234.

Journals, &c.—*continued.*

Royal Asiatic Society Transactions: China Branch
Article on Land Tenure, 56, 57.
Royal Institution Proceedings
Papers by Galton, 43, 46, 47.
Royal Society Proceedings
Papers by Galton, 47, 52, 64.
Transactions: Medico-Legal Society
Paper by Lieut.-Col. Henry Smith, 172, 173.

French
Archives de l'Anthropologie Criminelle
Article by Locard, E., 53, 86, 87.
Nouveau Journal Asiatique
Article by Klaproth, H. J., 208, 218.
Revue Scientifique
Article by Varigny, H., 77.

German
Archiv für Kriminologie
Article by L. Engelhart, 168.

Japanese
The Chrysanthemum
conducted by F., 28.

Swiss
Gegenbauer's Morphologisches Jahrbuch
Article by Otto Schlaginhaufen, 239, 240.

Miscellaneous
Cassell's Family Magazine
Article by Hopkins, T., 249.
Knowledge
Article by F., 18, 52, 137.
Listener, The
Broadcast by Dr. Hoover, 254.
Nineteenth Century, The
Articles by Galton, 48.
„   Spearman, E. R., 73, 74, 120.
Notes and Queries
" Facsimile Discrepancies," 68.
Sunlight
Articles by F., 20.

Juridical Review, The. See JOURNALS.

JUR-Y-IES

acceptance by, of fps., 220.
not bound to, 227.
distinctions in procedure between England and Scotland, 198.
reliance of, upon fp. experts, 173.

JUSTICE

fps., " powerful aids to," 121.
" powerful auxiliary," 54, 132.

Nature. See JOURNALS.

" NATURE COPY "
of fps. of criminals, suggested by F., 17.

NATURE PRINT-S-ING
referred to by F., 14, 15.

NASMYTH, JAMES
reference to thumbprint, 31, 40.

NAVY. See ARMY.

NEVADA CASE, 225.

NEW OXFORD DICTIONARY
" Dactyloscopy," only in Supplement of, 87.

NEW SCOTLAND YARD. See also SCOTLAND YARD.
connexion with fp. evidence in Ruxton case, 195.
  evidence by experts on fp. from, 4, 228.
F. appears as unknown to officials, 5.
practice in Glasgow, 4.
record of fps. kept at, 104.

News of the World. See under NEWSPAPERS.

NEWSPAPERS
  Boston Transcript, The
    cited by New Oxford Dictionary, 87.
  Bradford Telegraph, The
    report of L.C.J. Alverstone's judgment, 233.
  Daily Chronicle, The
    review in, of F.'s " Guide," &c., 243.
  Glasgow Herald, The
    obituary notice of F., 35.
    reference to fp. case, 161.
              ,,   lecture on fps., 167.
    special articles on fps. in, 4.
  News of the World
    alleged confession by Ruxton, 198.
  St. James's Gazette
    leader on fps., 39, 142.
  Saturday Review, The
    notice of F.'s " Nine Years in Nipon," 28.
  Scotsman, The
    reference to fps. for medical diplomas, 253.
  Statesman of India, The
    letter in, 96.

  Temps, Le
    reference to questions to French Government *re* fps., 253

POLICE—*continued.*

Henry, Sir E. R., London, Commissioner. See B.
  association with fps., 97.

Hoover, J. Edgar, Washington, U.S.A., Director. See B.
  opinion of his experts on Ruxton thumbprint, 194, 195.
  tribute to F. by, 64, 247, 248.

Jones, P. Norton, Calcutta, Deputy Commissioner
  assists with facts in Kangali Charan case, 90, 96.

Kendal, Sir Norman, London, Assistant Commissioner
  assistance by, on various points, 34.
  verifies convictions in Metropolitan fp. cases, 159.

Nunes, Guillermo J., La Plata, Chief
  introduces Vucetich to fps., 77.
  orders search for fps. in Rojas case, 84, 150.

Rawson, Thomas, Bradford, Chief
  verifies facts as to Bradford area cases, 159, 233.

Reyna, Almandos, Luis, Plata, Director. See B.
  tributes to Juan Vucetich, 77.

Sannié, Charles, Paris, Director
  vouches present position in France of fps., 52.

Sillitoe, P. J., Glasgow, Chief
  addresses Montreal Conference, 199.
  corresponds with Washington F.B.I., 194, 195.
  originates fp. bureau in Glasgow, 4, 5, 104.

Vollmer, August, Berkeley, California, Chief. See B.
  article by, 87, 250.

Vucetich, Juan, La Plata, Director. See B.
  originated first fp. bureau in world, 78.
  life and work detailed, 75.

Fp. Superintendents : Detectives : Experts : Inspectors

Alvarez, Eduardo M., La Plata, Inspector
  discovered fps. in first recorded murder case, 150.

Battley, Harry, London, Chief Inspector. See B.
  articles on fps., 106, 149.
  no reference to F., 106.
  publication by, 105.

Brewester, F., Calcutta, Expert. See B.
  reference to F., 108.

Collins, Charles, London, Superintendent. See B.
  witness in trial of Stratton Bros., 100, 101.

Cromwell, Oliver U., Bradford, Detective. See B.
  work as photographic expert, 151.

Dinnie, Edward W., Wellington, N.Z., Senior Sergeant
  expert witness in trial of Dennis Gunn, 171.

Fowler, John A., Sydney, N.S.W., Inspector
  evidence by, upon forgery of fps., 170.

Hammond, Bertie J., Glasgow, Superintendent
  examines Chinese fp. of 1839, 59.
  obtains derm print from corpse of victim, 194.
    Washington experts confirm identity, 195.
  only expert Crown witness in Ruxton trial, 183, 187.

Lal, Govind Behari, Delhi, Inspector
  brilliant work in " Trunk Crime " case, 174.

U   305

Police—*continued.*

MacKenzie, Norman, Edinburgh, Detective
assists in Ruxton murders investigation, 199.
Nicolson, Arthur Frederick, Exeter, Chief Clerk
connexion with Bradford area, 151.
Scobie, Thomas S., Edinburgh, Detective
assists investigation of Ruxton murders, 199.
Scott, J. A., Delhi, Superintendent
collects facts in " Trunk Crime " case, 177.
Talbot, Thomas, Bradford, Inspector
connexion with early Yorkshire cases, 151, 155.
Zwirz, Frederick E., New York, Expert
opinion on Chinese fp. signature of 1839, 59.

Fp. Bureaux : Identity Services

Argentina
La Plata
first established in world, 113.
reference to work of Reyna Almandos, 77.
     ,,   ,, Vucetich, 75.
statistics, 104.
success in Rojas case, 84, 150.

Great Britain
Bradford
reference to early cases in area of, 151.
success of, 151, 233.
Edinburgh, 6.
assists in Ruxton case, 199.
Glasgow, 4, 152.
established, 104.
statistics, 104.
success in Ruxton murders, 5, 152, 160, 167, 183, 199.
London
established in 1901, 97.
record of cases prior to 1909, 151.
statistics, 104.
Wakefield
established in 1905, 157.

France
Paris
present position of, 52.

Ireland
Belfast, 104.
Dublin, 104.

United States
New York
application to, for fp. examination, 59.
work by Deputy Chief Inspector, 65.
St. Louis
first set up, 81.

SEX
whether discernible from fps., 38, 39.

SHAVING
of fps. F. found no variation, 19, 138.

SHANKS, W. SOMERVILLE, R.S.A., 255.

SHERIFF COURT, GLASGOW, 3, 6.

SHOE. See BOOT PRINTS.

SILLITOE, P. J. See under POLICE.

SILVER DISC
fp. on, 251.

SINGLETON, MR. JUSTICE
judge in Ruxton case, 190, 193.
opinion on value of fp. evidence, 191.

SLATER, OSCAR
absence of search for fps., 164.
trial of, 161.
observations on, by William Roughead, 164, 168
critique by L. Engelhart, 168.

SMITH, HENRY, LIEUT.-COL.
paper by, 172, 173.

SMITH, SYDNEY, PROF. See B.
advocacy of birth fp. registration, 88, 252.
citations from treatise by, 88, 165, 193, 194, 252.
dermal fps., experience of, 200.
edits later editions of " Taylor," 244.
tribute by, to F., 244, 245.

Smithsonian Institution Report, The. See JOURNALS.

SNAILS, Chinese name for whorls, 31.

SOCIETIES : SCIENTIFIC. See SCIENTIFIC SOCIETIES.

SOCIOLOGICAL SOCIETY
F. member of, 35.

SÖDERMAN, HARRY. See SODERMAN & O'CONNELL.

SÖDERMAN, & O'CONNELL. See B.
reference to, work of, 65.
comment thereon of Dr. Heindl, 66.

SOLE PRINTS. See under FINGERPRINTS.

SOLEIMAN. See SULAIMAN.

SOOTY FPS., 8, 149.

SPAIN : SPANISH, 104.
letters of F. and Herschel translated into, 19.
terms for fps., 79.

SPEARMAN, EDWARD R. See B.
" Known to the Police " by, 74, 120.

SPIRITUAL FATHER OF FPS. See FATHER OF FINGERPRINTS.

Statesman of India, The. See NEWSPAPERS.

STATUTES. See B.

STEIN, SIR AUREL (MARC). See B.
discoveries of fps. in Eastern Turkestan, 131, 132.
documents examined by Prof. Chavannes, 202.

STOUT, SIR ROBERT
first conviction by, on single fp., 233.

STRATHERN, JOHN DRUMMOND, 2, 5.

STRATTON BROTHERS. See LAW REPORTS.
trial of, for murder, 36, 100, 101, 151, 231.
evidence of identification from fp., 101.
criticism of, by F., 101.
victims, Thomas Farrow and wife, 107.

SUICIDES
identification of, 81.

SULAIMAN. SULEIMAN, &c.
observations of, as Arabian traveller, 131, 204, 209.
variations in name of, 217.

Sunlight. See JOURNALS.

SWEDEN, 65.

TABOR, MR.
reference to, 30, 55, 110, 114, 239, 249.

TAGS. See ARMY.

TALBOT, THOMAS. See POLICE.

T'ANG, DYNASTY
fp. legends of, 211, 212, 215.
period of, 65, 202.

TATTOO MARKINGS, 20.

TAYLOR, ALFRED SWAINE. See B.
 reference to F. in his work, 244.
  Prof. Sydney Smith's emendations, 244, 245.

TECHNIQUE
 not dealt with, except generally, 255.

TELEGRA-M-PH. See MAIL.

Temps, Le. See NEWSPAPERS.

TEP-SAIS
 Herschel distinguishes from fps., 121, 124, 132.

THOMPSON, GILBERT
 Galton alludes to, 55, 239.

THOT, LADISLAO. See B.
 " Criminalistica " by, 83.

THUMB : MARKS : PRINTS : PORTRAITS. See FINGERMARKS.
 clay thumb marks, 201.
 Galton enquires into Chinese connexion with, 39.
 " Mark Twain's " first reference to, 41, 142.
 practice of bankers in China referred to by Herschel, 123.
 reference to, by James Nasmyth, 31, 40.
 reference to, in letters in *Science*, 46.
 referred to, by F. in his 1880 *Nature* Letter, 14.
  in World of Wonders for 1883, 40.
 used by Bewick, 30, 40.

THUMB NAILS. See NAIL MARKINGS.

TICHBORNE CASE
 F. refers to, 17.
 Herschel refers to, 12.
 Maugham, Lord, no reference by, to fps., 20.

Times, The. See NEWSPAPERS.

Times, The Law. See JOURNALS.

TOKEN SIGNATURES
 Herschel refers to, 123.

TRIALS. See B. for Trials : and Reported Cases.

TRITTON, DR. A. S.
 opinion of, on Arabic quotations, 205.

" TRIUMVIRATE, FP.," 127, 129.

WIGMORE, JOHN HENRY. See B.
references to work of, 146.

WILDER, HARRIS HAWTHORNE. See " PERSONAL IDENTIFICATION."
death of, 120, 246.

WILLS
authenticated by fps., 250.

WILLS, WILLIAM. See B.
citation from, 96.

WINDSOR CASE, 153.

WINDT, KAMILLO, 19.

WIRE. See MAIL.

WOODCUTS
of finger and thumbmarks of Thos. Bewick, 30, 40.
    ,,   Mrs. Ch'ên, 57, 58, 59, 60, 61, 177.
    ,,   James Nasmyth, 31, 40.

YANG, KUEI-FEI
stories of this Honourable Lady, 211, 212, 218.

YETTS, PROF.
opinion of, cited, 209.

YEDO BAY
F. finds fps. on pottery ware in, 1, 18, 137.

YULE, HENRY. See B.
" Cathay " of, cited, 207, 208.

WORLD OF WONDERS, THE, 40, 142.

ZWIRZ, FREDERICK E., NEW YORK. See POLICE
gives opinion on Chinese fp., 59.